Work That Makes Sense

Operator-Led Visuality

Creating and Sustaining Visuality

on the Value-Add Level

GWENDOLYN D. GALSWORTH

VISUAL-LEAN® ENTERPRISE PRESS

PORTLAND, OREGON

Visual-Lean® Enterprise Press
Division of Quality Methods International Inc. (QMI)
607 NE 32nd Avenue
Portland, Oregon 97232
503-233-1784 (phone)
503-233-3091 (fax)
admin@visualworkplace.com (email)
www.visualworkplace.com (website)

Galsworth, Gwendolyn D.
ISBN: 978-1-932516-30-2
Editor: Aurelia Navarro
Book Design: Brook Kirklin
Printing: ETC. Printing Services, Grand Rapids, Michigan
Printed in the United States of America

Visual-Lean®, Visual Office®, and Visual Machine® are federally registered service marks, globally licensed to Quality Methods International Inc.

All photographs in this book are used by the permission of the person and/or company represented or cited.

Printing number
    10 9 8 7 6 5 4 3 2 1

La Poesía

And something ignited in my soul,
fever or unremembered wings,
and I went my own way,
deciphering
that burning fire,
and I wrote the first bare line,
bare, without substance, pure
foolishness,
pure wisdom
of one who knows nothing,
and suddenly I saw
the heavens
unfastened
and open.

by Pablo Neruda
translated by David Whyte

By The Same Author

Books

Visual Workplace-Visual Thinking

Visual Systems

Visual Workplace-Visual Order Associate Handbook

Visual Workplace-Visual Order Instructor Guide

Smart Simple Design

DVD Training System and CDs

Visual Workplace-Visual Order DVD Training System (with Spanish subtitles)

Visual Workplace-Visual Order Resource Folio CD

Work That Makes Sense Resource Folio CD

Leading for an Effective Implementation CD

Training for an Effective Implementation CD

Licensed Training Implementation Suites

Work That Makes Sense

Visual Displays/Production Control Boards

Visual Workplace/Visual Machine®

Visual Adherence: Visual Standards & Visual Controls

Achieving Zero Defects: Visual Guarantees (poka-yoke systems)

Visual ScoreBoarding: Problem Solving for the Chronic, Complex and Costly

Becoming a Leader of Improvement-1: A New Role for Supervisors & Managers

Becoming a Leader of Improvement-2: A New Role for Executives

Management by Sight: Visual Displays/Production Control Boards

Creating an Enterprise-wide X-Type Matrix & Operations Roadmap

Smart Simple Design: De-Complicating the Enterprise Through Variety Effectiveness

VisualEdge Off-the-Shelf Training Packages

The Basics of Visuality

The Building Blocks of Visual Thinking

Automatic Recoil/The Visual Where: Borders

Visual Mini-Systems/Visual Inventiveness

The Four Power Levels of Visual Devices

The Five Reasons for Workplace Visuality

Machine Lubrication: Visual & Effective

Contents

Leadership Task List

Foreword by Brent Allen

Many companies have a full box of improvement tools—lean, six sigma, kanban, 5S, TPM, to name a few. When these are deployed, company leaders get results, often promising results. But these results are also often not sustained. The solution, they are told, is to make sure the effort is *operator-led*. But that goal often seems even more elusive.

A new business paradigm is required.

In her book, *Work That Makes Sense* (WTMS), Dr. Gwendolyn Galsworth provides such a paradigm when she shares her comprehensive methodology for implementing the visual workplace through operators—operator-led. First, operators are shown specific procedures for implementing workplace visuality in their own areas—from smart placement and the visual where, to mini-systems and the four power levels of visual devices. Great examples, great photographs, and systematic step-by-step methods show how. Galsworth teaches that "how" extremely well, providing chapter after chapter of the principles and techniques that operators need to drive out waste through visual solutions. This, the mechanics of visuality, is the first dimension of this excellent book.

The book's second dimension is even more powerful: the cultural change and how leadership is widened to include operators. Galsworth does this better than I have seen anywhere else—in any book, program or methodology—positing a new business paradigm for us to consider. She calls that leadership paradigm: *I-driven*.

At the heart of I-driven leadership is the realization that operators do not know how to lead *because* they have not been given the opportunity to learn to do so.

Lifetime manufactures a wide range of innovative lifestyle products. Thanks to 1200 hardworking men and women, we are leader in several of those markets. After 30 years as an executive with this fine company, I am convinced that most supervisors would love to get their operators to take on more responsibility and make more decisions. Their question is how?

Managers and operators want the same thing. But how do we get it? I found the answer—one I had sought for a very long time—in Galsworth's implementation framework. A successful continuous improvement work culture must find the balance point between *structure* and *free will*.

This is at the heart of Galsworth's I-driven approach—her approach to visuality and her approach to creating a work culture for excellence. Her book clearly identifies what category of decisions operators can and cannot make. In the week-long WTMS training for trainers Galsworth led at Lifetime, I saw this in action when operators were presenting a list of visual improvement projects they had identified. She asked them to circle the ones they could do and the ones that were management's. They did, taking on many tasks as their own. I was taken aback. Prior to that, not only operators but managers would have listed **all of them** as management's job. I suddenly realized that the answer to the question who gets to lead is about giving operators permission, time, and authority to lead. To lead what? *To lead themselves.* Once given, operators willingly accept *and* meet that challenge.

The fact that Galsworth's approach has structure—shape, rules, and accountability—provides managers a way to contribute to continuous improvement and to excel. You need to retain structure so the place doesn't get blown up and to communicate an abiding respect for managers and their legitimate role. That same structure allows operators to freely determine *how* they want to fulfill their own need to contribute and excel—operator-led visuality. A spirited and engaged workforce is not about anti-management. It is about a system where both sides of the equation succeed. It is *not* either/or but *both*. This is a great definition of teamwork.

And yet a third element is needed and also found in this exceptional book—the one that gets added to teamwork so the enterprise can grow to a new horizon. That third element is *exactness*.

Work That Makes Sense teaches us that visual devices translate information into exact behavior. That is its primary purpose: embedding and sustaining exactness through visual solutions. And this can only come about in a culture of free will—an I-driven culture. The third element for enterprise excellence—for creating the continuous improvement work culture I have sought for Lifetime—is exactness: the exactness that visuality, and every other improvement method, requires for its success.

Exactness cannot be demanded. The level of exactness required for continuous improvement to become a way of life at a company can only be given voluntarily, through an act of free will.

Free will, structure, and exactness are a shifting balance point. This is the new business paradigm that Galsworth offers us. This is an I-driven enterprise. Once learned and operationalized, this paradigm allows the organization to take on anything, any new improvement effort.

I have been a student of management for 30 years, read countless management books and gone to many seminars. I have never found a better, more powerful system of transformation than Galsworth's. That comes through on every page of this book. She does that better than anybody.

Brent R. Allen
Vice President of Operations
Lifetime Products, Inc.
Salt Lake City, Utah

Foreword by Rhonda Kovera

Fifteen years ago, my partner, David Stearns, and I took a deep breath and made a bold move. We started a company, Visual Workplace Inc. (VWP), in order to provide products and services to companies wanting to go visual.

At the time, and like so many other companies, we made the early mistake of thinking that visual was the same as 5S. Then we figured it out.

Please don't get me wrong. 5S is a very important first step on every company's journey to enterprise excellence. But I worry when I search the internet for what's new in the visual workplace and the little I find is nearly always under 5S—everywhere. 5S is the first thing companies think of when we talk to them about visuality. And we find that many of them shy away from even using the word *visual workplace* because they think they are being redundant; they think it is the same as saying 5S.

That is why we are so delighted with Gwendolyn's new book, *Work That Makes Sense*. It doesn't just define what a visual workplace is, it shows you step by step by step how to transform your company into a visual work environment. It describes in detail tools, processes, and outcomes that are so far beyond what is understood as the visual approach by most people that I feel sure that anyone who reads this book will never confuse 5S and visual again. They will know that *workplace visuality* (Gwendolyn's term) will build your safety, quality, and on-time delivery specifications in the work environment, that visual devices will let you spot abnormalities at a glance, that visual solutions will build standard work and your KPIs into daily operations, and much much more.

Work That Makes Sense represents an opportunity for all organizations, not just manufacturing, to apply some extraordinary concepts to their workplaces—service professions, education, health care. The tools and concepts in this book provide operators, the experts, with concrete ways to improve their own workplace in a way they can and want to be responsible for. Whether you are an operator, nurse, mechanic or teacher, the common sense practices in this book and hundreds of common sense examples will show you what a visual workplace is and how to apply it to your own world.

In fact, I think you will discover in this book (or already know) what David and I discovered so many years ago: the visual workplace is its own distinct approach to excellence, with its own distinct benefits, and its own distinct implementation methodologies.

Yes, you are right: The visual workplace is not the same as 5S. It is greater than that. And it is greater by far than "a place for everything and everything in its place." But even more, you are right in recognizing your own 5S efforts will slide back into disorganization—they will fail—without the visual workplace.

I'd like to say this again: No matter how much a company tries, it will never be able to sustain its 5S outcomes if it does get visual. In fact, around my company we say: *You won't get lean until you get visual.* And we are so convinced of that, that it has become our company motto. And that's a little scary because we really are saying that a company will fail at lean if it doesn't implement the visual workplace.

In a way, David and I have a selfish reason for wanting you to read Dr. Galsworth's book, *Work That Makes Sense*. VWP now provides systems that allow a company to create its own visuals in-house and on-demand for a fraction of the cost to buy them. David and I want to take that much further. We want to offer companies do-it-yourself tools to get and stay visual—to imbed and sustain lean gains through visuality. Yet until our customers understand that there is much further to go, we cannot really do that.

To go much further, we need a new horizon. And it seems the only way for us to get a new horizon is to make one. We are convinced that this book will go a long way in helping that to happen.

Rhonda Kovera
CEO and Co-Founder
Visual Workplace Inc.
Grand Rapids, Michigan

Acknowledgements

This is a book for and about value-add associates—you. And I have waited nearly twenty years to write it. I could not have written it sooner because I did not know enough about visuality, about the workplace or about you. Now I do. This book is my gift of thanks to you. Any of its errors are my own and no reflection on that thanks. After twenty-five years of working with you, side by side, sharing what I know, learning what you shared, I can only say it has been magical and rewarding beyond measure. Thank you. I hope the pages of this book capture some of my respect and affection for you, and my abiding gratitude.

All in all, I feel the luckiest of people. I work in a field I love. And, besides encountering brilliant visual thinkers everywhere I go, there are people in my life who are willing to help me with that work.

First and foremost, Aurelia Navarro, my esteemed editor. Aurelia has the skills and judgment in her field that allow me to excel in mine. One could want no more from an editor. Except that she is also a friend who supports my work as though it were her own. If I thought Aurelia's mettle had been tested on my previous books, this one, *Work That Makes Sense*, set a new definition of "against all odds." The details shall remain quiet. But my thanks can only be loud and long. Aurelia, without you, this book would never never have happened. Thank you!

Also of enormous help were: Chris Choryan of ETC. Printing Services (Michigan)—I didn't know it would be so hard or you would be so patient, skilled, and pleasant throughout; Angela Willis and Mindy Garlington of PrintSync (Oregon)—even though this project was not given to you, you came through for us again and again so that it could happen; Brook Kirklin, our brilliant and (praise the Lord) enduringly cheerful graphic designer—you took over this project at the eleventh minute of the eleventh hour and made it work. Thanks go as well to graphic designers Kristen Britten and Lubosh Cech.

To you who allowed me to enter your companies and assist on your journey to workplace visuality, thank you. Your vision got me started. Your resolve held things fast when the continuous improvement road got bumpy as it seems to always. But it was your willingness to take on a new paradigm on your journey to excellence—workplace visuality—for which I am enduringly grateful. You are the pioneers.

My heartfelt thanks in particular to:

Pratt & Whitney and **Hamilton Standard** (Connecticut): Clark Shea, Al Lapa, John Christian, Tom Dancy, Mike Feltrin, John Ghann, Al Lapa, Stanley Mickens, Richard Scorzafava, Gordie, Tom Cormier, Cynthia Matroni, Theresa Paul, Brad Slater, John ("Yago") Yacavone, Howard Ferrara, Ed Brey, and the

P&W and Hamilton Standard Team.

United Electric Controls (Massachusetts): David Reis, Harvey Chambers, Paul Plant, Bob Rando, Fred Ritzaw, Lee Sacco, Bruce Hamilton, Annie Yu, Maureen Hamilton, Pat Wardwell, Bill Antunes, John Pacheco, Luis Catatao, Michael Holmes, Beverly Scibilia, Mildred Williams, Randy Campbell, Cindy Barter, Ellen Brill, Randy Brown, Maria Helena Cabral, Randy Campbell, Theresa Carroll, Carlos Chaves, Bob Comeau, Mike Contardo, Tony Cruz, Maureen DiRusso, George Farraher, Dan Fleming, Krikor Frounjian, Shahag Hagopian, Vee Hagopian, Joan Hurton, Pam King, Doug Kuntz, Jesse MacArthur, Debbie Martin, Frank McKenna, Andrea Minasian, Mary Rose Mix, Manny Monteiro, Judy Moon, Ryta Mullen, Cheryl O'Connell, Lilia Orozco, Janet Prescott, Regina Santos, Manny Sousa, Kelly Tonner, Steve Torres, Hieu Tran, Michael Vailliant, Glen Whittaker, Arthur Barter, Levon Khatchadourian, Joe LePage, Aram Minassiam, Berg Narjian, John Mondello, Fernando Rego, Ed Velosa, Gerry Yuskauskas, Guy Alger, Cindy Allen, Gladys Appleby, Frank Barter, Tom Brennan, John Burke, Bill Colby, Chris Cronin, Judy DeMartin, Mark DeNovellis, Jodie Glennon, Diana Hajain, Don Holm, Chris Jaffier, Don Jones, Joe Lyons, John Machado, George McGary, Al Nashawaty, Charlie O'Hearn, Manny Pereira, Janet Raposo, Bob Sanders, Jim Silva, Joe Silva, Joan Sampson, Dave Smith, Terry Sousa, Bud Tucker, Dave Vaughan, Allan Waugh, Dave Williams, Pat Woods, and the UE Team.

Fleet Engineers and sister company, **Lee Industries** (Michigan): Wes Eklund, Brett Balkema, Tim Olt, Kenny Cain, Laura Dewald, Steven Hascher, Dan Herzhaft, Craig Tobey, Dennis Johnson, Larry Kaufman, Gary Buys, Roscoe Clark, Greg Hancock, Al Stone, Jeff Hamm, Robert Oldaker, Garry Boos, Mark DeWitt, Roger Stalzer, Stefanie Bennett, Bruce Boos, Cindy Boos, Harold Coleman, Patti Falbe, Mike Hart, Diane Schmiedeknecht, Terry Verhulst, and the Fleet and Lee Industries Team.

Denison Hydraulics (now Parker Denison/Ohio): Ken Theiss, Joseph Linehan, Steve Harvey, Bill Cornell, Paul Baker, Larry Moore, Rick Ell, Dorothy Wall, Sheila Bowersmith, Michael Church, Ron and Judy Lake, Dave Dobbins, James Justice, Mel Foreman, Mark Bell, and the Denison Hydraulics Team.

Royal Nooteboom Trailers (Holland): Henk Nooteboom, Marc De Leeuw, Roy Kuipers, Frits Foekens, Frank Bogels, Max Janssen, Kees Smeeman, Coby Herman, Henk Hop, Victor Geertruida, Jan Peters, and the RNT Team. **Lifetime Products** (Utah): Richard Hendrickson, Brent Allen, Cliff Holstein, Jared Steele, Sandy Turbyfill, and the Lifetime Team.

Alpha Industries (now Skyworks/Massachusetts): George Levan, Ken Bushmich, Annie Yu, Ellen Babson, George Cassello, Russ McGibbon, Earl Scranton, Sau Tran, Bernice Pereira, and the Alpha Team. **Curtis Screw** (New York): Carl Falletta, Bruce Kilbin, Dave Stanley, Kent Young, and the Curtis Screw Team. **Greene Rubber** (Massachusetts): Patricia Broderick, Eladios Cruz, Ed Davis, Janine DeGusto, Carlos Gomes, Sheila Morton, Daniel Rossetti, and the Greene Rubber Team.

Parker Hannifin (California): Curt Williams, Matt Furlan, Troy Gerard, and the PH Team. **Lockheed Martin** (Texas): Larry Pike, Mark Swisher, Michael Joyce, Marty Harnish, Margie Herrara, John Casey, Robert Boykin, and the LM-Aero Team. **Cobham Aerospace** and **Rolls-Royce** (global): Peter Dobbs and Stephen Pollard. **Plymouth Tube** (USA): Rick Keller, Donald Van Pelt, Jr., and the PT Team.

Harris Corporation (Illinois): John Saathoff, Sue Osier, Janet Jones, Carolyn Rabe, Pat Humke, Deanna Butler, Beverly Sparks, Janet Jones, Carolyn Rabe, Buzz Harlan, Melody Sparrow, Larry Penn, Dewayne Bullock, Lynn Vollmer, and the Harris Team. **Delphi Automotive** (Indiana): Jim Luckman, Jerry Hall, Junior Oliver, Francis Davis, and the Delphi Team. **Scania Trucks** (Holland): Lars Stenqvist, Henk Heijden, and the Scania Team.

Trailmobile/Canada: Tom Wiseman, April Love, and the Trailmobile Team. **Seton Name Plate** (Connecticut): Beverly Nichols, Richard Mini, Joyce Clark, John Barrett, David Martin, and the Seton Team. **Hitchcock Industries** (Minnesota): Ronn Page, Carleton Hitchcock, Jonathan Hitchcock, Mike Suchy, Melanie Haggard, Tim Auelt, Wes Gustafson, Ron Halliday, Adam Koronka, Mike Robbins, Ken Trottier, Troy Zuelzke, and the HI Team. **Delphi** (Mexico): Armando Botti, Socorro Garza, Florencia Martinez, Mark Brown, and the Delphi Team. **Sears Parts & Repair Services** (California): Angie Alvarado, Frank Lopuzinski, Georgeann Georges, Marv Thaxton, and the Sears Team. **Schlumberger** (Kansas): Barry Landon, Mark Metzger, Joseph Wilson, and the Schlumberger Team. **Wilson Transformer** (Australia): Jon Retford, Steve Damm, Mauro Stefani, and the Wilson Team. **Vibco Vibrator** (Rhode Island): Karl Wadensten, Linda Kleineberg, Susan Heater, Lucy Manley, and the Vibco Team.

Friends in the business world who helped along the way: Shigeo Shingo, Ryuji Fukuda, Richard Schonberger, Jeff Madsen, Don Guild, Sherrie Ford and Steve Hollis, Chris Rutter, David Visco, Tony Manos, Martin Hinckley, Anne Marie Chester, Robert Miller, Joy Brisighella, Steve von Niederhausern, Ross Robson, Jake Raymer, Shaun Barker, Ha Chau, John Kim, Brenton Leitch and Gaye Parsons, Keith Hornberger, Paul Harbath, Michel Greif, Annie Yu, Steve Reed, Paul Olsen, Don Dewar, Phil McCready, Oscar Roche, Ben Chopping, Colette Choryan, David Noble, Karen Miklusicak, Bruce Hartman, Sarah Howe, Jon Tudor, Brian Levitan, Norman Bodek, Don Fitch, Joe Rizzo, Louis Stephenson, Tricia Moody, Marley Lunt, Malcolm Jones, Elaine Thorndike, Aleta Sherman, Lavon Winkler, Todd Allen, Cynthia Christie, John Croft, Alice Lee, Michel Baudin, Jerry Bussell, Claude Kennedy, and Don Norman.

David Whyte, poet, author, and an early inspiration to find my own voice and speak it. He is also the source of the image that far too many of us leave the better part of ourselves in our cars when we go to work, with the window slightly cracked so we can reclaim it at the end of the day.

Jeanne Walters, Rhonda Kovera and David Stearns, and Carol Shaw for their trust and support.

The QMI Team: Georgia Spence, Leslie Carver, Harald Hope, Jill Pruett, Linda Faes, and Merlin the Cat.

Personal friends who care and cared for me: Kathryn and Andrew Kimball, Mataare, Jacqueline and Robert Miessen, Dawn Bothie, Barbara Paster, Debaura Shantzek, Rosemary and Neil Tomkinson, Rania James, Jan Caviness, Sara Kane, Marcy Roban, Judy Barry, Sarah Sporn, Diana Brynes, Diana Asay, Pamela Thomas, Marilynn Considine, Annette Mason, Sharon Ward, Janabai Raymundo, Clifflyn Bromling, Tonya Bednarick, Marlena Gangi, Camilla England, Sally Schwager, Dr. Wei Li, and John Clegg.

My remarkable teacher, Swami Chetanananda, with a lifetime of gratitude.

My family, for all that you are to me: Gary Galsworth, Robert Weigler, Ondine Galsworth and Forrest Boone, Daniel Spencer Galsworth, Martha Millwood and Jessica and Julianne, Stacy Joyce, and Karen Cathcart—and to my array of parents, Geraldine, George, and Donato.

Philip Hylos, Edmund Noch, Samuel Bear, and Anderson Merlin for their wildly creative participation in my life and the flawless, unwavering guidance of their hearts. It is your song I sing.

Gwendolyn Galsworth
Portland, Oregon
2011

Preface to Revised Edition

This publication represents the revised edition of *Work That Makes Sense*, an implementation manual on operation-led workplace visuality.

The first release came out in May 2010. Though we worked strenuously to meet our vision of that opportunity, when we had the volume in hand it fell short of what we envisioned, planned for, and desired. For one thing, the nearly 600 photos in the first release needed more room to breathe, be seen, and be understood. The page-by-page discussion also needed more detail; and the combination of the two—photos and text—needed a more creative formatting solution.

In January 2011, we released the book anew, having addressed these concerns, I hope, successfully.

It bears repeating that this book is not a management overview of the logic and application of visual technologies. I have written other books on that important topic, with several more to come. This book is for operators, for people who work on the line, in direct interface with customers or materials or both—what I call the *value-add level*.

I have always wanted to produce a book that spoke to, honored, and supported the vision, knowledge, skill, resolve, imagination, and intelligence of the people on the value-add level of the enterprise—whether factory, bank, military depot, hospital or open-pit mine. I particularly wanted it to be in the voice of "you and I" so I could speak directly, setting up a dialogue or conversation. Many times during the writing of this book, I felt, almost heard, that exchange. It was a palpable experience.

A word about the photographs. First, a number of the photos in this book are already a part of my previous books, videos, presentations and/or webinars. They have been seen before—in some cases repeatedly. While I considered replacing them with a fresh set of examples to demonstrate the incredible scope and depth of the field of visuality, in the end a different motivation persuaded me to include repeat solutions. They are simply the best. Almost iconically, they illustrate core visual concepts and principles. I call them "teaching examples" because they hold and reveal visual elements exceptionally well. They teach us. We learn from them, not just about the mechanics and technical considerations of visuality, but also about higher level considerations that the visual workplace is capable of producing—psychological safety, tolerance, trust, respect for diversity, the corporate intent, alignment, and, ultimately, unity.

Second, though the majority of examples come from a manufacturing setting, this is not a book about visual manufacturing. Because visuality is a universal language, its core principles and concepts are universal as well. There is no company or person visual information sharing cannot help and support. If you work in a non-manufacturing setting, such as mentioned above, don't let the manufacturing nature of the examples deter your study. Take the opposite approach. Study them and uncover their secret mechanics; then apply that to your own workplace. And when you create great teaching examples of your own, send them to me. And I will look to include them in a next book, along with other first-rate solutions that come my way.

At the start, at the end, and at all points along the way, I hope you find this book useful to your purposes and inspiring to your heart and mind.

Gwendolyn Galsworth
January 11, 2011

Work That Makes Sense

Operator-Led Visuality

Visual Workplace Basics

Many people believe they know what a visual workplace is— but it is so much more than is commonly understood. In a thriving visual workplace, one of the greatest benefits is work that makes sense.

In this first book section, we enlist the support of company management and recognize the expertise you already bring to your work. Then you get an overview of visuality, including basic definitions and principles and the *Ten Doorways*. We show you how visual devices translate vital information into exact behavior—your own or other people's.

Then you learn about eight elements—or building blocks— on which a visual workplace is built. The first is *I-driven*, an approach emphasized throughout this book that affirms that what *you* do, think, say, feel, and create matters—a lot. We return again and again to these eight elements as the visual learning and application continue.

Next, you learn the basics of getting ready to launch a visual conversion—and your supervisors and managers start to learn about Leadership Tasks they must undertake to ensure your efforts are well-supported as you create dazzling visual inventions in your area.

As part of this, you and they learn about five hands-on tools for achieving the first set of visual goals: a visual showcase, measurable bottom-line results, and an on-going attitude of learning.

Chapter | One

Introduction to The Visual Workplace

A Word at the Start to Managers

This is a book for operators—those employees responsible for converting materials into shipped products or transforming protocols into delivered services. That is their job.

How many times in the last decade have you heard company executives—even yourself—proclaim that *people* are your organization's most valuable resource? That employees on the value-add level are the experts of their work, and that they must be allowed—empowered—to organize their own work and work area to better suit their needs and the needs of high performance? This, you were told, is the doorway to a spirited, engaged, and aligned workforce—and to the empowerment indispensable to enterprise excellence.

But what does this really mean? How does a company create an empowered workforce while strengthening the bottom line?

This book addresses that, telling you both the what and the how—what true empowerment is and how the organization achieves it. But we discuss these over-arching concepts with two important differences: we discuss them as part of a visual workplace and directly with your value-add workforce—the people you say you want to empower or empower more. Whether you refer to these hardworking, inventive individuals as associates, technicians, operators, hands-on employees, touch labor or workers, they are—as Rolls-Royce puts it—the *experts*.

Every great change requires three things: inspiration (a vision of the horizon), a vehicle (the means for getting there), and a pathway (the map to the destination). These three elements are described in this book in the context of workplace visuality. In 25 years of research and implementation, I have never discovered a more dynamic, creative, and complete approach for operator-led visual conversions than the *Work That Makes Sense* methodology.

And what does that conversion look like? Work areas aglow with tangible intelligence and coherency, speaking through visuality with precision, relevance, and completeness—thanks to the visual language value-add associates have learned to diligently and inventively imbed there.

That is the subject of this book, and it is addressed to your value-add employees. These excellent contributors will find an ample fund of visual workplace concepts, principles, tools, methods, encouragement, teaching, and examples in these pages. And they will be successful *only if*….

Managers, executives, and supervisors, this *only if* is yours.

- *Only if* you become an active part of that transformation will it happen.
- *Only if* you demonstrate your commitment by actively supporting and encouraging people in these tasks will it be realized.
- *Only if* you provide value-add employees with the visual workplace training and supplies they need—along with a quiet place where they can think and experiment—will these same associates decide to convert their areas to the high level of operational functionality the visual approach is designed to achieve.
- *Only if* you designate separate time for visual improvement can it realistically happen in the face of pressing production demands.
- *Only then* can you look forward to a workplace that speaks with the precision, relevancy, timeliness, and tangible completeness that the language of visuality provides.

These *only ifs* are the reason you are the first person I address as this book begins. You are essential to the return on the investment you made when you purchased this book. That investment is one of both money and hope. Throughout this book you will find notes to guide your thinking and actions in support of those outcomes—principles and practices of leadership, commitment, and engagement. You are encouraged to read, practice, and apply them.

Which brings me to the final *only if*.

Only if you read this book cover to cover (not just scan it) and *only if* you deeply absorb it, will you learn to become the ally of the change you say you want. Whether you are an executive, supervisor, manager or CEO, *your involvement is indispensable to the success of this transformation.* And there will be no success for you to support without the release and empowering of the human will that is resident in the people who work closest to where value gets added in your enterprise. They are the *power* in *empowerment.* Only with the transformation of their role from doers to thinkers to implementers will you gain the prosperity, stability, and market scope you long for and expect. And that can only happen with your active and knowing participation.

A Word at the Start to Value-Add Associates

The *Work That Makes Sense* process described in this book is specifically designed to help you gain control over your work and the outcomes that work is meant to produce—as I like to say it, control over your corner of the world.

Since your managers and supervisors need to be partners in this process, there are notes to them throughout the book. But you are the reason this book was written. You are the hero of its pages.

In them, you are invited to consider a new way of seeing—and a new way of solving. I call that new way: *Visual Thinking*. The destination is called a visual workplace.

In a visual work environment, you and your colleagues will find what you need when you need it, know correct quantities and mixes at a glance, meet every deadline on-time, and perform complex tasks with precision and confidence—because you have designed it that way.

At its core, workplace visuality is a language: the language of excellence imbedded into the physical landscape of work. As a language, it will gain popularity, common usage, and power as more and more people in your company begin to "speak" it. I hope it will become your language as well.

Fellow traveler on this wondrous journey, let's get started.

You are the Expert

You are an expert at what you do. You know your job. Whether that job is in a bank, lumber mill, medical facility, military depot, food, chemical or pharmaceutical processing plant, restaurant, oil field, engineering or marketing office, retail outlet, or automobile factory—you are good at what you do, whatever you do and wherever you do it.

Yet that doesn't mean that everything at your work always happens as expected or according to plan. Not everything is always perfect—not in your company or, for that matter, any company; not in your work area or any work area.

On most days, though, knowing your job means that you know what is supposed to happen. And it does. But there are other days when it just doesn't. In fact, sometimes what is *not supposed to happen* happens for so many days in a row that work seems more like drudgery than a job you know well—a struggle instead of a flow. On days like that, work can begin to seem like some kind of insanity. It just doesn't make sense.

Oh sure, there are reasons for that—and you know them. If someone were to ask you, you could list plenty of them. In fact, on some level, all the reasons that things go wrong are right. That's not gibberish. It's just a way of saying: You are right about knowing what causes most problems in your area. To which you might say, half-jokingly…*at least I am right about something!*

The fact is you are not only an expert at the work you were hired to do. You've also become an expert at spotting the problems that keep you from that work.

The real question is: what to do about those problems? Will you become skilled as well at solving those problems, an expert at eliminating them—not just during your shift but permanently?

This is a book about finding those answers and building them into the very process of your work. In that way, the work itself tells you when you are right, when you are wrong or on your way into—or out of—either. The workplace learns to speak. You turn it into a visual workplace—and you are about to learn how.

- How to transform an information-starved work area, step-by-step, into one that is information-rich.
- How to take the struggle out of your work day and put the sense back in through visual information sharing.
- How a robust set of principles, concepts, terms, and methods can help you identify problems at your work that are caused by missing information; and then
- How to minimize or eliminate problems completely through solutions that are visual.
- How to use a set of hands-on implementation tools so you and others can carry through on your ideas and inventions and actually put them into place in your work area.
- How to use the power of the mind, our own natural strength, to help identify the need for visuality and fulfill it.
- How to create work that makes sense by designing a workplace that talks to you in a precise, accurate, complete, and practical language, a language you understand because it is your own language, your own visual language—and that language will make sense.

In short, you will become a *Visual Thinker*.

What is a Visual Workplace?

We'll start by defining a visual workplace:

A visual workplace is self-ordering, self-explaining, self-regulating, and self-improving; where what is supposed to happen does happen, on time, every time, day or night—because of visual devices.

If you remove the last four words—*because of visual devices*—you remove the engine that drives that definition and its outcome as well. Without visual devices, the outcome of *on time, every time, day or night* becomes impossible. Why? Because it is visual devices in the workplace that ensure that what is *supposed* to happen *does* happen. That is their primary purpose.

Here's the definition of a visual device:

A visual device is a mechanism or thing intentionally designed to influence, guide, direct, limit or even guarantee our behavior by making vital information available as close to the point-of-use as possible to anyone and everyone who needs it without speaking a word.

Photo 1.1 In the early days, gas was pumped out of the ground into a clear glass cylinder that showed what you were getting, including if the gas was dirty (a big problem at that time). From there, it flowed by gravity down the hose into the car. Only the calibration marks on the cylinder express true visual information sharing—for viewing and measuring the gas as it flows out.

Photo 1.2 The modern gas pump is so highly visual that, with a little help from you, it easily substitutes for the gas attendant and the cashier.

Look at the workplace known as our local gas station and the evolution of the gas pump in Photos 1.1 and 1.2. Early on, visual information sharing was almost absent. Then as the technology became more complex and the number of people needing gas soared, the need for visual devices also increased. The modern day gas station is flooded with visual devices that make it possible for even the most untrained driver to complete the transaction of *gas-for-money* safely, precisely, and with no supervision. Just try to get the kind of gas you need in the right quantity without the help of visual devices and mini-systems. Impossible!

Photo 1.3 The car is a visual machine.

Consider the car itself (Photo 1.3). Examine it closely—inside the car where the driver sits, under the hood, under the chassis, in the trunk—and you will find no less than 144 visual devices that help you drive the car, maintain it, and, when it breaks down, repair it or pay someone to do it for you. Over 110 million cars and trucks use U.S. roads and highways every day and all of them are *Visual Machines*®.

Visual devices make our roads and highways safe and highly functional for us, our family, and friends. For bus, taxi, ambulance, and truck drivers everywhere, these devices form a vital part of their workday. Visuality on our roads and highways serves as a gigantic adherence mechanism, providing a common language of at-a-glance rules that makes our economy—and the prosperity that follows—possible.

Look at the Photo Cluster 1.4 of vehicle and roadway visual devices below and appreciate the sanity and safety they bring to our everyday life. As you do, realize that these devices did not fall out of the sky. They didn't happen by accident. They happened by design, intentionally.

Photo Cluster 1.4

As a visual thinker-in-the-making, do the following as you consider these devices: remove them in your mind's eye from all the vehicles and roadways on the planet. Now imagine the impact of that for our world. Imagine the problems, delays, accidents, insurance claims, heartache, and expense in an everyday world without visual devices.

In the language of visuality, there is a single word for these headaches: *motion*. *Motion* is corporate enemy number #1 and is defined as *moving without working*. You may be familiar with the term *waste*—well, motion is like that, only much more specific, as you will soon discover.

The Translation of Information into Behavior

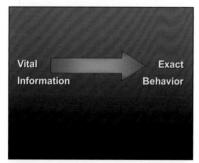

Figure 1.1 The basic transaction of every work day.

The world of work shares a single basic transaction, used millions upon million of times a day: the translation of vital information into human behavior. You see that simple formula in Figure 1.1.

But operationalizing this formula is not that simple. Workplace information changes quickly and often: schedules, customer requirements, engineering specifications, operational methods, tooling and fixtures needs, material location, and the thousands of other details on which daily life in the enterprise depends.

To share that information, most companies depend on classroom and OJT (on-the-job training), binders of SOPs, reference manuals, online instruction, and blueprints to share that information—supported by lots of supervisors and managers who answer our many questions (Figure 1.2). These are all indirect methods, and they have varying levels of effectiveness.

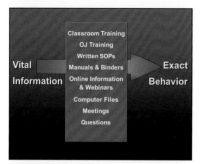

Figure 1.2 Management believes indirect methods will produce the needed behaviors.

The belief is that, once we get the right information, we will do the right thing, the right way, on time and safely. We will behave, as it were, in keeping with that information and good things will result—namely, well-made products, delivered on time and/or well-provided services, presented with a smile. Those same companies assume, incorrectly, that these indirect methods are capable of translating vital information into exact behavior.

The truth is more like this. You begin your day determined to produce outstanding results. Then the unexpected happens: you grab the wrong material (or the wrong material is delivered and you didn't know it); you make the wrong model (because you couldn't quite decipher the work order); you use the wrong tool (because the right one could not be found); you over-heat the part (because the gauge on the oven had slipped); and so on and so forth. You intended to do the right thing—but the wrong thing happened.

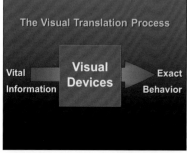

Figure 1.3 Visuality converts information into exact behavior.

What would it be like if the physical workplace itself could make that translation, instead of books, manuals, computers, training hours, coaching, and so on? What would your work day be like if the floors, instead of just holding you up, actually helped you do your work, actively and precisely? What would it be like if the walls assisted you in that—as well as the tools, tables, shelves, carts, materials, machines and other objects in your work area? What if they too became active partners in helping you reach your daily work outcomes—safety, quality, cost, delivery—day after day, week after week, year after year?

This is exactly what happens when we create a visual workplace. When we populate the physical work environment with visual devices, we make an active partner out of that environment. When we do, we ensure that the complete, accurate, and precise information we need is available when and as we need it, as close to the point-of-use as possible.

Look at Figure 1.3. Visual devices become the translation point between vital information (your standards) and the exact behavior or outcome that information is supposed to produce. Instead of the indirect methods described above, the physical workplace itself—these devices—influence, guide, direct, limit or even guarantee that we do the right thing safely, precisely, completely, repeatedly, and reliably.

They transform your physical work area into a gigantic mechanism for adherence, with an impact that is equally gigantic. And it is also simple. You are free to do your work, excellently well. This is precisely why you came to work in the first place. To be a hero. To command and execute excellence—to do ordinary things extraordinarily well.

Visual devices are the translation point between vital information and the exact behavior the information is supposed to trigger. Your journey to a visual workplace begins and ends with them.

Visual Devices Are Everywhere

Visual devices are everywhere in the community, helping us do the right thing, on time and safely, without speaking a word. They guide, direct, and protect us so seamlessly that we barely even notice them. And yet they are powerfully a part of our daily life. Look at this terminal gate at a large metropolitan airport in the States (Photo 1.5).

Notice the yellow marking or line in the middle; in the language of visuality, this is known as the *flow line* or *critical path*. See the black letters and numbers in the yellow cross bars at the end of that flow line (easier to see in Photo 1.6)? We call them *addresses*. The white markings on the left of the flow line are called *borders* as are the red-hatched areas on each side. These are all visual devices—flow line, borders, and addresses. Together, they make up a visual mini-system: a system of visual devices, all aimed at a specific outcome.

Photo 1.5

Question 1: What is the purpose of the yellow bars at the end of the line? Why are they there?

Answer 1: They hold the names of the plane types that use this gate: 727, DC-10, 757, 747, and 777. Each yellow bar indicates the exact spot the plane (by type) must stop its wheels.

Question 2: Why? Why is it important for each plane to stop with such precision?

Answer 2: So that the jet way (or passenger bridge to the right) can quickly and easily connect with the plane's passenger door. Why? So passengers can leave the plane quickly and safely and get on with the reason that brought them to this airport in the first place—a flight connection, business in town, or Grandma's birthday party. That can happen with precision because of this visual system.

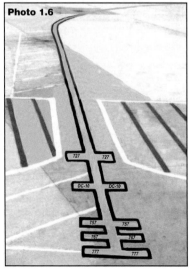
Photo 1.6

The other visual devices at this gate are: the white hatch marks in the lower left that pinpoint the catering function; the white hatch marks in the upper left target baggage handling; and the red-hatched areas to the left and right warn us that rotating turbine blades are nearby.

Let's Think

Think some more about what you see here. Think about how these devices function on the micro level and what their macro impact is. Here are three points.

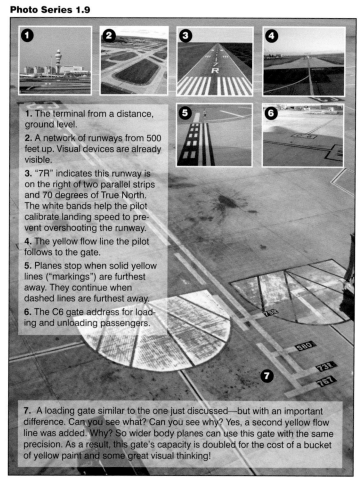

1. The visual devices in this system enable the pilot and ground crew to have a "conversation." Sitting 20-30 feet above the tarmac with the nose of his plane blocking the view, the pilot cannot see his plane's address—the stop point (Photo 1.7). But the ground crew can; and they share that information with the pilot by means of another visual device: signal wands (Photo 1.8).

2. This splendid system of devices is built directly into the "floor" or tarmac and allows the two stake holders—pilot and ground crew—to connect accurately and quickly so they can do the right thing for their customers, the passengers on the plane.

3. This visual mini-system doesn't just benefit pilot, crew, and customers—it also benefits the airline. Once the passengers get off the plane quickly and safely, another group can board just as smoothly; and the plane flies to a new destination. That's the way the airline—and the airport—make money. Nearby towns and cities benefit, as well as the entire regional economy. And, whether you are a pilot, ground crew member or work elsewhere in the airport, when planes take off and land safely and on-time, you get another dose of job security.

All this is thanks, in good part, to the visual mini-system at this gate and the way it builds vital information directly into the process of work. That's the power of a visual workplace.

Photo Series 1.9 contains many airport-based visual solutions including the large photo with a visual device similar to the one we just discussed—that yellow flow line, now doubled. Once a workplace (in this case, an airport) learns how to speak visually (without saying a word), you can bet that visuality will spread and deepen. In this series, the examples show the tarmac, runways,

Photo Series 1.9

1. The terminal from a distance, ground level.

2. A network of runways from 500 feet up. Visual devices are already visible.

3. "7R" indicates this runway is on the right of two parallel strips and 70 degrees of True North. The white bands help the pilot calibrate landing speed to prevent overshooting the runway.

4. The yellow flow line the pilot follows to the gate.

5. Planes stop when solid yellow lines ("markings") are furthest away. They continue when dashed lines are furthest away.

6. The C6 gate address for loading and unloading passengers.

7. A loading gate similar to the one just discussed—but with an important difference. Can you see what? Can you see why? Yes, a second yellow flow line was added. Why? So wider body planes can use this gate with the same precision. As a result, this gate's capacity is doubled for the cost of a bucket of yellow paint and some great visual thinking!

and the airport terminal itself. They are all speaking the same visual language.

Next time you go to the airport (especially in a larger city), notice how visual devices help you from the moment you enter the airport property. The next time you fly, get a window seat and watch as the plane taxis. You'll see lots of visual devices, for pilots, ground crew, and support services (Photo 1.10). These devices do this so seamlessly, we hardly notice them. We simply obey—we and the thousands of other people who use that airport daily. We do the right thing because it is so easy to know what it is.

Photo 1.10

Together, these devices create a level of operational excellence that would be impossible to achieve without them—everything and everyone functions to plan, safely, accurately, precisely, completely, and on-time. What is true for the airport is true for so many community locations. If they are visual, they are almost certainly also safe, well-run, productive, and prospering. We live in a visual world because we are visual beings (and not the reverse). Keep your eyes open and you will see visual devices everywhere!

Before we look more closely at the pre-visual workplace, let's clear up a possible misunderstanding. The purpose of a visual device is to carry a message—vital information. But, such a device can and often does use any of our five senses. Please read Inset 1.1 for more on this interesting knowledge point.

Inset 1.1 Visual vs. Sensory Devices

Calling the devices you see in this book visual might be a bit inaccurate. Why? Because such devices can use any or all of our five senses—not just our sense of sight—to share information and deliver the message. Take a look.

1. Sight. Our most frequently used sense is sight. We are visual beings therefore we live in a visual world. The highways are thick with road signs like the one you see here, telling us vital things.

2. Sound. The ringing phone delivers the message that someone wants to talk to us. In the workplace, beepers on trucks and forklifts warn us when they are backing up and may be heading our way.

3. Smell. Gas in its natural form is colorless, (nearly) odorless, and highly combustible. You can't see it, can hardly smell it—and yet it can kill. In visuality we say: it carries no message, no warning. That's why a rotten-egg smell is often intentionally added—so we can remember to turn stove off or detect a leak before a fire or explosion. The smell became a "visual" device.

4. Taste. A toddler puts everything in her mouth, including that bottle of poison you forgot to throw out. After too many were harmed, a bad taste (and often smell) is now routinely added to send the message: "UGH! Don't drink me!" An opposite message is sent when cherry flavor is added to otherwise bad-tasting medicine.

5. Touch. Small, raised bumps imbedded in walkways (called "tactile paving") are used extensively on crosswalks and train platforms to alert the visually impaired of danger. The blind receive this message through the tips of their canes; others through the soles of their shoes.

The Pre-Visual Workplace

By now, you get it. An airport is a workplace and the visual devices we see there ensure that what is supposed to happen does happen. They ensure work that makes sense. So why not bring them into your own company, into your own work area, onto your own bench or desk?

Photo 1.11 A visually-competent area.

The vast system of visual devices that make our airports safe, productive, and profitable can do the same there, though the exact devices will differ because your operations differ.

To make sure you understand the power of visuality, let's use our imagination. Remove the visual devices you just studied from the airport gate (Photo 1.11). In your mind's eye, erase the yellow flow line, addresses, and white and red borders. What does that gate look like now? Probably like Photo 1.12. And what is the impact of that?

Photo 1.12 A recipe for motion.

Would it still be as safe to work at that gate? Would it be as productive? For you? For your customers? Would passengers still have a satisfying experience, safely and smoothly coming and going as their needs required? Would that huge white airplane you see in the upper left even be able to land at an airport where gate operations were not visual? What do you think?

Now ripple your mind out and remove all the visuals you saw in the airport photo album. Turn that airport into a pre-visual workplace—where there are no visual devices, zero visual information sharing. What would that mean? What would be the impact of that?

How many planes per day could land or take off safely in an airport that is not visual? Even if the government didn't require such devices, would you risk flying in or out of that place? Would other people? Think about the consequences of an airport without visuality and then the consequences for the community it supports.

Now apply that same logic to your own work area—the place where you spend 35-40 job hours a week (plus overtime). To what extent does that location speak to you—in a language that makes the meaning of that place and the work that goes on there clear, correct, precise, complete, and available at-a-glance? To what extent is your work area visual right now?

In today's world, information is the bedrock of our daily life, so much so we hardly notice until it's not there anymore. Easy access to information is vital to our way of life, and visuality is the main way we access it. Think again of our roads and highways. They are populated with visual devices that powerfully and precisely guide and direct us on our way. We barely notice them because they are so much a part of what we expect—what we have come to rely on—to help us do the right thing, and avoid the wrong thing. The result? We can get where we want to go, safely, and on-time.

Why Not in the Workplace

Why not bring the power of visuality to our banks, hospitals, factories, mines, military depots, engineering and marketing offices, retail stores, restaurants, utility plants, processing facilities, schools and universities, movie lots, and construction sites? Why not bring visuality to the entire world of work?

In a pre-visual workplace, we are forced to rely on our words, alone, (whether written or spoken) to convey information and meaning. As a result, we stay busy reading, or talking and listening (they're called "meetings")—or talking too much and listening too little (also "meetings"). You know how that goes. Even when the information we need is in a report or binder—or, heaven help us, somewhere in a computer—it is never really close enough. It is not where we need it—at our fingertips, at the point of use.

If you ever spent an hour searching your computer for a file you worked on only yesterday, you know exactly what this means. The information is in there somewhere but you cannot find it and so you cannot use it. And even if you do find it, you really only need part of it, not all 15 screens.

Photo 1.13

The pre-visual workplace is always hungry for information, starved for the information that is either there "somewhere" or simply not there. In either case, information is missing—details that can usually only be found in the mind or memory of someone else. But what if that colleague is out ill or just began a two-week vacation? What if he or she is at yet another meeting or just got promoted? What happens is: We're stuck. When all is said and done, the result of missing information is this: We can't do our work, not all of it or not yet or not exactly, completely, safely or on-time (Photo 1.13).

I began this chapter by declaring you an expert at what you do. I know this is true and so do you. But in an information-starved work area—a pre-visual workplace—you will never get to show that to me, you, or anyone else. Instead, you are going to do a lot of wandering around and asking questions—and a lot of listening to answers that are not really the answers you need. Or you just might decide to skip all that and guess—take a chance out of desperation or determination to get on with your day. Or you may decide to do nothing, to simply stop and wait.

Yes, you are good at what you do—but in an information-hungry, pre-visual work area, chances are slim that you are going to get to do it.

Regardless of the type or size of your organization, information drives your day. If a single employee anywhere in the company cannot get the exact information he or she needs, when and as needed, the organization has a

Photo 1.14 Information deficits are like fish that escape from a torn fishing net. If fishermen don't fix their nets, they'll lose a lot of fish.

rip in it. Like an otherwise strong fishing net (Photo 1.14), the size and number of these rips—of these information deficits—will determine the level of struggle we will have to deal with.

The *Ten Doorways* we are about to discuss show that each of us can learn to minimize or even eliminate those deficits for ourselves and for others—no matter the organizational level and no matter the cause.

The Ten Doorways:
Creating a Workforce of Visual Thinkers

This book is about how you, a value-add associate, can become a visual thinker and what that means to the enterprise. But that alone will not turn your company into a fully-functioning visual workplace. To become a robust visual work environment, your enterprise must engage everyone in making a visual contribution. Each employee must open a door that leads to higher and more complete levels of visual information sharing, relative to their own work.

Everyone must become a visual thinker: you, your supervisor, your manager, the material handlers, executives, planners, schedulers, doctors and nurses, machinists, assemblers, engineers, buyers, marketing and sales staff—everyone. And when everyone inside your company is involved, it's time for your supply chain to get on board.

That is why I say there are ten doorways into a fully-functioning visual workplace, each one opened by specific organizational groups or levels. I developed this ten-doorway framework (Figure 1.4) in order to show that each company level gets involved—and has to get involved—in creating a fully-functioning visual workplace. These doorways also tell us precisely what category of visual function each level is accountable for—which doorway each level owns.

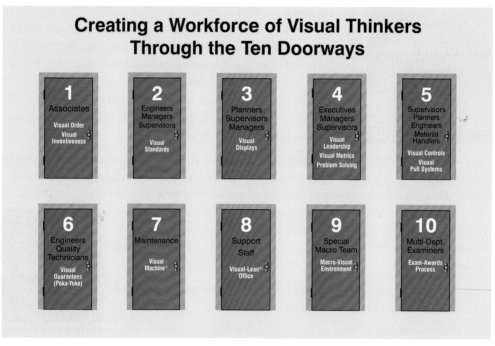

Figure 1.4 A fully-functioning visual enterprise is created with the participation of the entire workforce.

For example, engineers and supervisors own *Doorway 2: Visual Standards*. But that doesn't mean that you and other value-add associates are not allowed to create visual standards. You almost certainly will and should. It simply means that the company holds managers, engineers, and supervisors responsible for distributing accurate, precise, and complete technical and procedural standards across the organization—and then making them visual.

As an area associate, you own *Doorway 1: Visual Order/Visual Inventiveness*, the subject of this book. But that doesn't mean that engineers and supervisors—and all other employees—are not expected to also implement visual order (the visual where) in their respective work locations. They are! And they definitely will as visuality picks up speed and focus in the enterprise. But your group will take the lead in operations—because, above and beyond everyone else, the visual where is critical to *your* work. You have an urgent need to know where the things of your daily work are.

The point is the ten doors we are about to scan are not restrictive or exclusive. Anyone in the company can contribute a visual solution for any doorway. But specific groups are held accountable for making sure that specific categories of visual function are implemented in the enterprise, no matter what.

Now let's take a short walk through each of the ten doorways.

Doorway 1 • Value-Add Associates • Visual Order/Visual Inventiveness

The first doorway belongs to you. As an expert on the value-add level, focus first on installing the visual where in your area. Knowing precisely where things are, at-a-glance, removes a ton of struggle. The borders in Photo 1.15 make the exact placement of a cable wheel easy. The device in Photo 1.16 ensures that we'll pick the right part. After the visual where, start inventing visual solutions to help work make more sense for yourself and others. In Photo 1.17, Pete, a welder, uses a magnetic tag to alert the forklift driver he needs a load of 1990s next. You'll see hundreds of operator-level visual solutions in the chapters to come.

Photo 1.15

Photo 1.16

Photo 1.17

Doorway 2 • Engineers, Managers & Supervisors • Visual Standards

Doorway 2 is about making the two types of operational standards visual: 1) technical standards (your product and process specifications); and 2) procedural standards (your work methods and SOPs). Supervisors, managers, and engineers own this doorway because they are responsible for providing accurate, precise, complete, and timely standards—and then, in a visual workplace, making them visual. Photo 1.18 is a visual standard showing the right and wrong way of taping an electrical wiring harness. Photo 1.19 shares the SOP for crushing a part.

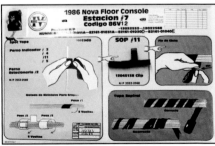

Photo 1.18

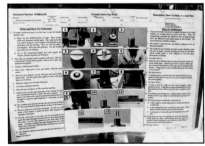

Photo 1.19

Doorway 3 • Planners, Supervisors & Managers • Visual Displays

In Doorway 3, supervisors, managers, and planners create visual displays (production control boards) so they can track what needs to be done, in what quantity, by when, where, and by whom. There are as many formats for visual displays as there are needs for them. The display in Photo 1.20 tells us the release schedule for ECNs (Engineering Change Notices), with a spot for follow-up needs. Photo 1.21 is a maintenance display for all current work orders, arranged by what's completed (green), what's new (yellow), and what's overdue (red). We call this: "Telling the truth as that truth changes."

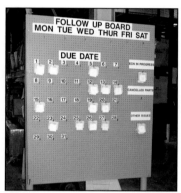

Photo 1.20

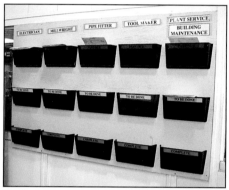

Photo 1.21

Doorway 4 • Executives, Managers & Supervisors • Visual Leadership + Visual Metrics + Visual Problem Solving

Company leaders are responsible for: (1) maintaining focus on the vision, mission, and goals of the enterprise; (2) driving towards them through measures (key performance indicators); and (3) solving problems permanently. Doorway 4 helps leaders make that happen visually. This threesome is visuality's response to the need for *hoshin* (Japanese for "compass") in every enterprise. Photo 1.22 shows the gap between our last best performance (100% on-time delivery) and today's (93%). Such metrics drive the company's annual plan, for example using the X-Type Matrix (Photo 1.23). The matrix then gets translated into an Operations Roadmap for action on the value-add level (Photo 1.24).

Photo 1.22

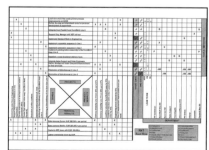

Photo 1.23

Photo 1.24

Doorway 5 • Supervisors, Planners, Engineers & Material Handlers • Visual Controls + Visual Pull Systems

5

Supervisors
Planners
Engineers
Material
Handlers

Visual Controls

**Visual
Pull Systems**

Determining the order and flow of materials into your area is the role of planners, engineers, supervisors, and material handlers. They own Doorway 5. Their first task is to control material quantity and usage, achieved in Photo 1.25 by the red-line visual control that limits the number of boxes in this area to 18.

The second task is to implement visual pull systems—creating pull by limiting quantity or volume. Photo 1.26 shows a 4-part kanban square that ensures there is always enough (and just enough) material to operate. "Don't worry," this device says, "you won't run out. But you also can't hoard material. We took away the room."

Photo 1.25

Photo 1.26

Doorway 6 • Engineers & Quality Technicians • Visual Guarantees

6

Engineers
Quality
Technicians

Visual
Guarantees
(Poka-Yoke)

Engineers and your Quality Department are responsible for product and process quality. Doorway 6 focuses on the smartest, surest, quickest way for that to happen: visual guarantees (*poka-yoke* systems). First, your quality techs learn how to build 100% source inspection into the process of work; then they teach you how to do it. The result? You become masters of cause on the attribute level. No more mistakes.

Photo 1.27 is a masking template that prevents us from picking the wrong drill bit in final machining. The device in Photo 1.28 makes sure we assemble all 72 clips—because they are pre-counted and waiting for us on this board.

Photo 1.27

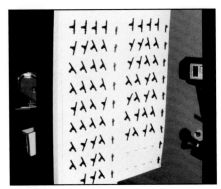

Photo 1.28

Doorway 7 • Maintenance Department • Visual Machine®

If production in your company relies on machinery, your Maintenance Department can stay very busy. In Doorway 7, Maintenance seeks your help in getting the machines to speak through visual devices. When machines become visual, everyone knows how to run and maintain them—at-a-glance. And when a visual machine needs a fix, we know it almost before the machine does. Plus, because the machine speaks, maintenance can make its repairs more quickly. The green in Photo 1.29 shows us, at-a-glance, the acceptable range for this bladder gauge. The device in Photo 1.30 helps to make sure dull tools get sharpened and sharpened tools get returned—visually.

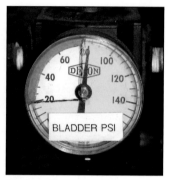

Photo 1.29

Photo 1.30

Doorway 8 • Support Staff • Visual-Lean® Office

Research shows that nearly 70% of all costs begin in company office and support areas. Doorway 8 helps office staff make their areas speak so that they, too, can tell at-a-glance what's right, what's wrong, what's fast, what's slow—and how to make corrections. When pull is added to that equation, lean is added to visual. The result is the visual-lean office, a visual conversion using the first six Doorways, this time exclusively in the office setting. In Photo 1.31 we see the visual where for the corner printer. David (Photo 1.32) posts his full address over his desk—so we know which products he's responsible for purchasing.

Photo 1.31

Photo 1.32

Doorway 9 • Special Macro Team • Macro-Visual Environment

As areas gather speed on the visual journey, the company forms a special team to coordinate visuality across the enterprise. That is Doorway 9 and your macro-visual team (Photos 1.33 and 1.334), comprised of ace visual thinkers who pay attention to the big picture. They identify the need for and create visual linkages between departments, and pinpoint visual best practices-in-the-making. Thanks to them, visual information sharing deepens and grows across the enterprise and down the supply chain. Value-add associates—you!—also sit on this team. I hope you say yes when this opportunity comes along.

Photo 1.33

Photo 1.34

Doorway 10 • Multi-Department Examiners • Exam-Awards Process

Doorway 10 houses QMI's Exam-Awards Process, a framework developed for companies well-advanced in visuality that want to make sure visual practices are tied together and continue to grow for maximum success. Doorway 10 examiners assess each area (Photo 1.34), using a set of visual principles and practices known as visual scorecards (Photo 1.35). Examiner teams are comprised of master visual thinkers from all levels of the organization, including yours—value-add associates—after you have learned to make your own work areas speak, loud and clear, through workplace visuality.

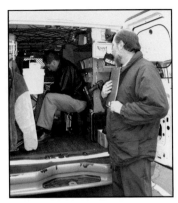

Photo 1.35

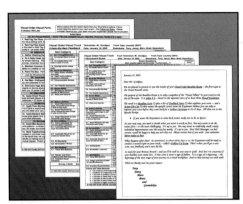

Photo 1.36

There they are, the Ten Doorways and how these doorways are used to create a workforce of visual thinkers in the enterprise, with each company function making powerful visual contributions to take the struggle and guessing out of their own work. The result? An enterprise populated by hundreds, even thousands, of visual solutions—not just on the production floor but equally in support offices, sales and marketing, the lobby, and the board room. And then, sooner or later, visuality jumps organizational boundaries into your company's supply chain.

Imagine what it would mean for your company to become a fully-functioning visual work environment—what that would mean for your internal and external customers, for the work that gets done in your company and for the people who do it. Imagine what that would mean for you.

The Benefits of a Visual Workplace

As you are beginning to understand, a visual workplace is for everyone who works in your company because it is created by them. The benefits of this are many. Here are seven.

Benefit 1: Work Happens. When vital workplace information is wrong, incomplete, confusing, late, or simply missing (all called "information deficits"), problems occur, even chaos. But when that same information is clear, correct, precise, complete, on-time, and available at-a-glance, you—and the people around you—can get on with work. So the first benefit of creating a visual workplace is simply this: work happens.

Benefit 2: Sense of Safety. The second benefit of a visual workplace is that people learn they can depend on themselves for good outcomes—and they can depend on others as well. When the work environment is rich with vital information that you and everyone else can access at-a-glance, each person begins to feel a new sense of safety—safety in body, mind, and heart. We reach a new level of trust with our work environment and with the people who work there. In this way, visuality puts us powerfully in the driver's seat of our own work. And there's plenty of room on that bus for everyone.

Benefit 3: Visual Thinking. Third, when a problem arises due to missing information (information deficits), you and your colleagues are able to spot that right away and eliminate it quickly through visual solutions. In this way, you and those around you become scientists of your own work and masters of cause. You become visual thinkers.

Benefit 4: Partners with the Physical. The fourth benefit of workplace visuality happens because—through visual devices—you have made a partner out of the physical workplace (Photo 1.37). For example, you learn to expect more from the floor than simply its capacity to hold you up. You start to see the physical objects in your area in a new light—the desks, carts, benches, machines, tools, parts, shelves, cabinets, walls, and so on. Instead of "just things," you realize that each of these items can help you in your work if you give it a voice to speak—if you make it visual. This partnership deepens our appreciation and use of the inanimate things that populate our lives.

Photo 1.37 Maryanne made a partner out of the top of her desk when she fixed her ounces-to-liters conversion chart directly on it, along with a sample materials label. (Seton Name Plate/Connecticut)

Benefit 5: Bottom Line. The results of the above are powerful improvements in product and process quality, lead time, safety, employee morale, on-time delivery, and cost. Visuality impacts measures and metrics—your key performance indicators (KPIs)—directly and significantly.

Make no mistake: When you share vital information visually, what is supposed to happen does happen. You and your entire work area perform better than ever, in ways that inspire others and go straight to the bottom line.

Here's a sample of actual Doorway 1 results from several companies already on the visual journey:

- 15%-30% increase in productivity
- 70% reduction in waiting
- 70% reduction in material handling
- 54% reduction in walking
- 96% improvement in quality
- 68% reduction in storage requirements
- $2,555,000 scrap reduction (yearly)
- 7,132 hours of machine downtime eliminated (yearly)
- 60% reduction in floor space requirements
- 100% elimination of rework

Pretty impressive—thanks to associates like you who learned to think visually.

Benefit 6: Company-wide Alignment. Benefit six happens when visual solutions in your area get linked up with those in other areas. The organization becomes connected as though it were a human body. Like your own physical body, the company knows what's happening in all of its parts and can begin to function more holistically. When all work areas are visually connected, communication between them becomes smoother, more accurate, more precise and complete, and timely. Alignment follows. The enterprise knows—and can know—itself.

Look at Figure Series 1.5. Here you see an organization from the perspective of an individual (A) and a bunch of individuals (B). Clearly, while everyone is busy, there is no enterprise alignment—and without alignment there can be no empowerment. But an aligned and empowered workforce is perfectly evident in (C), with everyone still busy, this time working for common outcomes.

Benefit 7: Unity. The seventh benefit of workplace visuality is the big picture: visuality liberates information and, as a result, it liberates the human will.

That is, when we take information out of our minds, filing cabinets, and computers—and install it, instead, into the physical workplace in the form of visual devices and mini-systems, we can move through our work day with confidence, skill, and flow. As we do, we contribute to our own well-being and the well-being of others. We feel powerful because we are powerful. A deep part of ourselves brightens and

Figure Series 1.5

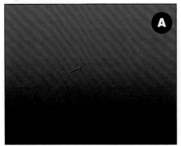

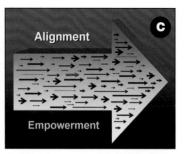

A. Here is a well-intentioned individual in a company without workplace visuality—pedaling away in a direction she thinks is a good one for the organization.

B. Here are a bunch of well-intentioned individuals in a company without workplace visuality--each pedaling away in a direction they think is a good one, many of them opposite.

C. And here is the same company after implementing workplace visuality across many of the Ten Doorways, with an aligned and empowered workforce one of the happy results.

engages. That part is called: our will.

That will, which each of us has in equal measure, is the part that decides—decides to act or not to act, decides to improve or not to improve, decides to participate or not to participate. That will needs information to embrace its power. That is why the will often gets dusty, testy, or even distorted when information is scarce, wrong, incomplete, or too late. Stressed and confused, we lose touch with our true self—our true will—and begin to feel powerless to change, impact, or improve our lives. In the face of that stress and confusion, some of us withdraw, become passive, and appear not to care. Others strike out, become aggressive and seem to care too much—in the opposite direction.

These two situations are not polar opposites. They are instead symptoms of the same problem: information deficits—missing information. Visual information sharing cures both; it is this problem's antidote. When we liberate information through visuality, we liberate the human will. Liberated, that will—our will—is free to decide…to decide, for example, to follow the corporate intent, to say yes to the company's vision, goals, and objectives—or elect not to. In either case, the decision is powerful and life-changing.

Saying yes means that we join in and align with what the company wants because we see there is good in it for us too. This is not giving up on our own dreams; it is realizing that in helping the company succeed, our own dreams can be made more real. This is a moment of mighty agreement. It cannot happen if we do not feel safe in body, mind, and heart. It cannot happen in an information-scarce work environment.

Benefit seven is the result of adding all the previous benefits together. You get something that is both the result of and greater than that sum. You get unity—an organization so aligned, synchronized, and energized in its own excellence that it demonstrates the higher values of human endeavor—generosity, harmony, common purpose, shared destiny, a growing excellence, and a built-in flexibility that allows the enterprise to succeed beyond usual definitions. Prosperity in the fullest measure of that word blossoms.

Such a company becomes a touchstone and inspiration to other companies and to society at large, pointing the way to a new horizon of possibility. We learn from that kind of organization, even as it continues to learn and grow from the higher role it has embraced.

This may appear a grandiose claim in a simple book about workplace visuality. But it is not. It is a truth that many companies have repeatedly experienced. Not always in the fullness of that promise—of what is ultimately possible. But always with a promise that the next stage of excellence can emerge if the company keeps going, and the next stage after that, and the next and the next.

So you are invited to begin—to begin to learn about and apply the visual concepts, principles, tools, and methods presented in this book. This is an invitation to become a part of something greater by becoming greater yourself as you help that great thing happen: a fully-functioning visual workplace where what is supposed to happen does happen on time every time day or night—because of visual devices. Become a visual thinker.

> ## You miss 100 percent of the shots you never take.
>
> Wayne Gretzky

Chapter | Two

The Building Blocks of Visual Thinking

There are two definitions fundamental to this chapter, both of which you have seen before. The first is the definition of a *visual workplace*:

> *A work area that is self-ordering, self-explaining, self-regulating, and self-improving…where what is supposed to happen does happen on time every time, day or night—because of visual devices.*

The second is the definition of *visual thinking*:

> *Your ability to recognize motion (the enemy) and the information deficits that trigger it—and then to eliminate both through solutions that are visual.*

You must understand both terms and how they interact with each other if you are to achieve a fully functioning visual work environment. And to do that, you must first understand the *Eight Building Blocks of Visual Thinking* (Figure 2.1).

One Simple Reason: Too Many Questions

There is one simple reason why a visual workplace is needed: People have too many questions. Some of these questions are asked but most of them are not. When people don't ask questions, they do one of three things: (1) they do nothing and just

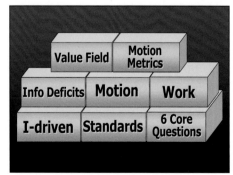

Figure 2.1 The Eight Building Blocks of Visual Thinking.

wait until the answer shows up; (2) they go hunting for the answer; or (3) they make stuff up and go with their own best guess. Sometimes that "stuff" works; many times it doesn't.

You may wonder why people don't just ask the questions they have. That answer lies in the mysteries of the human heart. Some of us don't ask questions because we don't want to appear ignorant or uninformed. Others don't ask because they know that nobody has the answer anyway—so why bother. Still others have *not* been told the truth in the past (intentionally or not), so they have learned not to trust the answers they are given. Still others of us don't ask:

- Because we've come to resent having to ask questions in the first place—especially the same questions over and over again, such "What do I do next?" or "Where is the material for this job?" or "What are the specifications for this order?" Ordinary questions like these can rob us of our dignity if we have to ask them repeatedly.

- Because the person we must ask (who may also happen to be our boss) is, for example, half our age and brand-new to the company—whereas we've worked here twenty-three years. Our per-sonal pride keeps us from asking.

These are not uncommon reasons for people to hesitate to ask questions; and there are doubtlessly other reasons. And when the preceding conditions combine, we might find ourselves faced with asking the same dumb questions, twenty times a day, of a person half our age who thinks his/her main job is to answer questions. So we refuse to go after the very answers we need and, instead, get angry or go numb, do nothing or—as mentioned, just make stuff up.

If we repeatedly don't get plain, accurate, and complete answers to our questions, we may start asking other kinds of questions, eyes skyward…for example: "Is this what I'm here for? This?! Chasing down tiny answers to the same old tiny questions I asked yesterday, and the day before that, and the day before that? Oh dear heaven, show me the way out of here!"

For those less philosophically-inclined, the inner protest might sound more like: "What the heck is this? Chasing down the same stinkin' answers, day in and day out! I've had it! I'm outta here!"

Neither person may actually quit. We all have bills to pay and loved ones to support. Besides we may genuinely like our job and the company we work in—if only the struggle would stop, if only it made more sense!

So we stay—or at least our hands and our feet do. But we may leave the better part of ourselves in the parking lot, in our car, with the window slightly cracked so that part is still alive and waiting when the workday is over.

This is not what we signed up for when we agreed to this job. It is not how most of us want to earn our daily bread. Most of us want to earn our living in a meaningful way, doing our work, and expressing excellence. Faced with the insanity-of-tidbits, some of us go numb; others go ballistic.

At the center of this situation is an issue that affects and shapes much in our daily work life, not just in the United States but in the world of work around the globe. That issue is: "Who gets the power?" That is: "Who gets the power to have the answers—when and as we need them—complete, accurate answers that are on time without special effort?"

Not so very long ago, our society learned that *information is power*. That is exactly why many people feel dis-empowered when asking questions—and others feel far too powerful when answering them. One way or the other, asking/answering questions has become a play of power, highly destructive to the journey to excellence. More about this in a few pages when we talk about *information hoarders*.

Since the primary purpose of a visual workplace is to make answers to vital workplace questions readily and easily available, without speaking a word, we better look at the question of questions carefully.

Building Block 1: I-Driven Visuality

When you look closely at all the workplace questions you ask—or anyone else asks—you discover that only two questions drive them all.

The First Driving Question: The Need-to-Know

The first of these two driving questions is: *What do I need to know?* That is:

> *What do I need to know that I don't know right now in order to do my work—or in order to do my work better? What information do I need?*
> (Figure 2.2)

Figure 2.2 The first driving question.

Need-to-know questions can be very basic. If you work in a factory, an urgent need-to-know question might be: "Where are my pliers?" In a hospital, it might be, "Where are the patient charts?" In an accounting office, it might be, "Where's that report I was working on yesterday?"

Yes, these are plain questions but how many people will you have to ask to get the plain answer: "There! There are your pliers." "There! There's your cart." "There! There is your report." All the while you mutter, "What's it doing there anyway?"

For more plain questions, look at the boxes below (Figures 2.3 to 2.5), listing typical questions across three kinds of workplaces.

FACTORY *Need-to-Know Questions*	HOSPITAL *Need-to-Know Questions*	ACCOUNTING OFFICE *Need-to-Know Questions*
• Where are my pliers? • What am I supposed to run next? • Where is the material for that order? • Where are the fixtures for that changeover? • How do I change over this machine? • When will that sub-assembly be ready? • Who's on vacation today? • Where is my supervisor?	• Which patients do I look after today? • Where are their charts? • When will the doctors visit today? • Does this kit contain everything I need? • How many beds will be freed up this week? • Who is my supervisor today? • Where is my supervisor?	• Where is the report I worked on yesterday? • When exactly is that report due? • What appendix do I include? • Who do I give this correction to? • How do I deliver this confidential file? • How many more reports need to be completed today? • Where is my supervisor?
Figure 2.3	**Figure 2.4**	**Figure 2.5**

Plain as they may sound, these are the kinds of questions that drive workplace visuality. How? Because once you track down the answers to your need-to-know questions, you then translate those answers into visual devices and imbed the answers, visually, directly into your work area, into your value field—so you never ever have to ask those questions again and no one ever has to answer them! Keep going from there—through cycle after cycle of translating your questions into visual answers—and you will build a robust visual work environment.

Photos 2.1 and 2.2 are reminders of need-to-know solutions you saw in Chapter 1.

Photo 2.1 Rick Ell built this tooling fixture, color-coded by model. Now he can tell at-a-glance which tool to use when he changes over his machine.

Visuality is I-Driven

Please notice that the first driving question does not read: "What do WE need to know?" It reads: "What do *I* need to know?" That *I* is you.

If it did read "what do *we* need to know," then you'd face yet another challenge before you could convert your answers into visual devices: a meeting! If the question read "we," you'd have to meet with others in your area to discuss and decide which are the most important need-to-know questions, what the possible answers are, and is it really necessary to bother with any of them anyway. You'd meet, present, discuss, analyze, plan, probably vote, and certainly meet again. And there is no guarantee that enough people would agree that you need to know what you know you need to know—let alone agree on the form of a visual device that would imbed the answer. A dreary prospect at best.

Photo 2.2 This is a masking template trimmed in black that prevents us—100%—from taking the wrong machining drill bit. A second template, in blue, has different cutouts for a second model.

But the question does not say "we." It says "I." And since that "I" is you, you are in the driver's seat of your own visual inventiveness. Good idea! After all, you know which questions you need answered better than anyone—because they are *your* questions. And you know your work. And that means you also know what stands in the way of getting that work done. So there's no requirement for you to present, discuss, analyze, plan, or vote on anything; doing so would probably defeat the very purpose in your asking in the first place. Simply ask the questions that drive you (crazy) and answer them. Then translate those answers into visual devices—so you never have to ask those questions again. And to that we all say: "Hurray!"

We have confidence in that "I" and so do you. That "I" is us, too. The starting place for all workplace visuality—for you and for us—is the "I." (By the way, that holds true for all ten of the Ten Doorways presented in the Chapter 1.) That's why we say: *The visual workplace is an I-driven process—an I-driven methodology.* Because it is so important, let's make the point again, using other words:

- The visual devices you create are triggered by *your own* need-to-know.
- Your need-to-know drives the visual devices you create.
- You, and you alone, are the person who decides what your need-to-know is and what the visual device will be that answers it.
- As long as your device does no harm to, and does not interfere with, someone else or their work, other people do not have to agree with you.

- In the visual workplace, *you* are in control of *your* corner of the world.

And if you are concerned because you share your bench or desk with others, we will discuss some simple ways of handling that later in this book.

Figure 2.6 The second driving question.

The Second Driving Question: The Need-to-Share

As you read through the above discussion, did you find yourself thinking: "I" "I" "I"—that sounds pretty selfish. Where do other people fit in? What about teams? What about "we?"

Good point. But don't worry. The "we" in a visual workplace enters powerfully into the picture with the second question that drives workplace visuality: "What do I need to share?" That is:

What do I know that others need to know that I need to share in order for them to do their work—or for them to do it safer, better, faster or at less cost? What information do I need to share? (Figure 2.6)

Notice this second question is still formed around the "I." It is still I-driven. But instead of you driving the question, this time you respond to it. The second question drives you. Where? To the next level of visuality in your area, triggered by the needs of others. Your focus, which was squarely on yourself before, is now turned outwards to others. "How may I help you?" is another way to say this.

At the heart of this second question is the recognition that each of us has knowledge and know-how that other people need in order to do their own work better and/or more safely—whether those other people are co-workers, a supervisor or manager, internal suppliers and customers, or external suppliers or customers. They are all our colleagues, our work companions. We are all on the same team, whether we will ever sit together in the same room. And they are all customers of the information you know. Here are some common need-to-share questions, across the three workplaces we looked at before (Figures 2.7 to 2.9).

FACTORY	**HOSPITAL**	**ACCOUNTING OFFICE**
Questions from Others that Trigger the Need-To-Share from You	*Questions from Others that Trigger the Need-To-Share from You*	*Questions from Others that Trigger the Need-To-Share from You*
• Planner: What are you working on now?	• Co-Nurse: Which patients are mine today?	• Operator: Who buys sintered metals for the J-190s? We're almost out.
• Planner: When will it be ready?	• Newcomer: Where do you keep the blankets?	• Supervisor: When will that report you owe me be ready?
• Supervisor: Where is the order you just completed?	• Nurse from other area: Where is the emergency kit?	• Purchasing Officer: Who do I give these corrections to?
• Accounting: When will my report be ready?	• X-Ray: When are you sending Mr. Smith?	• Co-clerk: How many copies do I make of this joint report and who gets it?
• Co-Operator: What's my next changeover, when, and where d'ya put the fixture I need that you used yesterday?	• Admission: How many beds will be freed up at the end of the week?	
• Quality: Where are those defective parts you told me about?	• Social Services: Is Mrs. Riley ready to go home?	
Figure 2.7	**Figure 2.8**	**Figure 2.9**

As you again see, these are simple questions, often repeated. Why should anyone have to struggle to get these answers? Here are two need-to-share visual devices (Photos 2.3 and 2.4). Read each caption to increase your understanding. Who knows? You may be able to use these very solutions to share information in your own area.

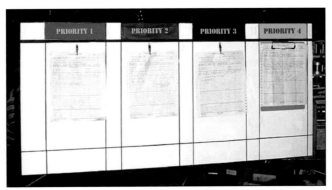

Photo 2.4 Two associates created these boards for newcomers and visitors that share, at-a-glance, the components made in their cell.

Photo 2.3 Supervisor Paul Plant needed a reliable way to share work order priorities with his department—this visual display shows priorities: 1, 2, 3, 4.

More About the Need-to-Share. Sometimes, people don't ask us directly for the answers they need. Instead, we see them wandering around our work area with no apparent purpose. As you'll learn soon, they are in motion (moving without working). That motion is the sure sign that information—an answer—is needed. When you observe that happening, politely inquire: "You seem to be looking for something. Maybe I can help.…"

Bingo! Now you'll get the question. And you'll give the answer. And then—just as with the need-to-know—you'll turn that answer into a visual device so that neither that person nor anyone else ever has to ask that same question again; and you will never need to answer it again. Why? Because you will have imbedded that answer into the physical workplace where it will be available to anyone and everyone who needs it, at-a-glance, without speaking a word.

This is exactly what happened to Sheila Bowersmith, a first-rate machinist and master visual thinker at Denison Hydraulics, when she saw Karen, the new planner, wandering around her area. Sheila quietly asked if she could be of help—and the rest is history (Photo Series 2.5).

Photo Series 2.5 The Need-To-Share: Customer-Driven Visuality.

Karen asked, "Could you tell me what you're running right now?" Sheila told her and then decided to never have to answer that question again. So she taped a yellow rectangle on the side of her machine, welded a heavy clip at the top, and put whatever order she's running there. When her machine was idle, a big NONE was visible so Karen—and anyone else—would know (see red circle). (Denison Hydraulics/Ohio)

The point is not that we don't like other people or don't like answering their questions. We simply know that our work life (and theirs) is about something greater than chasing down informational tidbits. Visuality, starting with the two driving questions, clears the way so we can pay more attention to our actual work function.

Please read "The first question is free" rule in Inset 2.1 and apply it. Your managers and supervisors know they spend too much time asking and answering the same questions over and over. The rule applies to them as well as to you.

Inset 2.1 The First-Question-Is-Free Rule

Some people mistakenly think their real job is to answer questions. That may be true if you are a customer-service rep or reference librarian. But for everyone else, learn and apply the *First-Question-Is-Free Rule* and turn those questions into visual answers.

1. Notice. Notice the first time you are asked a given question. For example, if you are a team lead/supervisor, someone will probably ask at the start of every shift: "What am I supposed to make/do now?"

2. Answer. Answer the question the way you always do—clearly, completely, and politely—but with this difference. As that person walks away, say to yourself: "That's one."

3. Wait. Wait until you are asked that same question again—by that same person or anyone else: "What am I supposed to make/do now?" As before, you answer clearly, completely, and politely.

4. Create. As that person walks away, say to yourself: "That's two! The first question is free. And now that I've heard that same question a second time, it's time to create a visual device so I never have to answer that question again—and no one ever has to ask it!"

Linking the Need-to-Know and Need-to-Share

As with all visual information, the impact of visually answering your need-to-know and need-to-share questions is more than simply imbedding those answers in the physical landscape of work.

Because other people in your area are engaged in creating visual solutions as well, there is a remarkable multiplying effect. The result is an impact far greater than the number of devices in a given work area. Similar to dropping a pebble in a stream, the ripples last longer and reach further than the first splash.

Figure 2.10 Begin by answering your need-to-know questions and gain control of your corner of the world.

Look at the ripples (concentric circles) in Figure 2.10. This is an image of you, applying the first driving question: What do I need to know? The visual answers that result define your locus of control. You gain control over your corner of the world.

Now let's do the multiples. We started with you, a single "I", answering the need-to-know. Figure 2.11 shows what happens when other visual thinkers-in-the-making join you. A fabric of visually-competent work stations begin to populate your department. Each visual thinker chases down the various forms of motion that make work a struggle for him or her and eradicates (or minimizes) the information deficits that caused them. The result is a new level of individual competency and pride, across the work area.

Time for the second driving question: What do I need to share? With that question, you reach beyond your immediate work station and look to visually share vital information with those around you. Those visual answers define your sphere of influence—help you provide for people outside your immediate area, as you just saw in Sheila's visual solution. Notice how far that influence extends (Figure 2.12).

Soon other visual thinkers will join you in generating need-to-share devices. Doing that creates a fabric of intention, improved performance, and good will across the organization. This network of connections weaves the enterprise together—area by area, person by person, and visual device by visual device (Figure 2.13).

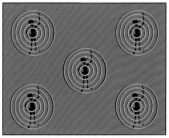

Figure 2.11 As others in your area (or other areas) join in and answer their need-to-know questions, a fabric of visually-competent work stations emerges to support company and personal outcomes.

Figure 2.12 When you shift to the need-to-share, you reach out and help others with their work—better, faster, and safer.

Summing Up the "I"

When you begin to implement visuality in your own work area, you start—you must start—by responding to your own need-to-know. Why? Because those are the questions that you know best! As you build a firm foundation of visual answers to this question, you get more and more control of your corner of the world. Then you turn to others and help them get the answers they need. You share the vital information they need through visual devices you create on their behalf—you share.

The I-driven approach is a deeply team-minded process, one that asks each of us to take personal responsibility both for ourselves and for helping others. Just remember that the "I" resides in all of us. So when other people in your area begin inventing visual solutions to their need-to-know, they are using their own "I" as the anchor. Same with your supervisor; she'll plug into her own "I" to create visual devices that serve her need-to-know because it's *her* need; only then will she move on to *her* need-to-share.

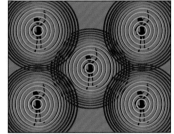

Figure 2.13 Then, when people begin to create need-to-share devices, the entire area—and soon the whole company—gets visually linked.

Ditto for managers, engineers, marketing people, and the CEO as each of them starts participating in the visual conversion of your company. The "I" becomes the anchor for each of them—their "I." The result is not chaos or anarchy as some might fear. The result is: a splendid self-ordering, self-explaining, self-regulating, and self-improving work environment that makes sense to each and every person in it. The result is: a visual workplace, true, wide, and deep.

I-driven is the first building block of visual thinking.

Building Block 2: Standards

Let's look again at the definition of a visual workplace:

> A *visual workplace is a self-ordering, self-explaining, self-regulating, and self-improving work environment—where what is supposed to happen does happen, on time, every time, day or night—because of visual devices.*

The second part of it states that in such a workplace "what is supposed to happen *does* happen." What exactly does that mean? What is supposed to happen?

The answer is: your work standards; your standards are supposed to happen. That brings us to *Building Block 2: Standards.*

Your Standards Are Supposed To Happen

When we use the term standards in workplace visuality, we are not referring to the time or accounting standards used in bids, quotes, and contracts. Instead, we mean the information that defines exactly *what* we are supposed to do and *how* we are supposed to do it—the *what* and the *how*. More precisely, the *what* refers to your technical standards and the *how* refers to your procedural standards (see Figure 2.14).

Figure 2.14 What is supposed to happen.

Your Technical Standards. A technical standard is a product or process specification, dimension or tolerance—the detailed requirements found in engineering worksheets and drawings. These requirements are the precise values you add as you convert material into a product (or as you develop and deliver a service) your customer wants to buy.

Here are examples of technical standards:

- outer diameter (OD)
- inner diameter (ID)
- pressure sensitivity
- coil resistance level
- cut length
- heat-treat temperature
- gloss level
- exact degree of radiation for this patient site
- dilution level for Taxotere (a chemotherapy drug)
- required response time on a fire claim
- required end-of-the-month sales figures

Once you identify the spec (the technical standard), your next step is to make that spec visual. When you do, you visually anchor that spec—that technical standard—in the physical landscape of work.

Look at the example on the next page of a visual guarantee (or poka-yoke device—one of the four power levels of visual devices presented in Chapter 10); it reliably captures a certain type of quality defect and prevents it from traveling downstream (Photos 2.6 to 2.9). This is a technical standard translated into a visual device—and a very powerful one at that.

Photo 2.6
Problem: On some plungers, the outer diameter is too large to slide inside the bushing without rubbing. This hard to see defect was rarely discovered before Final Test.

Photo 2.7
Challenge: Develop a way to ensure no defective plunger travels downstream.
Solution: Imbed the answer to the question "Is this a good plunger?" as deeply as possible into the process itself. Create a visual solution.

Photo 2.8
Visual Solution: First a plate is mounted on the blue bin, with a hole in the center the size of the bushing.

Photo 2.9
With the bushing mounted on the plate, the operator drops each plunger through and checks its size. If the plunger gets stuck, it is set aside. The attributes "talk" to each other.

Your Procedural Standards. A procedural standard is a method or an SOP (standard operating procedure)—a pre-set sequence of steps that tells you how to do or make something or perform a task. Procedural standards tell you exactly how to achieve your technical standards. In short, procedural standards create outcomes.

Do you need to form a 2-inch aluminum ingot into a .50 millimeter thick coil? Follow the step-by-step road map that is your procedural standard.

Do you want to insert an I.V. precisely into a patient's arm? Follow the SOP for that. Same with programming that CNC machine in the radial department. Follow the SOP for that. Here are more examples of procedural standards:

- How to rivet a bolt
- How to set a feed rate
- How to weld a rounded joint
- How to changeover the winder machine (in less than nine minutes).
- How to tighten a four-nut wheel
- How to verify a chemotherapy regimen
- How to close out the monthly books

Once you identify a problem SOP, then make it visual. When you do, you anchor that SOP into the physical landscape of work. Here is a simple and very effective example (Photos 2.10 and 2.11).

Photo 2.10

1. Problem:
The terminal endings of these electric harnesses are often damaged and become unusable.

2. Cause: The endings get banged on the floor when they are hung on the storage poles unevenly and too low.

Photo 2.11

3. Solution: Invent a way to make sure we hang harnesses evenly and high enough when we store them on the poles. That's our new SOP.

4. Visual Solution: Show where "too low" is on each pole with red tape to remind us not to let the harnesses hang below that point.

Combined, your procedural and technical standards are at the heart of all operational excellence. They cause reliable, repeatable, cost effective, high quality work to occur—the absolute bedrock of all outcomes and the core of all profit making in the enterprise. They create outputs your company's customers want to buy and will buy—and that is exactly "what is supposed to happen."

Standards are the second building block of visual thinking.

Building Block 3: The Six Core Questions

Take a closer look at both your technical and procedural standards ("what is supposed to happen") and you'll notice that they are made up of a specific set of answers—the answers to one or more of only six questions. In visuality, we call those the *Six Core Questions*:

- Where?
- What?
- Who?
- How Many?
- How?
- When?

Answers to these questions represent the details of every standard. They also represent all possible answers to the two driving questions—your need-to-know and need-to-share. When you answer those six questions visually (translate them into visual devices), the details of both types of standards and questions become visually imbedded, available to you and everybody, at-a-glance, as part of the process of work. The workplace speaks—at last able to tell us *where* things are, *what* needs to be done, by *when*, by *whom* (or by *which* machine or tool), in *what quantity*, and precisely *how*.

See Photo Series 2.12 for visual answers for each of these six questions. The *six core questions* are the third building block of visual thinking.

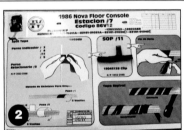
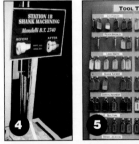

Photo Series 2.12: Six Core Questions

1. Visual Where. This standing sign tells us exactly where the J-190 brackets are, even though they will be moved in an hour.

2. Visual How. This clear, crisp SOP visually shows us the right and wrong way to tape a wiring harness. (Notice the chart is in Spanish and dated 1986.)

3. Visual When. This standing sign tells us (among many things) the duration for the epoxy cure cycle, at the exact point of use—the epoxy cure oven.

4. Visual What. This sign stands in front of a large Mandelli machining center, showing us what the unit looks like before and after the operation.

5. Visual Who. Leave your name tag in place of any special (and expensive) tool you take so the person who needs it next can find you—and so you know that we know that you had it last.

6. Visual How Much. Sheets of vinyl slide off this machine and stop, thanks to the edge on this wooden off-load platform operators built. Operators then cut sheets to size, using the wooden straight-edge and the red sizing marks you see here.

Building Block 4: Information Deficits

Once we understand the six core questions and their importance, our task becomes simple: Find the missing answers to those questions and convert them into visual devices. Another term for these missing answers is: *Information Deficits*—the fourth building block of visual thinking.

Look at the work bench in Photo 2.13, the *Before*.

> **Question:** How many six core questions are answered there?

> **Answer:** None! There's no where there or what, when, who, how many or how. This area is full of missing answers—full of information deficits. Because this a cut saw area, it is also very dangerous—motion of many kinds.

Photo 2.13 Cut-saw work bench *Before*.

Photo 2.14 Cut-saw workbench *After* the answer to the where question was installed.

In Photo 2.14 (the *After*), we see an area that is not just neat, clean, and safe, it is also highly visual, the way it is supposed to be. Motion has been minimized.

Missing Answers Trigger Motion

Motion is triggered when answers vital to work are missing, wrong, late, incomplete, unavailable, or simply not known. Another way to say this is: I do not know—and I do not share (Figure 2.15).

Information deficits have a powerful negative impact on a company. First (as already discussed), when vital workplace information is repeatedly not available, we become immune to a sense of urgency at work. No one wants to wander around all day, chasing down the same teeny tiny bits of information. It is hard to imagine a more degrading experience or one that is more a waste of time. And if these tidbits should be held by a select few individuals who withhold them from the many, insult is added to injury. (See Inset 2.2 for more on this, *Information Hoarders*.)

Figure 2.15 The two conditions that trigger motion.

The damage done to the bottom line through missing information is disastrous and huge. A company's performance measures tell the story—its KPIs (Key Performance Indicators). From ordering errors, defects, rework, scrap, and the chronic late deliveries these trigger—to the number of machine repairs, long changeover times, and material handling mistakes, to accidents, long cycle and manufacturing lead times, error-laden sales reports and collection activities, information deficits hurt the entire business. Their power is in their absence—the absence of answers.

Like holes torn in a fishing net, something of value escapes with every missing answer. These rips may start so small that we don't notice the tiniest escaping fish. Over time the holes get bigger—the information deficits multiply. Not only does the loss of so many small fish add up but now the big fish escape as well (Photo 2.15).

Photo 2.15 Visuality repairs the net.

Learning to See. What to do? The first goal in minimizing (or even eliminating) this sorry state of affairs is to learn to see what isn't there: those holes—those information deficits. But that's a hard assignment when chasing down missing answers has become a routine part of the work day—a way of life in some companies. We barely notice these chronic abnormalities and, instead, write them off as business as usual. The result is this: when our work area overflows with information deficits, we simply get busier and busier and try harder and harder. We hardly have time to notice that we don't get much work done.

Information deficits are the fourth building block of visual thinking.

Building Block 5: Motion

Motion is defined as "moving without working."

Motion comes in a thousand familiar and unfamiliar forms and disguises. Here's a sample: wandering, wondering, searching, guessing, checking, checking again, handling, handling again, or simply waiting.

Sometimes, when motion gets really thick, the only thing you can do is stop. That makes stopping yet another form of motion (Figure 2.16).

But the most common and dangerous forms of motion are connected with questions, a familiar topic already. Look at the red box in Figure 2.16: asking, answering, interrupting (to ask), being interrupted (to answer), and waiting for answers.

Questions have a peculiar multiplier effect that makes them very dangerous. Here's what happens.

When you interrupt someone to ask a question (no matter how urgent or genuine)—or when someone interrupts you to ask one—two people are automatically in motion, you and the other person.

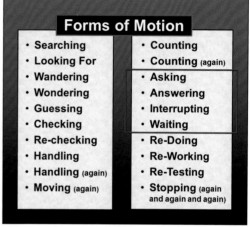

Forms of Motion

• Searching	• Counting
• Looking For	• Counting (again)
• Wandering	• Asking
• Wondering	• Answering
• Guessing	• Interrupting
• Checking	• Waiting
• Re-checking	• Re-Doing
• Handling	• Re-Working
• Handling (again)	• Re-Testing
• Moving (again)	• Stopping (again and again and again)

Figure 2.16 Common (and dangerous) forms of motion

The motion caused by questions is like a contagious disease—you start by asking one person a question and if he/she does not know the answer, then he/she asks a second person; and, if that second person doesn't know the answer to your question, chances are he/she will ask a third person—and so on until a whole roomful of people are contaminated, until they are all in motion.

Should I go on? Did you know that research shows that it takes the average person (like you and me) 6 to 15 minutes to get back on task after each interruption? Yikes!

That is just why motion is called Corporate Enemy #1. It spreads into every corner of the enterprise and eats away at value. (See Inset 2.3 to understand why I use the term *motion* as the name of the enemy, not *muda*, *waste* or *non value-adding activity*.)

What Motion is Not

Before we go further, let's make clear what motion is not. You are not in motion if:

- You are taking a break.
- You are at lunch or chatting with a friend.
- You are calling home or in the rest room—and things like that.

My intention is not to turn you into some tireless robot—the Energizer Bunny who just keeps going and going. None of the above activities are motion. They are, instead, ways we maintain our humanity at work—our sense of community, safety, and personal comfort. So please don't worry about engaging in them. They are part of who we all are as people. They are not the enemy.

Do It or Don't Do Your Work. Notice your motion and you are a step away from detecting the information deficit that caused it—that caused you, for example, to spend 45 minutes looking for your pliers.

But maybe you are thinking: "Wait a minute! If I need my pliers to do my work and I go looking for them, how is that bad? How is that the enemy? How is that motion? I have to have my pliers if I'm going to get my work done!"

First, you are right: You do need to find your pliers so you can do your work. But also recognize that looking for your pliers is not the same as using your pliers. It is not the same as working. The correct logic runs like this: "If I am looking for my pliers in order to be able do my work, then I am obviously not yet doing that work while I am looking for them." That's all we are saying.

There is a name for that—for anything you are forced to do or you cannot do your work. It is a name you already know: motion. Motion is anything you have to do or you could not do your work; but it is *not* your work.

Inset 2.3 Motion vs. Non-Value-Adding/Waste/Muda

The definition of motion I use throughout this book is the same as Toyota uses in its *Seven Deadly Wastes*: *moving without working*. In visuality, however, we use motion to define problems triggered by information deficits and the unintentional placement of function. While you might think that the terms muda, waste, and non-value-adding activity are used to mean the same thing, I do not use them interchangeably. Here's why.

Non-Value-Adding Activity: Many years ago, I noticed that the term "non-value-adding" caused heartache for people whose jobs were, in fact, non-value-adding: inspectors, expediters, rework operators, material handlers, supervisors, and managers—to name a few. Far too often, when these fine individuals heard me call their jobs "non-value-adding," they concluded that they, as people, were "non-value-adding." Nothing is further from the truth. But when I saw how my words affected them, I decided not to describe people's jobs that way anymore.

Waste: Waste is a general term. Motion is specific; it is always tied to a specific unanswered core question and almost always tied to a specific person—me or you. It is my legs that carry me all over the area trying to answer the question: Where are my pliers? I own that question. I own that motion.

Muda: Muda means "waste" in Japanese. I prefer to use a word that doesn't need translation and, as mentioned, has a more exact meaning.

Here are other examples of motion—the activities that associates like you are forced to do just to be able to do their work:

- Mary is forced to remove a pallet of pumps because they are wrong; she can not start the job.
- Victoria has to re-check the spec or risk making the wrong order.
- Tyrone is forced to count the units again because someone "borrowed" his order sheet.
- Nurse Betty has to go to the pharmacy for a new batch of medications because the batch number is missing from the first one.
- Hank has to find his pliers or he can't begin to assemble the unit.

Another powerful way to bring home the multiplier impact of motion is to realize that time is its shadow: *Time is the shadow of motion* (Figure 2.17). Every time we have to chase down an answer, the clock is ticking. All the time we are looking for a missing tool, that same clock is ticking. It is the clock of our life and the life of the company. However much we may want to work, without that answer, without the tool, we cannot. Either we never get our work started—or, once started, we never get back to it. Instead, chasing down answers eats up our day. It is a numbing experience and witness to motion's destructive power in the workplace.

Figure 2.17 Time is the shadow of Motion.

Motion is the fifth building block of visual thinking. You'll learn other powerful ways to spot it before the end of this chapter.

Building Block 6: Work

Have you noticed? While we were just explaining that motion meant moving without working, we neglected to say what working means. We'll do that now to complete your understanding of motion.

Working means moving and adding value. That is, we must move in order to add value—in order to convert material or procedures into products or services our customers want to purchase.

Value is not added by accident or by magic. We don't work on Star Trek's Starship Enterprise, at least not yet! On the Enterprise, when Captain Picard wants a cup of tea, he doesn't have to boil water—nor does his staff. He simply stands in front of the replicator (not a vending machine) and says aloud "Earl Grey tea, hot!" Earl Grey tea, piping hot, instantly materializes from the inside out, along with an exquisite Wedgewood tea cup and saucer that hold it. *Q* (a rather advanced ET in Picard's world) doesn't even need to say "cup of tea" when he wants one. He merely thinks it. No, our world isn't like that—not yet.

In our world, if we want a cup of tea or an F16 fighter jet, we must move in order to create it—in order to add value. We must engage our muscles and our mind in order to build a sub-assembly, grind a housing, load the cable, check a part, administer a medication, or produce a proposal. Yes, we must move to add value; we must work. And that means that motion is moving and *not* adding value.

Work is the sixth building block of visual thinking.

Building Block 7: Value Field

When and where do you add value? The answer is: When—and only when—you are in your *Value Field*. Only then can you add value—only then can you work. It's as simple as that. Your value field is a specific location. It is where work happens.

Look at Photo 2.16: the running track at Tuft's University in Boston. That track is a runner's primary value field. No matter how much time a runner spends working out at the gym, finding the right shoe or eating the healthiest foods, only when she runs on the track is she in her primary field of value.

Photo 2.16 Running track at Tuft's.

Only then is she about the business she has trained for, year after year. And look at the visual details built into that track surface! Olympic careers can begin and end here. Move a hurdle up or down an inch, and some Olympic hopeful may break an ankle and say goodbye to the Games.

It's the same way for you. Since you can only add value when you are in your value field, anytime you are not there, you must be in motion—and you can only do your primary work when you are in your primary value field.

Noticing your motion by whether or not you are in your value field is the powerful new way to spot motion we promised earlier: Track your motion based on your value field.

Here's that logic again:

1. Since motion is the opposite of work, and...

2. Since you can only do your work when you are in your own value field...

3. Then you know that if you are not physically in your value field, you are in motion—because you cannot be working.

4. Therefore, anytime you are not in your value field, you are automatically in motion. (Remember: Even though you're not in your value field during a break or the like, you're also not in motion).

Photo Series 2.18 shows three views of the assembly bench value field created by Bill Antunes (United Electric Controls, Massachusetts). It is worth a close read.

Bill Antunes, a master visual thinker, solders his subassemblies on this white bench. His primary value field is in the center, with a secondary value field on the left and another on the right for his tools.	Here is a close-up of Bill's solder arm, mounted on a shelf. At night he pushes it back and pulls down the white board that holds his work order during the day.	His hand tools are to the right in another pull-out shelf. Bill doubled the shelf's thickness and cut holes for each tool for easy pick-and-put. We see so many of the eight building blocks in this system.

Primary or Secondary Value Fields

Here's the tricky part: we almost always have more than one value field. In any given department, work can take place in many locations. The good news is that we usually have only one main value field—where we actually do value-adding activity: our work. We call that our primary value field. Other key areas within your department support that work; they are called our secondary or supporting value fields.

At first, you may find it challenging to separate the two—your primary from your secondary value fields. This may be because you have never thought about your work like that before. For example, if you are a machinist, you will quickly understand that your machine is your primary value field—that's where the material you load is converted into something of greater value for your customer; and the dies rack, changeover tools, and waiting materials are all in support of that.

But what if you run six machines—which is primary? In this case, all six may be equal, just used for different models or sequential operations. If you are a medical technician in X-ray, then clearly the X-ray machine is the point from which you measure all motion; that is your primary value field. But if you are a nurse, your primary value field may be less clear. Is it the patient, room by room, or the main nursing station where you undertake so many valuable services on behalf of the patient? It is the same issue for managers and supervisors: Is your main value field your desk? Or is it the areas you walk through as you assess and coach, monitor and expedite?

The important thing right now is to raise the question and clear up your own thinking by discussing it with others and listening to their thinking. With enough time and input, the distinction will become clear. Be patient with yourself and others. Raise the question and the answer will arrive. Think.

Value field is the seventh building block of visual thinking.

Building Block 8: Motion Metrics

The final building block is *Motion Metrics* (the term "metric" means "a standard unit of measurement"). A motion metric is a mechanism or yardstick that we use to track or measure motion—to find out how much motion there is.

You can track your motion a number of ways, including the one we already discussed at length: tracking the number of questions you ask or are asked. Here are four more (Photo Series 2.19): your own eyes, a stop watch, a pedometer, and/or a frequency check sheet.

Photo Series 2.19

Your Own Eyes
Use the power of observation.

Stop Watch
Measure time away from your value field.

Pedometer
Measure distance traveled from your value field.

Frequency Check Sheet
Track how many times you leave your value field—and why.

When you track your own motion, you get rock-solid evidence of the level of struggle in your daily work. Here are four examples from the same company, Harris Corp./Illinois.

- Janet, an assembler in electrical cables, watched her pedometer rack up 5.5 miles in walking in a week—and she never left her department.

- Her colleague, Linda, who was confined to a wheelchair, used a frequency check sheet that showed she left her value field 42 times in three days for work-related reasons. She said since she hadn't realized she was in motion, she never before thought of those side trips as a problem but always felt the pressure.

- Deanna, the supervisor in that same area, kept track of the questions she asked—and was asked—per shift. By the third day, she had already piled up 72 questions she had answered, and 123 she had asked. She now knew for sure that the motion called questions was eating up her time.

- Down the aisle in the same company, Buzz, lead operator in Final Test with 27 years on the job, saw his stop watch record 2 hours and 35 minutes that he spent outside his area on a single shift (not counting breaks or lunch). "No wonder I can't get my work done," he flashed.

Motion metrics give us a concrete way to see for ourselves why we cannot get a full day of work done.

Measure Your Motion

Here's what I'd like you to do: Pick a motion metric and track your motion for one week. At the end of that week, study what happened and why. Then look for ways to reduce your motion through visual devices. A few pointers:

- Track your own motion—and no one else's.
- You don't have to share what you discover with anyone else—unless you decide to. Your motion, for the time being, is strictly your own business.
- The important thing is for you to recognise you are in motion at least part of the time you are on the job. Notice that and notice why.

Motion metrics are the eighth building block of visual thinking.

Putting It All Together

That concludes our detailed discussion of the eight building blocks of visual thinking—and how they work together to help us eliminate motion and the information deficits that cause it. *The Cycle of Visual Thinking* in Figure 2.18 sums this up nicely. Please keep it in mind as you move forward.

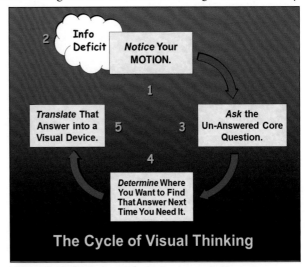

Figure 2.18 Eliminate motion step by step, cycle after cycle.

Step 1: Notice your motion.
- Look! I just left my value field. That means I'm not working anymore. I must be in motion.

Step 2: Name the information deficit.
- Hmmm, if I am in motion, it must have been triggered by an information deficit—a missing answer. What was it?

Step 3: Ask the un-answered core question.
- Which of the six core questions is linked to that information deficit of mine? Which question do I need answered?

Step 4: Decide where to physically install the visual device that captures the missing answer so it is both exact and handy.
- Where should I locate the new device? How close can I get it to the actual point of use?

Step 5: Translate that answer into a visual device.
- Now I'll turn that answer into a visual solution—and I won't ever need to ask or answer that question again because the answer will be firmly installed as close to my true value field as possible.

Excellent! Then at the least sign of new motion, the visual thinker starts the cycle again. That visual thinker is you!

Using the knowledge you just learned is exactly how you—and others in your area and throughout your company—can take the struggle out of work and begin to populate the work environment with dozens, hundreds, even thousands, of visual devices and mini-systems. The result? An enterprise of splendid visual functionality—self-ordering, self-explaining, self-regulating and self-improving…where what is supposed to happen does happen, on time, every time, day or night, because of visual devices.

About the Visual Examples in This Book

If you have already read any of my other books, you will know that some of the photographic examples in this book are the same as I use in other of my books. This is not because we do not have enough photos to offer new ones; in fact, we have about 35,000 photos of visual solutions in our database.

We use some of the same ones because of the depth of visual information they contain and the core visual concepts and principles they reflect. I call such high-level solutions "teaching examples." The mere act of seeing and studying them reveals many layers of application, from their operational impact to their power to reorient the work culture towards greater precision, alignment, tolerance, and harmony. Please bear this in mind as you see the repeats.

Also, although the majority of the examples in this book are from manufacturing, the visual workplace is a universal workplace, whatever the setting—bank, hospital, open-pit mine, military depot or automotive manufacturing. Visual is a universal language. There is no company or person that visual information sharing cannot help and support because it is first and foremost a language. So you move through the pages, examine the principles and concepts in the many visual solutions from the viewpoint of your workplace and look for applications that will help your work.

> Things do not change.
> We change.
>
> Henry David Thoreau

Chapter | Three

Your Implementation Tool Box

Knowledge and Know-How
The Three Outcomes
 Achieve a Showcase
 Achieve Trackable Bottom Line Results
 Adopt an Attitude of Learning
Your Implementation Tool Box: The Five Tools
 Tool 1: Your Vision Place
 Tool 2: Your Laminated Map
 Tool 3: Your Visual Workplace Hit List
 Tool 4: Visual Workplace Supplies
 Tool 5: Visual Workplace Blitz

Knowledge and Know-How

To this point, you have learned a good deal about basic visual concepts and the building blocks of visual thinking. Your knowledge of what visuality is and why it is important is vital as you start improving your work area, visually.

But you will need more than knowledge. You will also need know-how: how to implement visuality so it moves forward, takes deep roots, and keeps growing. Knowledge and know-how. Know-how and knowledge. They go hand-in-hand every step of the way, each strengthening the other as your visual conversion unfolds (Inset 3.1).

> **Knowledge vs. Know-How**
> - Knowledge is the *what*: What principles, concepts, definitions, and practices are needed.
> - Know-how is the *how*: How to put those principles, concepts, definitions, and practices in place—how to implement them.
>
> **Inset 3.1** You need both.

The know-how needed for a successful visual conversion of your area is a shared responsibility. You and other area associates own a large part of it. The rest belongs to company leadership: supervisors, mid-level managers, and senior managers—whether plant manager, hospital administrator, depot commander, company owner or CEO.

This chapter focuses squarely on that: What you and your colleagues do—and what supervisors, team leaders, managers, and executives do—to effectively implement, grow, and sustain visuality in your area.

These two sets of tasks are crucial but different. The main pages of this book are always addressed to you, the operator-experts. Leadership (management) tasks appear as blue insets throughout the same pages.

The Three Outcomes

There are three outcomes that define success as you and your colleagues convert your area to visuality. They are:

1. Achieve a visual showcase.

2. Achieve trackable bottom-line results.

3. Adopt an attitude of learning.

Outcome 1: Achieve a visual showcase

The first thing you want as a result of implementing visuality in your area is a *Visual Showcase*—a work area where you have drilled deep into the details of your operations and made them visual. I say it like this: *Implement visuality one-foot square and one-mile deep.*

A work area that has reached the showcase level demonstrates what a well-developed visual work environment looks like and how it functions. When we visit such a showcase, our own eyes tell us why visuality is important; we understand. Newcomers and visitors understand as well—along with people from areas in the facility that are not yet visual. And when they do, they get inspired and want their own areas to look and run like that also—as well as the entire enterprise.

I often hear it put like this: "I want one like that!" To make sure you remember your progress, your management will take photographs of your area regularly (see *Leadership Task 1*). So the first outcome you focus on is achieving a visual showcase.

Leadership Task 1: Take Photographs

Take plenty of *Before* photos—before associates change anything. Do this for all areas, all shifts. Begin today. Then take another set of photos week-by-week (on the same day of the week, if you can, at about the same time) so you have a moving history of visual improvements as they happen. Take photos weekly even when nothing has changed. No matter. Over time, you'll collect the story of the visual journey in the area.

- As a rough guideline, take ten different shots of each department per week.
- To track an area's visual progress further, pick a single spot and regularly take a weekly photo or two from there. Like a tree across the four seasons, these photos allow us to see the area visually transform over time (Photo 3.1).

Photo 3.1 Spot point.

Outcome 2: Achieve trackable bottom-line results

As each area makes its way to showcase level, it's important to be able to see visuality's positive impact in terms of trackable, bottom-line results. Management usually takes the lead in tracking this since tangible proof of return on investment is one of their main measures. But you can certainly participate—and, in the case of self-directed teams, take the lead.

In due course, the benefits of visuality must positively impact your performance measures—quality, delivery, cost, and safety (QDCS). You may know these as KPIs (Key Performance Indicators). As your visual rollout gains momentum, look for improvement in them.

Here's how you or your supervisor can do that: collect KPIs just before the visual conversion begins in your area (we call that *the launch*). Continue to do this week-by-week, comparing the actual results as you go along (see *Leadership Task 2*).

Within six to nine weeks of launch, you are likely to see a positive drift in your KPIs, sometimes sooner. That steadily increases over time thanks to the visual devices you and others create and the information deficits that dissolve as a result. In five to six months, expect to see results in your area as good as (or better than) those shared in Chapter 1. Remember?

- 15%-30% increase in productivity
- 70% reduction in waiting
- 70% reduction in material handling
- 54% reduction in walking
- 96% improvement in quality
- 68% reduction in storage requirements
- $2,555,000 scrap reduction (yearly)
- 7,132 hours of machine downtime eliminated (yearly)
- 60% reduction in floor space requirements
- 100% elimination of rework

Leadership Task 2: Your Baseline Set of Metrics

Before you launch the Work That Makes Sense methodology in the areas you have targeted, collect a baseline set of measures (or metrics) for each of these areas. Collect the current level of Key Performance Indicators (KPIs). In most companies, these are routinely collected. All you need do is print out the latest results and put it in a binder. Do this again every week but not less than twice a month.

In six to nine weeks (or sooner), you will begin to see a positive drift in the direction of those measures. What needs to increase will begin to increase. What needs to decrease will start to go down. That's when and how you and others will recognize that the visual improvements underway in each department are translating into better performance and improved bottom-line results.

Other metrics: Two additional measures show visuality's positive impact: (1) management's tracking of improvement time utilization (see the *Leadership Centerfold* in this chapter); and (2) associates' tracking motion metrics via a stopwatch, pedometer, frequency check sheet, or questions asked and answered (for review, see Motion Metrics in Chapter 3/Building Blocks of Visual Thinking.)

These are impressive bottom-line results and not uncommon for an effective I-driven visual conversion on the value-add level. So the second outcome you focus on is achieving trackable bottom-line results.

Outcome 3: Adopt an attitude of learning

Most of us already realize that learning is our life-long job, no matter what company employs us. The third visual workplace outcome targets the conversion of our mind, heart, and beliefs as we convert the work area to visuality.

Continuous improvement is an opportunity to both streamline the physical workplace and help ourselves grow as individuals. As we change the process, the process changes us and we learn. We learn what works and what doesn't, what we like and what we don't, what we got right and what we got wrong; and, as importantly, we learn the difference between demands and preferences.

Safety, for example, is always a requirement; we demand it. But the way I like to have my workbench laid out is a preference; I favor my way but your layout is also "interesting." I know that I'm an adult and so are you; therefore neither of us need get bent out of shape if the other person doesn't agree with us, exactly. We just learn to stay open and sort things out.

For Outcome 3, we adopt an attitude of learning. We learn to stay open so, for example, we can appreciate mistakes as opportunities to learn. We may even get so interested in mistakes (including our own) that, instead of hiding them or blaming them on others, we study them and become scientists of our own work. We come to realize that mistakes are part of what makes improvement a journey, not a destination.

When you learn to adopt an attitude of learning in the face of change, you can learn to stay open and bear the discomfort of not knowing the exact result. Over time, you come to accept things about yourself and others; and where acceptance is beyond your reach, you are willing to adopt tolerance. I may learn, for example, that I:

- Prefer to be in a leadership position, out in front of a change; or
- Like to hang back, with a wait-and-see attitude; or
- Get cranky because I'm not sure I like change in the first place.

Whatever my personal preference, though, I agree to stay open and remember that not all other individuals will be like me. And I will allow myself—and others—to change.

As Gotama, the Buddha, told a student a thousand years ago when she asked how to navigate life's tricky parts: (1) Show up; (2) Tell the truth; and (3) Stay open. That was the Buddha's way of saying: Adopt an attitude of learning.

So these are the three outcomes that tell us if our visual workplace implementation is a success:

- Achieve a visual showcase
- Achieve trackable results
- Adopt an attitude of learning

Which is most important? All three. They are equally vital to your success. Now let's look at the five tools in your *Implementation Tool Box* that will help you get in and get going.

Your Implementation Tool Box: The Five Tools

With those outcomes firmly in mind, you are ready to begin to learn and implement. We use five key implementation tools to help us to stay inspired and to focus, target, and drive workplace visuality so our visual improvements sink deep roots and keep growing—so they are sustainable.

The five tools are:

1. Your Vision Place (to help you stay inspired)
2. Your Laminated Map (to help you stay focused)
3. Your Hit List (to help you target)
4. Your Supplies (to help you invent)
5. Your Blitz (to help you drive)

1. Your Vision Place...a tool to help you stay inspired

Name a place you have actually been *where what was supposed to happen did happen because of visual devices.* Name your vision place.

Maybe it was a nearby factory, hospital, or accounting office—a place where high levels of visuality made you dream about your own work area looking and functioning like that. Such a location is called a *Vision Place.* The purpose of a vision place is to inspire us on the outside until there's a vision place of our own on the inside—inside our own company and inside our own work area.

If there's no hospital or factory like that near you, find a community location that is highly visual—the post office, for example, or county library. Or these restaurants and retail outlets, famous for the many

user-friendly visual devices that help customers and employees alike: Friendly's Ice Cream Parlor, McDonald's, and Home Depot or Lowe's (Photos 3.2 and 3.3). Or if you live in Orlando, Florida, Disney World is the vision place of choice (Photo Cluster 3.4).

Photo 3.2 Lowe's visual checkouts.

Photo 3.3 McDonald's: Visual McKing.

There are only three requirements for choosing a vision place: (1) It is highly visual; (2) You have actually been there yourself—physically in person (not just heard about it or seen it on video); and (3) It is within easy driving distance (10-15 miles)—so you can visit it often to remind yourself what visuality looks and feels like in action until a vision place exists at your own work.

Photo Cluster 3.4 World-class Vision Place: Disney World.

Choose your vision place now and write it down so you remember. Then, if your visual efforts get stalled or you forget what you are working for or why, visit your visual place—and you'll say, "Wow, this place runs like clockwork. It's so smart. They've made everything visual. Hey! I want one like that!"

You saw this phrase—"I want one like that!"—when we talked about *Achieving a Visual Showcase*. See the connection? Your visual showcase becomes a vision place inside the company once you achieve it. Let your vision place be a constant source of information, inspiration, and understanding on your own journey to a visual workplace.

2. Your Laminated Map...a tool to help you focus

When faced with a large job, some people get overly ambitious and want to do everything at once, only to end up getting nearly none of it done. Others, faced with a large project, start feeling so overwhelmed even before they start that they *never do start*. The same can happen when we are faced with converting our work area visually. There's so much that needs to be done.

That's why the *Laminated Map* is in our Implementation Tool Box—to turn big projects into bite-sized tasks. The right use of the laminated map allows us to say "yes" to the few and "wait" to the many. It helps us to decide where to begin, in six easy steps. Here are the steps in detail (Figure Series 3.1).

Step 1. Get a paper map of your work area and laminate it.

Figure Series 3.1 Laminated map step-by-step.

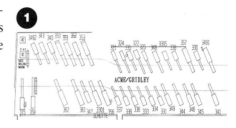

If you do not have an architectural drawing of your department's floor plan, a hand-drawn map will do—as long as it is large enough (20 inches by 30 inches) and somewhat to scale (precise dimensioning is not important).

- Your laminated map does not need detail, such as equipment layout, electrical outlets, plumbing, coolant systems or the like (but if your map already has those, that is also no problem).

Step 2. Draw a boundary around the entire outside of the area.

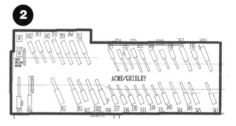

Working with your colleagues, use a dark, *non-permanent* marker to draw a complete boundary around your department, whether it has walls or not. (If you make a mistake, use water and a Q-tip to change it.)

Step 3. Divide the floor plan into its natural work areas.

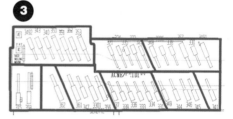

On your map, divide your department's floor plan into its natural sub-areas or sections, based on any combination of factors that makes sense to you—product types, functions, customers, etc. Use your dark, non-permanent marker to draw a boundary, border or outline around each sub-area.

- Make sure every square foot of your floor plan is bordered or outlined, even closets, staircases, sinks, hallways, aisles, and restrooms (if they are within your department's boundary). Just include each of these within one sub-area or another. This is because, in implementing visuality, every square foot of the physical work environment will eventually be made visual. So pair those small functions within a large section of the floor.

Step 4. Put a blue-dot sticker on each sub-area.

Place a removable blue dot on every sub-area on your laminated map. A blue dot means: We have not committed to implement here—yet! See Inset 3.2 for precisely what each dot means.

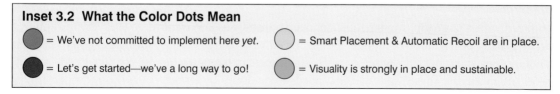

Inset 3.2 What the Color Dots Mean

◉ = We've not committed to implement here *yet*.   ○ = Smart Placement & Automatic Recoil are in place.

● = Let's get started—we've a long way to go!   ◐ = Visuality is strongly in place and sustainable.

Step 5. Decide where to begin.

With a blue dot in each sub-area, you and your colleagues are now ready to decide where to begin to roll out visuality in your area. Select the sub-area or areas to target first.

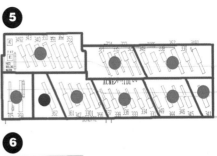

When you have selected your target areas, switch out the blue dot for red. Red means: *Let's get started—we have a long way to go!* This is where you will begin to implement visuality, systematically.

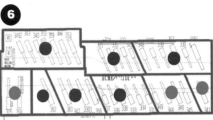

- To start, limit red-dot areas to two or three so you and others feel in control and not overwhelmed by all that is yet to be done. Slow and steady wins the race.

Step 6. Begin to implement visuality—and keep going.

Now you are ready to apply what you learn about visuality, step-by-step. Change the dots, color by color, as you reach each visual milestone in a given targeted area.

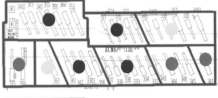

- The blue dot in a sub-area gets changed to red dot as soon as you—or anyone else—begins to apply visuality to it; nothing more is needed. These dot changes allow you and others to visually track the visual progress in your area. If you wish, mark the date of that change on the dot itself. And take photos of your map as the dots change color, using your camera's date stamp to keep closer track of the process.

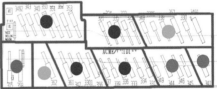

- Post your map on your area's bulletin board (see *Leadership Task 3* and Photo Cluster 3.5).

Leadership Task 3: Visual Workplace Bulletin Boards (Photo Cluster 3.5)

Each area targeted for visuality needs a Visual Workplace Bulletin Board for posting various items and notices: the department's Laminated Map, training schedule, Visual Hit List (explained below), Improvement Time Tracking forms (explained below), and other special announcements. With an eye towards uniformity across all targeted areas, work out the format, size, look, color, feel, and location of this board. Then make it self-explaining and easy to spot, use, and update—in other words, make sure it is visually functional and appealing.

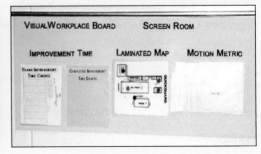

Leadership Centerfold: Your Improvement Infrastructure

In our hope for a quick and easy solution to all workplace challenges, we sometimes mistakenly think that improvement success is simply the result of good ideas, carefully implemented. Just as buildings require infrastructure to function safely and well, so your visual conversion requires an internal structure. Management needs to put this behind-the-scenes framework in place before the first associate is trained or the first brilliant idea is discussed. Called the company's *Improvement Infrastructure*, it is the organization's insurance that steady progress will continue to be made, learning applied, and hard-won gains sustained. As with buildings, the absence of a strong internal framework may go unnoticed until the building (or, in this case, your visual implementation) begins to fail. By then, there is often little we can do to save the situation—so we shake our heads and wonder why more strength and reliability were not designed into the structure at the outset.

The six elements below are what I use to help my clients make a successful journey to a visual workplace. When effectively implemented, these elements can enable an organization to reach the ultimate destination—a fully-functioning visual enterprise that is also sustainable.

1. Vision Place
2. Systematic Methodology
3. Excellent Transfer Materials
4. On-Site Leadership
5. The Laminated Map
6. Improvement Time Policy

Two of these six (Vision Place and the Laminated Map) are included in the Implementation Tool Box for associates discussed in this chapter. As managers, you use the same two but, as you will read here, with a strong leadership emphasis. The other four are exclusively your responsibility: Systematic Methodology, Transfer Materials, On-Site Leadership, and an Improvement Time Policy.

1. Your Vision Place. Vision comes first, then transformation. Even though you may have never experienced a comprehensive visual workplace first hand, you have visited places where what was supposed to happen did happen because of visual devices; and, from what you saw, it happened remarkably well. Before you begin the visual journey, choose a location that can serve as your vision place—your touchstone for inspiration—until one exists within your own company (Photo 3.6).

Photo 3.6 Visuals at Lowe's.

2. Systematic Methodology. Vision without an implementation road map is only a hope. Select an improvement method with a proven track record for bottom-line results—in this case, related to workplace visuality. Then follow it carefully for at least *three cycles* before you change or remove anything. In that way, you will learn to understand and value the method as given, adapting it knowingly only after you have clarified your local needs. There are many such protocols but for your journey to a visual workplace, our method of choice is the Work That Makes Sense process—structured, principle-driven, systematic, and sustainable—with hundreds and hundreds of outstanding visual solutions to learn from and a crisp, robust set of steps to follow.*

3. Excellent Transfer Materials. How will you transfer visual workplace knowledge, know-how, and excitement to others? How will you inform and inspire others? You need a robust materials package to do so. For visuality, that package needs to include proven content that teaches a systematic method—including concepts, principles, models, frameworks, tools, and practices.*

As importantly, these materials must include scores, if not hundreds, of color photos of splendid visual solutions and explanations, not just from your industry but from many industries. Outstanding instructional materials are indispensable to learning and implementing visuality and producing sustainable and inventive visual transformations.*

4. On-Site Leadership. Company conversions do not happen overnight or by accident, not if gains are to be sustainable. Your company will need a compact team of high-functioning, emotionally sturdy individuals to lead, coach, and support your visual transformation. These individuals mostly work behind the scenes to plan, support, assess, and troubleshoot the rollout before and during the conversion process. They are responsible for the progress of the rollout, in terms of work culture and the bottom line.

I call this team the *3-Legged Stool*—each leg represents a different person or group willing and qualified to be held accountable for some aspect of the visual conversion and its success. They work together to support the seat of the stool—the targeted areas. The three legs are: the Visual Workplace Champion, Coordinator, and Steering Team (Figure 3.2). (Feel free to change these names to better suit your company).

Leg 1: The Visual Workplace Management Champion is the sponsor of the visual initiative—the person who authorized it and signed off on the resources (dollars, time, and people) needed to support the change. In a union shop, the champion often works hand-in-hand with union leadership. In addition to resourcing the visual conversion, he or she visibly supports the process, providing it with regular top management feedback, and going to bat for the implementation if the need arises. Once the process launches, the Champion's supporting role is largely behind the scenes.

Figure 3.2 An accountable team.

Leg 2: The Visual Workplace Coordinator is responsible for: a) the logistical and administrative details that support the implementation; b) coordinating activities between departments (such as maintenance and technical support); c) collecting and graphing improvement time usage; and d) serving as an internal coach to the process.

The Lead Team. Because the Coordinator job is a large one, he or she usually designates a group of two to four people to lend a hand (see small gray box next to the Coordinator's stool leg in Figure 3.2). In some companies, the Lead Team's role becomes more strategic; for example, each team member can be assigned to a targeted area to act as a visual coach and a management liaison. Whichever the case, this team can become an increasingly valuable asset to any serious implementation.

Leg 3: The Visual Workplace Steering Team is formed about two to three months after the initial launch and is made up of an hourly volunteer from each area participating in the visual conversion.

The exact names of Steering Team members depend on who volunteers. This team's mandate is to: a) stay in touch with how the implementation is unfolding within each area and across departments, b) look for ways to strengthen efforts, and c) recommend plant-wide standards and policies to the Management Champion so that visuality sinks deep roots in the enterprise and spreads.

Add a fourth leg to the stool if your company has its own in-house trainers to strengthen and support the visual roll out.

5. The Laminated Map. A conversion can stumble into serious early problems if a decision is made to implement too fast and too wide. No organization knows how to handle or absorb unlimited change right out of the starting gate. The company has yet to learn what to change as well as how to change.

(*See the QMI/Visual-Lean Institute pages in this book's Resource Section for information on complete self-standing train-the-trainer instructional packages, licensing, webinars, videos, and other QMI educational materials.)

The tool called the Laminated Map—this time used on a strategic or enterprise level—can be a big help in focusing resources and pacing the rate of change. In creating this laminated map, follow the same steps described in this chapter for associates, but for the entire company.

Briefly, managers border all departments on a facility's map; then they decide to which areas to say yes ("we'll implement there first") and to which to say wait ("we'll implement there later"). The same color-dot system that associates use on their scaled-down map applies here. In this way, managers can regulate the flow of resources that support the initiative, focus on achieving a showcase (a vision place, internal to the facility), and prepare—after their own hands-on learning—for an easier and more effective conversion in subsequent areas.

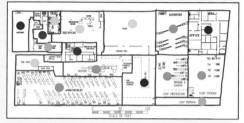

Figure 3.3 Company-wide Laminated Map on its way to green.

6. Official Improvement Time Policy. Any company committed to the journey to excellence is running full tilt. A company that is not yet on that journey also runs full tilt—but for other reasons. If either company does not establish an official improvement time policy, very little improvement will ever happen in that enterprise.

In the battle between operations and improvement for time, operations will always win. That is as it should be, since the company is in the business of delivering the products and services its operations create. Without an established Improvement Time Policy, however, there is a danger that needed improvement will never happen. Improvement will certainly never turn into a habit if we simply leave it to the willing who see the vision burning brightly before them and eke out small pockets of time to make magic happen. In their determination to find a way, these quiet heroes do themselves and the rest of us some bit of harm.

When they succeed in the absence of a clearly defined improvement time policy, they unintentionally send the message that separate time is not needed. It is the wise executive who sees through this double think and takes steps to establish an official improvement time policy. The lack of an established improvement time policy is one of the greatest corporate roadblocks to making continuous improvement a way of life. Here are three key points:

- Improvement time is separate from operations time and clocked as such.
- Improvement time is not associated with meetings or general house cleaning.
- Your improvement time policy is piloted for a few months and tweaked as needed until it works for its three stakeholders: the enterprise, operations, and continuous improvement.

But a written improvement time policy is only an intent. After the policy is written, it must be operationalized, tested, and tracked. For that we collect raw data (the actual hours used) on a tracking sheet which value-add employees complete, I-driven. This tracking sheet is either posted on the area bulletin board or, if the work culture is troubled, handed out and handed in privately. (See samples in Figure Series 3.4.)

In nearly thirty years of implementations, I have never found a more finely-tuned yet robust tool for diagnosing the true health and resiliency of a company's work culture than a written improvement time policy that has been operationalized.

This ends our overview of the six leadership tools managers need in order to resource, support, and drive the enterprise on its way to a fully-functioning visual work environment.

Figure Series 3.4 Samples of Improvement Time Tools.

1. Written Improvement Time Policy. This policy was signed by the ranking site executive plus her direct reports. Notice that the policy calls for a distinct separation of improvement time from any other time use, including actual work and meetings. This policy gets written first.

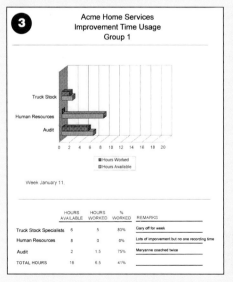

2. Improvement Time Tracking Sheet. This form is handed out to associates so they can track their time directly on it—each in their own hand, as shown here. No pleading. If associates do not submit their info, you have a valuable measure of your existing work culture.

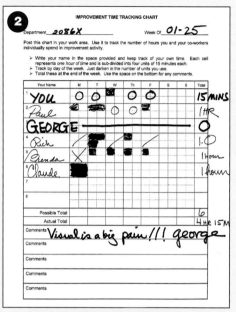

3. Improvement Time Usage Chart. The Visual Workplace Coordinator collects the people's usage data, area by area, and creates a chart such as this one to compare what the policy makes available to what is actually used. Another excellent diagnostic.

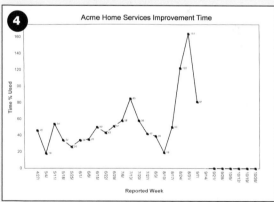

4. Improvement Time Trend Chart. The Coordinator prepares this trend chart for the champion, weekly—a valuable way to assess the extent to which the policy is working.

3. Your Hit List...a tool to help you target

The laminated map shows you how to target specific locations in your work area for visual improvement. Now it's time to define exact improvement tasks and projects to visually transform those locations—and keep going until you are done. This is a job for the third implementation tool: your *Visual Workplace Hit List* ("hit list" for short).

Your hit list is an inventory or register of tasks and projects that you and other associates in your area want to undertake—alone or with a buddy—in order to visually improve the department and take more struggle out of the work that goes on there. The hit list helps you target where to begin and how to keep going; and it tells you if and when you completed what you set out to do. In this way, you stay focused on your plan and use limited resources—including your own time—productively.

Here are four things to know about these hit lists:

- Your hit list is I-driven. You and your colleagues choose the tasks that get posted there.
- Just because you thought of an improvement task doesn't mean you have to do it.
- Just because no one else wants to undertake a given task, doesn't mean it should not get done.
- You can work alone; but if you decide to work with others, limit it to no more than two others.

Figure 3.5 shows a standard visual workplace hit list, reflecting a simple six-step procedure. Before I walk you through it, notice the headings: *Your Visual Workplace Project • Point Person • Start Date • Target Date • Status • Comments/Problems/Special Needs.* Since it is important to make your hit list work for you, use these headings as guides, not requirements. Change the language as you wish. Again, it is also perfectly fine to start your own hit list—just for you. The steps are exactly the same.

Step 1. Name the Task. Think about the challenges in motion you face in your work area and the information deficits that trigger them. Choose one such challenge and name it in the first hit list column ("Your Visual Improvement Project"). If more words are needed so others understand, add a few under the project name.

Step 2. Find a Point Person. Next, decide if you want to undertake this task yourself. If you don't, leave the point-person cell empty; another area associate will pick up the task or your supervisor will help. If you do want to undertake the task, decide if you want to do it solo—or with a buddy. If with a buddy, find that person or ask your supervisor to help find someone. Once found, you and that person decide who takes the lead (the point person) and who assists.

Visual Workplace Action Hit List

Department: Mag Test and Clinic | **Supervisor:** Donald x426 | **Visual Coach:** Maryanne x444 | **Date:** June 16

Your Visual Workplace Project Describe it in a few words. ↓	Point Person / Buddy	Start Date ↓	Target Date ↓	Traffic Light Status: Red X (started)	Yellow X (half-way)	Green X (done)	Comments Problems Special Needs
1. We are missing real time feedback on our defect tracking—huge info deficits.	Sue / Dave	5-14	5-25	●	○	○	We need 1/2" drill bits for plastic.
2. Incoming and Outgoing keep getting mixed up—by us and forklift drivers.	Gary / Henk	May 14	May 30	●	X	○	Please get us some more blue and green Floor-Mark.
3. The Stamper SOPs are too hard to get to, especially for newcomers.	Geo /	05/18	05/25	X	○		What can stick to the Stamper sides?
4. We need a match between parts and blueprints. Will do.	Mary / Dan	May 21	June 3	●			Who's color-blind in our area?
5. All shipping stations are disorganized in different ways. We need to develop at least three prototype benches.							
6. We want to develop a way to store + track test samples while in our area.	Dan / Joe	May 21	~~May 30~~ June 20	●	○		We need a white board by the door.
7. Our consumable supply area is a mess, no order, no visuality, lots of mix ups. We will fix.	Mary Pat / Nate	6-4	6-14	●	○	○	Can we work with purchasing, please?
8.							
9.							
10.							
11.							
12.							
13.							
14.							

Figure 3.5 Standard Visual Workplace Hit List.

- Remember: Just because you thought of a project (an important contribution), doesn't mean you have to do it. And just because no one else wants to do it, doesn't mean it shouldn't get done.
- Consider working with a second person so you have a back-up—another brain and an added pair of hands and eyes, especially if it's a big project. Or invite the new person in your area (or to the company) to join you and help. Or invite a colleague who you know wants to participate but hasn't yet thought of an improvement project of his own. Reach out. Improvement projects can be challenging, fun, and satisfying—so spread it around.
- If the project is a big one, break it down into two or three sub-projects or tasks; post these as separate hit list tasks. Tackling and completing smaller tasks make for early victories and keep the momentum going and interest high. Lots of base hits win a ball game just as surely as home runs.
- Supervisors start hit lists of their own for related tasks you can't handle (see *Leadership Task 4*).

Step 3. Set the Dates. Fill in the *Start Date* (the day you actually start the project, not when you post the task). Next, figure out the *Target Date*—when you (and, as applies, your buddy) think the project should be completed. The clock starts ticking when you start working on the project—and when you do, put a red dot in the first cell of your Project Status section. (Don't have the right color dot? Mark an *X*.)

- Reserve one column on your hit list for comments, worries, and/or special needs—for example, special supplies you need.

Step 4. Tackle the Project and Track Your Progress. As you get more of the project done, the status color shifts, like a traffic light. At the halfway point, put a yellow dot or an X in the yellow column.

- The yellow level is not exact but simply your fair opinion that the task has reached a middle point.
- If your Target Date arrives and there's still more to do, reset the date. That's the law.
- Capture comments, problems, and special needs. If you need more room, create it.

Step 5. Complete Your Project. At some point, your improvement solution is in place and you know it. Check off the final box and make sure to take a photo of your result.

Figure 3.6 A Photo Hit List. In this type of visual hit list, you use photos to track your progress—capturing the *Before*, the *Midway*, and the *After*.

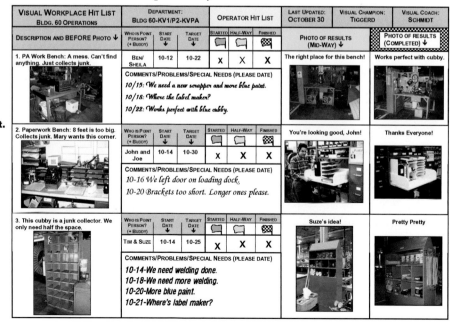

Step 6. Choose a New Project. Keep going. Name another improvement project. Tackle another information deficit. Your hit list is a powerful targeting device you can and should use repeatedly. Make it a permanent tool in your implementation tool box.

- Feel free to expand your use of the hit list to suit your needs. If a computer is not handy, ask your supervisor for access or to make the changes for you.
- Add photographs of your project to your hit list—before, during, and after (Figure 3.6).

Leadership Task 4: Hit Lists and Punch Lists for Supervisors & Managers

No matter how experienced and skilled, associates often discover that some, several, or even many problems in their area caused by information deficits are beyond their scope to address—sluggish machine repairs, murky quality measures, upstream ordering errors, and the like. Because the causes (and therefore often the solutions) to these problems lay outside the control of area associates, managers and supervisors must take them on. To that end, they start hit lists (aka, punch lists) of their own—with tasks that only management are in a position to tackle.

Higher-level challenges can also be handled through a *Macro-Visual Team* (Doorway 9/Chapter 1), a small group of ace visual thinkers who analyze and troubleshoot the overall implementation and often create higher-level visual solutions—for example, visual linkages between departments and across the organization. Managers and supervisors also bring other issues and concerns to this team. All get posted on a *Macro Team Hit List*, following the same format associates use—but with Macro Team members leading the charge.

4. Your Supplies... tools to help you invent

Here's a short story about Dave.
It's the Saturday morning Dave has been waiting for—enough free time to tackle the garage and create a nifty wall system for the new tools he got for his birthday. As long as he is done by 10:30—in time to take his kids to the practice—he'll be all set. At 8:15 on the dot, Dave opens the garage door, with the sheet of paper he has mapped everything out on. Brilliant! Dave is ready to make magic happen....

But wait a minute, where's that cardboard he needs? What about the paint and that blue tape he was counting on—and those metal drawer dividers? Where are Dave's supplies? "Oh darn, I'm gonna have to make a run to the hardware store—but I'll never get there and back on time. Darn! I'll have to wait for another Saturday I guess... but when? Darn."

Sad postponements of exciting improvement happen all too often—"I have this great idea but I don't have the supplies to make it happen!" The same can occur with the improvement projects on your hit list if you don't do your part. Your part is to:

- First, help your supervisor identify a list of basic supplies you need. (Make sure to include cleaning supplies; you need sparkling surfaces if your visual devices are going to stay in place, especially those borders, addresses, and ID labels discussed in Chapters 7 and 8); and then
- Make sure to tell him/her if you need any special supplies.
- Help managers think of easy ways to keep basic supplies well stocked and add new supply items as needed—because as your knowledge of visuality grows, your improvement supplies will need to grow as well.

Leadership Tasks 5 and 6 give more detail on getting this done. Photo Cluster 3.7 shows pictures of great supply storage solutions.

Photo Cluster 3.7
Visual Supply Carts: many choices.

Leadership Task 5: Create Visual Workplace Supply Stations

Managers and supervisors, you are responsible for identifying, ordering, stocking, and replenishing visual improvement supplies for your department.

You also need to identify a place to store them—a cabinet, rack, or shelves—so associates can get supplies quickly. Use a cart and they can pull supplies directly to point-of-use when needed and remove them when done. If the department is large, several carts are needed—so no one gets to be a "Dave."

Make sure whatever supply station you set up is highly visual. Borders, home addresses and ID labels are requirements. Also think about:

· A *Table of Contents* on or near the supply station (preferably with min/max levels indicated).
· A simple pull/kanban system to keep supplies well-stocked.

(Companies listed in this book's Resource Section provide a wide range of the supplies you will need.)

5. Your Visual Workplace Blitz...a tool to help you drive

A Visual Blitz is time set aside for a small team (or the entire department) to stop production activities and focus instead on improvement—by applying visual workplace principles and practices (Photo 3.8).

There are three kinds of visual blitzes:

- Visual Blitz: The department shuts down for two to three hours to work on hit list projects.
- Visual Mini-Blitz: Two to three sets of people stop work for a few hours to work on hit list projects.
- Visual Micro-Blitz: One or two people stop work for an hour or so to work on their hit list projects.

Photo 3.8 Associates at Denison Hydraulics work together during a Visual Blitz.

Leadership Task 6: Provide Spending Money

Photo 3.9 Renewable funding.

Some companies supplement basic improvement supplies by providing each area with a "brown bag of money"—$50 or $100 that associates can use at will to buy small things that make their job easier (Photo 3.9). When the money is spent, the bag is turned in with receipts and replenished with another round of cash. Consider this option for your company.

Are associates trustworthy? Most people are not surprised to learn that area associates are not only trustworthy but also meticulously careful about spending and tracking these funds—to the penny. There has certainly never been an ROI issue; this level of trust and respect feeds on itself, producing bottom-line benefits far beyond the dollars spent.

Throughout, a visual blitz remains I-driven; you and other area associates decide which improvement projects to undertake, with whom, and when. Your area's hit list forms the backbone. This means that the kinds of things that get improved during a blitz are driven by your ideas and insights—your need-to-know and, later, your need-to-share.

At first, your visual workplace trainer supports you and drives the blitzes in your area, keeping an eye on hit list projects, helping people buddy up, ensuring supplies are on hand, and coaching as needed. Gradually, your supervisor takes over; the following details begin at that point.

The Visual Blitz: Partnering with Your Supervisor. Here's how your supervisor helps you prepare for and participate in blitzes in your area. Your supervisor will:

- Help you find and hold your improvement focus through the use of the area hit list.
- Check in with you before each blitz to make sure you have any special supplies you need; be sure to tell him/her.
- Help you build your improvement vision, think ahead, and see a successful outcome in your mind's eye.
- Coach you to keep building the power of your visual solutions until they trigger the exact behavior you are looking for—in yourself and in others.
- Show photos of other people's visual solutions and point out specific visual principles to keep you thinking and inventing.
- Respond to your questions with questions. Because your supervisor wants to build your strengths, he is likely to answer most of your questions with another question. Something like this….

> - You ask: Hey, boss, how would you handle this type of motion?
> - Your boss responds: How would you?
>
> - You ask: Hey boss, why do you think this device doesn't work?
> - Your boss responds: Why do you think it doesn't work?

You may find this a little annoying. But sometimes it's the only way for your supervisor to get to know *your* thinking. He already knows his own!

- Help you follow the visual steps you learn in this book, reminding you to do first things first so you follow a systematic approach. (For example, when you start laying down floor borders, the floor surface must be squeaky clean. Rush past that step and all the effort that follows can come to nothing.)

- Take lots of photos, including *Befores* (so you don't forget the past), photos of visual solutions, and solutions-in-the-making—and of people (Photo Cluster 3.10). People thrive on attention, appreciation, and recognition. Taking photos of them and their ideas is a powerful way of expressing that. Tell your supervisor if you don't want your picture taken. He will respect that—no questions asked.

Photo Cluster 3.10 Videographer and subjects.

- Meet with you after the blitz to say "thanks" and, if there's time, to share photos/video and next steps.
- Check in a day or so later to admire what was achieved and find out if anything else is needed. (The company CEO may even stop by—time for more photos!)

See Photo Cluster 3.11 for the blitz in action. For more on what supervisors do during a visual blitz, see *Leadership Task 7*.

Photo Cluster 3.11 The visual blitz in action.

Leadership Task 7: What to Do During a Blitz

Here is a rundown of the finer points of the supervisory role during a blitz.
- Stay visible during the blitz.
- Where given a chance, work shoulder-to-shoulder with area associates, lending a hand, and modeling the behavior you want others to adopt.
- Share photos on the area bulletin board, on the web, in newsletters, and/or passed on to blitz participants to take home and show their families. If a camcorder is handy, why not make a blitz documentary?
- And remember, as supervisor, you are in charge of time from the outset. You decide what time can be spared for a blitz, realizing that making time for continuous improvement is part of your job. If your operations schedule is tight, a full visual blitz maybe be unlikely. Look for ways to spare a few people and schedule micro-blitzes instead.

So that's the what, the why, and the how of a visual workplace blitz, the final tool in your Implementation Tool Box. Regular blitzes will help you turn your improvement ideas into practical outcomes that take the struggle out of work. You are going to love what a blitz can do for your area and for you!

With the three outcomes (showcase/bottom-line results/attitude of learning) firmly in mind and the five implementation tools purposefully in hand, you are ready to launch the systematic visual conversion of your area.

Leadership Task 8: Avoid Standardizing Too Soon

Starting with the next chapter, the journey to visuality begins. The reader will encounter hundreds of visual devices, created by other people in other companies. As you consider these, here's a word of caution: avoid standardizing too soon.

Standards are the bedrock of operations. Standard work is the bedrock of pull, which in its turn, is at the heart of lean conversions. Because of these and other reasons, management tends to rush to standardization—in this case, standardizing on visual improvements—as an unalloyed, automatic good. Make it all uniform. Make it all repeatable. Make it all vanilla. This is often a mistake, certainly where the visual workplace is concerned—where Cherry Garcia rules.

Workplace visuality is an iterative process. We keep developing a visual solution until it triggers the required improvement in behavior. Rarely does this happen at the first cycle. Our first attempt is only a beginning, a draft. And that draft must get tested in real time. Is the motion minimized—or only reduced? Is this good enough or is it splendid?

If you, as a manager or supervisor, seek to standardize on the first iteration, you will not only rob individuals of becoming scientists of their own work as they observe, explore, and experiment, you will rob the company of ripping good visual solutions, with all their attendant benefits.

Instead of standardizing on early efforts, wait for the outcome worthy of the term *Visual Best Practice*. Now standardize on that, with the recognition that that practice will simply serve as a base for further improvement. Model this and instill it in others. Better makes us best.

This was one of Lockheed Martin's smartest moves during its visual conversion when the company was challenging for the government contract on the Joint Strike Fighter (which by the way it won). Not standardizing too quickly turned the entire enterprise into a laboratory and the employees into a workforce of visual thinkers.

Learn from the mistakes of others.
You can't live long enough to make
them all yourself.

Eleanor Roosevelt

Smart Placement

Where things are located matters. It matters so much that we are going to spend three chapters learning how to change the location of things so that the flow of work can be accelerated and slowed at will. This is the logic of *Smart Placement*.

First you learn this logic's fundamental formula: *Function + Location = Flow*—along with two powerful mapping procedures that help you see through the struggle in your area as you learn to see the flow of materials, people, and information into and through your department.

Then you learn the first seven of fourteen concepts called *Smart Placement Principles*. These will help you re-think the current placement of things in your area. While some may say these principles are simply common sense, the fact is they are not commonly used, let alone applied systematically.

The second set of seven principles focuses on larger, more strategic concepts such as flow design, design efficiency, the utilization of air, and innovation.

All fourteen principles are made to be applied. By the end of this section, you are ready and prepared to undertake the smart improvements you have pinpointed in the location of function (things). The result will be an increase in the flow and speed of materials, people, and information in and through your area. The transformation has begun.

Chapter | Four

Smart Placement: Logic, Meaning, and Mapping

The Logic: Function + Location = Flow

Smart Placement Begins with Thinking

Two Powerful Maps

Ideas, People, and Minority Reports

Step-by-Step Mapping Process

All of us know the value-mantra in the real estate industry: Location, location, location! Location is critical in the workplace, too—not just because you need to know where things are but because, to begin with, those things must be in the right place.

By *right place*, we do not just mean in a designated home location—as in "a place for everything and everything in its place." While that's important, it comes later; it is secondary to the process this chapter describes.

Instead, by right place, we mean the smart place for an item—the right location for it in relationship to every other item in the work area (and eventually in the company). We call this conscious and conscientious location of things—*Smart Placement*.

When all the items in the workplace are smartly placed in relationship to each other, the entire landscape of work becomes connected, letting material, information, and people flow into and through work areas with a minimum of struggle—a minimum of motion. Smart placement makes it possible to generate a flow of work that can accelerate (and de-accelerate) at will. Whose will? The will of your customer—and therefore yours.

When smart placement is not applied, the opposite is all too often true. When the objects in your work area—tools, parts, materials, consumables, benches, cabinets, shelves, chairs, and even trash cans—are physically placed without careful thought and intention, the result can be a tangled muddle that feeds motion instead of supporting a smooth and elegant flow of work.

Let's take a trip to Cycle Hub, a motorcycle shop in Portland, Oregon. The front of the store is filled with Triumphs, Nortons, BSAs, and other English motorcycles (Photos 4.1 and 4.2).

Behind the counter stand Mr. and Mrs. John Mahjor, shop owners and expert motorcyclists in their own right (Photo 4.3; see yellow circles).

Photo 4.1 Cycle Hub.

Photo 4.2 Showroom.

Photo 4.3 The Mahjors, store owners/cycle experts.

In the store's back rooms are mountains of astonishing clutter—monuments to motion (Photos 4.4 and 4.5). And smack in the middle of that clutter, on the side wall (just where the red arrow is pointing) is an oasis of order: the tool board (Photo 4.6). All of the tools needed to keep a bike in good repair are on that board—in order.

Photo 4.5 Chaos in the back room.

Photo 4.4 Just behind counter.

Photo 4.6 Smart Placement on the Cycle Hub tool board.

The tools are in smart placement (though, as you will discover, they are not yet *visual*), reflecting the importance Mr. and Mrs. Mahjor assign to the function those tools provide: to keep their cycles running. Yes, the location of function at work matters—a lot. Improve the location of function and you automatically improve the flow of material, information, and people into and through the area. The result? Motion takes a nose dive.

In this chapter, we learn about the logic of smart placement. The two chapters that follow this one then present the fourteen principles of smart placement and show you how to use them to build smart location into the physical landscape of work. No matter where you work—in a bank, factory, medical center, military depot, office or open-pit mine—when you apply this logic, you create powerful improvements in the design of your work area that pave the way to excellent visuality and superior performance.

The Logic: Function + Location = Flow

The smart placement process begins when you evaluate the current location of the items (things) in your work area—or as we say it: the current location of function.

In a manufacturing cell, for example, this means we look at the individual location of each machine, bench, tool set, incoming raw material, outgoing WIP, dies rack, commodity part storage, desk, and so on. In a hospital, this means the location of charts, medicines, consumable supplies, beds, desks, cabinets, racks, and so on.

In all cases, we recognize that each work item (thing) represents a *specific function*—a specific and particular use or purpose. A desk, for example, represents the paperwork function whereas a machine represents the conversion function—the conversion of material into product specifications, thereby adding value.

The concept of function plays a big role in smart placement. Only when you recognize the true function of an object can you place it correctly—smartly—in your work area. In understanding an item's true function, you also understand its relationship to other nearby items. As a result, you can position or locate each accordingly.

This is the central question in smart placement: What is the best location of function in your area—the smart location of things—so that the flow increases, so that is it safer, more aligned, and less costly? The answer is always *in relationship* to other functions (things) in that same area. All the things in a work area must function together in support of important outcomes—the product, process or service for which your department is responsible. Each item in your work area is (or should be) designed to contribute to that outcome—and it must do so safely and conveniently. If it doesn't, then change the item's location so it does—or get rid of it because it is an intruder. If workplace items are not smartly placed, their location will trigger the enemy: motion/moving without working.

Here is the formula that captures that thinking: *Function + Location = Flow*. That is the logic of smart placement.

Ask yourself:

- Are the visual devices you create triggered by *your own* need-to-know?.
- Is that computer desk in right relationship with the data I collect from my microscope on the other side of the room? Is it smartly placed?
- Are those tools on top of the cabinet in right relationship with my punch press? Are they smartly placed—or is there, for example, a safer location and/or one that is more convenient?
- What about those commodity parts in that cabinet? Is that the best position for them, with my bench 40 feet away and more than 15 trips required every shift to keep my bench stocked?

Let's look at a case study on the next page that shows us the smart placement formula in action.

Case Study

Here's a smart placement case study from Greene Rubber, a rubber stamping company near Boston.

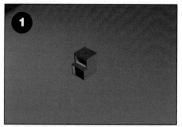

Here is the stamping cell with only its primary value field or function in place: a blue press for stamping small rubber parts.

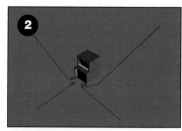

Right now, accessing that function (press) from any angle is safe, straight, and easy.

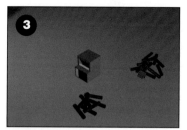

But the press needs material to stamp—rolls of rubber plus a fine red hand cart for moving the rolls.

It also needs dies. With hundreds of models, we need hundreds of dies, stored on the tall brown racks, with a nifty yellow step stool so we can reach the top shelves.

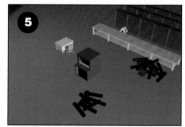

We're almost ready to start stamping —as soon as we have a long table where we can cut rubber into sheets and a desk and chair for our paper work.

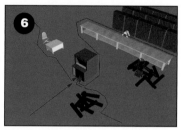

Eight workplace items—eight workplace functions. But accessing them (including the blue stamping press) is no longer so straight and easy. Look at the red flow lines.

Now let's look at the impact of those eight simple functions on the direction, volume, and complexity of the flow of materials, people, and information in and through the area—over three hours of lapsed time.

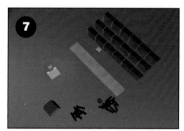

Here's a bird's eye view, a snapshot of the layout of function in the area.

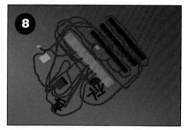

Same view, with motion revealed over a three-hour period. Dinner is served—we are having spaghetti.

Time to eat the spaghetti and get rid of the motion—caused by the unconscious location of function. Time for smart placement!

On the next page are the first four changes that happened when the Greene Rubber team applied the logic of smart placement.

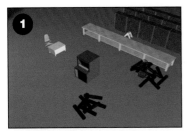

The first re-location of function: turn the desk and chair around, making it easier to slip in and out while doing paperwork.

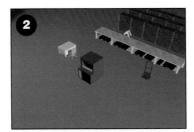

Now put the rolls of rubber under the long table (that shelf was always there—we just never thought of using it). Now materials are at point-of-use.

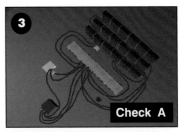

Let's check: Did those two simple changes make a difference? You bet! Look at the reduction in motion in the same three-hour span. And we did it ourselves. Can we do more?

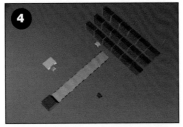

Wow, we can move the table closer to the blue machine, closer to point-of-use. That also clears access to the tall shelves. Great smart placement thinking. Can we do more?

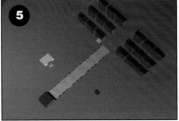

Why not open the tall shelves for have twelve points of access instead of six. Great idea—but we can't do it alone. We'll need management approval for outside help—and we got it!

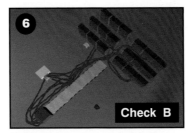

Did these two moves help? Let's check. Yes, look at this three-hour period: The flow is smooth, easy, direct, with a huge reduction in motion.

Greene Rubber's smart placement thinking really paid off. They moved from a congestion of motion (*Before*) to a much easier flow (*After-1*)—and then to a safe, fast, smooth, and accelerated flow (*After-2*).

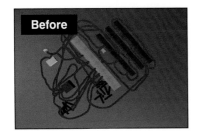

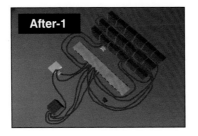

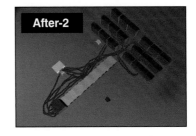

Smart Placement Begins with Thinking

The smart placement process we just walked through in the Greene Rubber case study began just as yours will—with thinking.

What is that thinking? First you discover the specific forms of motion caused by the unconscious or unintentional location of function in the area. Then you think through changes or improvements to that location that will minimize or eliminate motion. You consciously improve the location of area functions.

But note: Nothing has changed up to now but your thinking.

Only after that thinking is clear and complete—discussed, vetted, and agreed upon—do you turn to concrete actions: you move functions to match your new thinking. Only then do you get *visual*, laying down borders and addresses—the visual where you read about later in this book.

Let me say that again: Before you move a single trash can or lay down your first border, you need to understand the current design of your area: what functions occur where, and how materials (information and people) flow into and through your work area during the course of a single day. Next, you systematically examine that current design by applying the fourteen smart placement principles—and then think about and imagine improved locations for functions. Only after that is finalized do you make physical changes. The thinking comes first.

Two Powerful Maps

There is no better way to cultivate smart placement thinking than to develop the two powerful maps described below. Both maps use different colored sticky-notes to represent different kinds of functions (yellow for hard-to-move functions; blue for easy-to-move functions, pink for work-in-process; and green for consumables). Step-by-step details on developing and using both maps are at the end of this chapter.

Here is an overview. The first is called the *What-Is Map*. You and your colleagues develop this map so you can see the true extent of motion, as it is, in your area—motion triggered by the current location of functions. The second is called the *Could-Be Map (or Dream Map)*. At first, this map is identical to your What-Is Map; then you change it (sometimes radically) as you think through and apply the fourteen principles you will soon learn.

Between them, these two maps give you a concrete way to see, probe, think, imagine, and experiment with the logic of smart placement. Along the way, you will find and discuss many improvement opportunities. Some of these (the blue sticky-notes) are easy-to-spot and easy-to-handle changes that you and a buddy or two can safely undertake on your own. I say: They are within your control.

But you may have other ideas, some that seem to hold the promise of a breakthrough for your entire area. I call these "Big Ideas." How do you handle those?

Big Ideas: Changes Outside Your Control

As you travel deep into the logic of your area's current layout design, you may discover compelling opportunities for improvement that are outside of your direct control. Maybe these ideas require heavy lifting or are linked to functions that are bolted or wired in; maybe they are simply too dangerous to undertake without outside help. One way or the other, management approval is required.

Ideas, People, and Minority Reports

Sometimes, some of your most exciting ideas won't get approved; they are set aside. Usually, your management explains why (see *Leadership Task 9*); but you may still be unsatisfied with the result. And to that I say: *move on*. Getting cranky won't change the fact that a decision like that is not yours to make; it is out of your control to command. Instead, concentrate on the things you can change safely, easily, and quickly yourselves—small as they may be. These small ideas quickly stack up and create big changes. Let that momentum work its own magic.

Leadership Task 9: Handling the Big Ideas

Most of us have very active imaginations and, invited or not, love to envision possibilities. The smart placement section of the Work That Makes Sense process is often seen as an open invitation to do so. But it isn't entirely open because of the need for boundaries—for example, related to safety and cost.

Several times in this and the other two smart placement chapters, I make this point to associates: Just because you think of a terrific improvement idea doesn't mean it's going to get done—if it's not a thing under your control. In smart placement, we call this a "yellow"—or something that is "hard-to-move." It is also called a Big Idea.

Not handling Big Ideas correctly is where some smart placement efforts crash and burn. You as a manager or supervisor must not to confuse "I-driven" with open-handed permission. If you confuse that, associates might get the mistaken impression that just because they thought of an improvement, it is as good as done—even though it is in the hard-to-move category. That is simply not—and cannot be—so. Safety, costs, and plain old timing are important decision-making factors. If you promote other expectations, associates can rightly become discouraged, even angry, when one of their Big Ideas is not approved.

With the "yellows," there can be no such thing as coulda, woulda, shoulda. You can if you can; and if you can't, you can't. So stay open, listen to the improvement ideas of associates, and resist the temptation to over-promise, especially when an idea is out of your control as well. Be realistic and be honest. And if it's a no, make sure to get back to people with the real reason why.

Therefore, when we apply smart placement, we put a premium on collecting ideas, all ideas—ideas from everyone—because smart placement is, first and foremost, a thinking step. Ideas will be triggered simply by making the first map. Then more ideas will come as you apply the fourteen smart placement principles. Some ideas will target the detailed placement of specific items; others will be about the layout of a cluster of functions or even your entire area.

The point is this: At the thinking stage of smart placement, there is room for everyone's ideas.

But I want to go even further with this. I want you to stand by your ideas as well, even if they are not well received by other people, appear to be unpopular, or are simply different from what other people think. When this happens, instead of retracting your idea or bowing to the popular will, I invite you to go in the opposite direction: Develop your idea further, explore it, play with it; see where it takes you. Submit what I call a *Minority Report*—your concept of how smart placement principles could or should work in your area. This so-called "report" is your chance to develop your own unique design and demonstrate your thinking, peculiar though others may think it is.

At this stage in the process, you and your colleagues do not have to agree on a final set of ideas or changes. It is perfectly usual and acceptable for different people in the same area to see different solutions to the same challenges. This is especially true for common spaces—where people work closely in the same sub-area, for example, and/or share the same bench—either because of cross-manning or different shifts. In such circumstances, focus on staying open; adopt an attitude of learning, and listen carefully. That's what everyone else is supposed to be doing as well.

Getting people to agree on improvements related to shared areas is not out of reach. But it will require patience and tolerance, sometimes exceptionally so, before you and your colleagues can actually get to the point of moving forward together. The process is called *consensus*, and it is one of the four people tools you will learn about now.

Four People Process Tools

To make sure all ideas are encouraged and collected, the following *Four People Process Tools* are an important part of the smart placement process.

These four tools share a double purpose: (1) to help you and others find lots of different ideas about smart placement and put them on the table; and (2) to safeguard and even bolster tolerance, respect, and collaboration between people so all ideas get shared. The result? Our thinking gets clearer, stronger, and more complete—and we and others make better decisions with longer-lasting benefits.

1. Brainstorm. If you want other people to share their ideas, better make it safe for them to do so. Here are the six absolutes of brainstorming—I encourage you to adopt them:

- All ideas are acceptable and accepted.
- There's no such thing as a dumb idea.
- Ideas are collected first and evaluated later.
- Piggy-back on other people's ideas.
- Keep your non-verbal comments to a minimum—no squirming, sighing, muttering.
- Stay open.

2. Appoint a Gate Keeper. If the group gets too rambunctious or certain personalities dominate, let a group member take on the role of shutting the gate—temporarily—on bubbly, sometimes overbearing, characters while opening it for those who haven't had much of a chance to speak.

3. Use the Talking Stick. A Native American friend of mine told me about the talking stick and how his people use it in community pow-wows.

- Sit in a circle, around a table, for example, with a stick in the center (Photo 4.7).
- If you wish to speak, pick up the stick and speak. Everyone else in your group listens, without interrupting you, not even for questions—no comments, grunts, groans or squirms. When you are done, put the stick back into the center of the table.

- Someone else then picks up the stick and speaks.

Photo 4.7 A talking stick.

- The person with the stick speaks as long or as briefly as he or she likes. Some people simply hold the stick in silence—a long, calming silence.

- Keep doing this until no one picks up the stick.

- If you happen not to have a stick handy, use something else—an eraser, a remote control, a book.

4. Carry out Consensus. *Consensus* is the most involved of the four process tools. In fact, you can use the other three tools as part of your consensus process.

There's a lot of misunderstanding about consensus. Here's what consensus is not: It is not about getting your own way by getting other people to say yes. It is not about caving in and going along with others, against your better judgment. That's not consensus. That's just politics as usual.

True consensus requires two things. First, it requires an *active search* for disagreement. That means, we make a special effort to find out what other people are thinking and exactly what their objections are. We dig out the differences and surface the opposition in detail.

Second, when the details of the opposition are known, understood, and appreciated, consensus requires that we look for areas where we *can* agree until there is enough agreement for everyone to move forward together. We look for common ground.

In a sentence, true consensus is this: *The active search for disagreement until enough agreement is reached for us to move forward together.*

True consensus takes time, carefulness, and commitment. And it deserves a worthy focus. For example, it would be overkill (to say the least) to use the consensus process to get your family to agree on the type of pizza to order (at least it would be in most families). But it may be just the ticket as you develop smart placement.

So make sure to use these four tools as you share your smart placement thinking with others and they share theirs with you.

Minority Reports Are Welcomed (a repeat)

Even with the best process skills, though, there will be times when it is hard to convince other people about ideas that are different from theirs, especially if those ideas are a bit edgy. As I stated before, I want you to share those ideas anyway—but by showing them, not talking about them: Create a minority report (Photo 4.8).

A minority report gives you a chance to put your ideas into form—in your own Could-Be Map—so these get a fair hearing. People can listen to something they see better than they can hear something they are told.

Photo 4.8 Charles had a unique idea for a new layout in the retail department. He made his own Could-Be Map and presented it, on his own, to great applause. (Sears/California)

Mini-Case Study: Three Layouts.

The Cables Department at the Harris plant in Quincy, Illinois is responsible for assembling electrical wire harnesses for large radio communication systems. Only a few weeks before the visual conversion began, three cabling areas were merged into a single new department. The seventeen women from those areas were suddenly faced with a far more complex product flow than they were used to (Photo 4.9)—with the added challenge of never having worked together before.

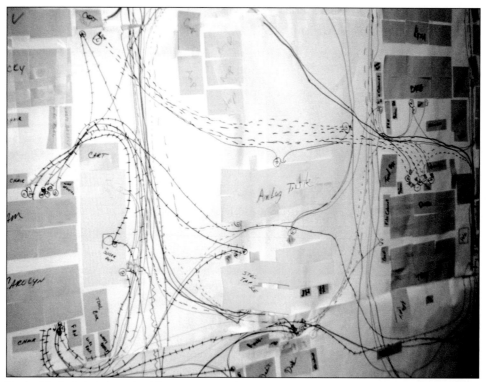

Photo 4.9 Each dashed or colored line represents a different product made in the area.

When the smart placement process began, these women, who didn't really know each other all that well, found themselves sitting around a very large table, mapping out the current layout of function (the What-Is Map). That went pretty well.

But then it was time to map out people's ideas about improving that layout (the Could-Be or Dream Map). Everyone expected the discussion to get pretty lively. But it didn't. The women simply sat politely and appeared to listen. Behind the scenes, however, the group broke into three factions, each organized around a different layout preference.

These evolved into three distinct minority reports (Photo 4.10)—but then the process stalled. People stopped talking.

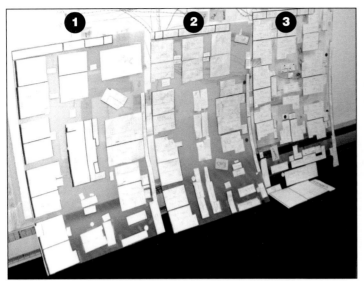

Photo 4.10 Three Layouts/Three Choices (on a heavy plastic backing).

Photo Cluster 4.11 Smart Placement Thinking in the Cables Group.

Happily, several area associates and Deanna Butler, their supervisor, had learned about true consensus (defined above) and launched the process. (Photo Cluster 4.11) Though it took several weeks to work through the details, the Cables group not only got a very fine new layout, they also got to know each other.

Mental walls left over from the old thinking came down and a new level of respect, cooperation, and departmental performance emerged. The seeds of trust were planted because each group had a chance, through the minority report format, to air its differences and preferences to an audience of their respectful peers. (And yes, the talking stick was used more than once.) The final new area layout contained elements from everyone's map for a flow that was sound, precise, accelerated. It made more sense.

Now let's walk through the steps of developing your own What-Is and Could-Be Maps, beginning on the next page.

SMART PLACEMENT MAPPING INSTRUCTIONS
Your *What-Is Map* and *Could-Be-Map*

Purpose

To document, and then improve, where functions (area items) are currently located.

Time

What-Is Map: 60-90 minutes
Could-Be Map: 90-120 minutes (can be done in smaller sessions)

Supplies Per Team/Table

4-6 blank sheets of chart paper (with faint pre-printed grid lines if possible)
Pencils with erasers
Several rulers
Several pairs of scissors
A roll of beige-color masking tape
Black, red, green, and blue markers (bullet point)
Yellow, blue, pink, and green sticky notes (2" x 3") (Can't find green that size? Use 4" x 6")
Clear removable tape
A small see-thru plastic bag

Creating Your What-Is Map

Work together and share tasks in following the ten steps in creating your What-Is Map. In Step 5 and Step 7, you will also make an exact duplicate of your What-Is Map that will serve as the base of your Could-Be Map.

Step 1. Decide which way you want to sketch your area's layout on the chart paper—portrait or landscape.

Step 2. Turn the chart paper that way and write the words "What-Is Map" at the top, along with the name of your area, today's date, and the people working with you today.

Photo 4.12 Sketching out boundaries.

Step 3. With a pencil, sketch the boundaries of your work area on the chart paper. Leave an outside margin of 1-2 inches around the edge of the paper (Photo 4.12).

- Use a solid pencil line —— for walls/other non-moveable structures. Use a dashed pencil line - - - for invisible/non-structural boundaries such as aisle ways that touch your area.

- Pencil-in brackets for doors (or leave a space). Use a wiggly pencil line for windows. Pencil-in any I-beams with a big **I**.

- Note: Start by using pencils—not markers! I've never seen a group not make a mistake in sketching out their work area. Use pencils at first and save yourself the trouble of having to correct a marker mistake. (But if you do make a mistake, use masking tape to correct it.)

Step 4. When you've completed these tasks in pencil, retrace your pencil lines in a bullet-point black marker. (Flat-tipped markers are too wide.)

Step 5. When you've completed Step 4, prepare a second sheet of chart paper, identical to the first—only name it the "Could-Be Map" and, as before, add your area's name, date, and team members.

Shortcut (Photo 4.13)

- Tape your What-Is Map to the table.

- Put your new sheet of chart paper over that map.

- In pencil, trace the outline (or boundaries) of the map underneath—along with the other structural features.

- When you have it right, retrace your pencil lines in black marker.

Photo 4.13 Could-Be Map Shortcut: Lay fresh paper over your What-Is Map.

Step 6. Make sticky notes for all items in your area—anything that has a floor or wall print. Color-match your sticky notes to one of the four categories of items.

Hard-to-Move	**Yellow=Hard-To-Move:** For items that are bolted down, recessed into the floor, wired in or the like—or too heavy or dangerous to move.
Easy-to-Move	**Blue=Easy-To-Move:** For items that you and a buddy could handle yourselves. Don't forget those wastebaskets and chairs. (If you work in a union company, follow labor rules and procedures.)
W.I.P.	**Pink=W.I.P. (Work-In-Process):** For WIP in the area—raw material, parts, orders, assemblies, sub-assemblies, finished goods, and so forth.
Consumables	**Green=Consumables:** For packing supplies, drill bits, lubricants, and so forth.

More on This Step
Cut your sticky notes to specific shapes. Combine sticky notes for larger items; cut them down for smaller ones.

- Make them as close to scale (proportional) as you can.
- Write the name of each item on its note. Be specific.

CNC Machine	Tool Cabinet	J-190 Parts	Brown Boxes

- Place each note on the paper exactly where the item is in your area right now— today.

Step 7. Now make a duplicate set of sticky notes for your Could-Be Map. Place them on that map exactly as they are on your What-Is Map. Work as a team (Photo Cluster 4.14).

Photo Cluster 4.14 Teams working on their Maps.

Step 8. When you think you are done, go to your work area and make sure that you have not missed any item—anything that casts a shadow.

- Take your map and put sticky notes, tape and scissors in a baggie.
- Don't be surprised if you've missed a few items. It happens …
- When you finish, return to the training room, and finalize your What-Is Map.
- Adjust your Could-Be Map accordingly. Then set it aside; either tape it on a nearby wall or fold it up on a nearby table. You will use it later.

Photo 4.15 Smart placement team from Hitchcock Industries (Minnesota) go to the floor to check their What-Is Map and find some things missing.

Step 9. Trace the flow in pencil first on your What-Is Map.

9a. In pencil, trace out how materials flow in and through your work area right now.

Note: You may not have time to trace the flow of people or information. Don't worry. Tracing material usually provides plenty of insight into flow congestion and motion.

Inset 4.1 Mapping: Why not use CAD? (Computer-Aided Design)

I am often asked why we do not provide people with CAD maps instead of asking them to draw their What-Is and Could-Be Maps by hand. "Think of all the time and bother they would save...." There are two main reasons for asking you to draw by hand.

1. Deeper Insights. I have found no better way for people to connect to micro and macro levels of motion in their current location of functions than to sketch out—using pencil and paper—the work area by hand. And then to populate it, by hand, with sticky notes, cut (by hand) to the size and shape of the things in that area. Because your own muscles are engaged, deeper levels of insight are triggered—and discoveries are more deeply understood and owned.

CAD maps have already done that work and, in a sense, rob of us of our thinking. You can be sure the technician who created those maps got to know the area very well, intimately. There a difference between using a CAD drawing and creating one. A deeper level of insight is triggered when creating these maps from scratch.

2. Smoother Working Relationships. Relationships between people often become smoother and more aligned when they join with others in the simple task of creating these maps from scratch. In the training field, this is called a normalizing activity—a way for everyone to contribute equally, with a high promise of success. The focus is outward—and not directly on each other. If the culture in a given work area is a bit touchy, doing these maps together can clear the way for better teaming (though you may need to use the talking stick for a while as well). It is also often a lot of fun.

Note: Some trainers like to keep CAD blueprints handy for people to refer to as they create their maps by hand. But I don't. I like the depth of understanding that comes from people recalling the area, without prompts; I believe that when they do, they notice a lot more about the location of function in their area. Later in Step 8, they will go to the floor and verify—and see what they missed.

Photo 4.16 **A** Harris Corp. team tracing many flows.

9b. Re-trace those with colored markers. Do you have different products flows? Show these by using different colors, double lines or dashed lines (Photo 4.16).

9c. Number each flow change (in pencil first; then in marker).

- Mark a #1 where the material enters your area.
- Mark a #2 is where it goes (or you go) next... (Photo 4.17 and Detail).
- Mark a #3 for the next stop or function that it (or you) go to next, and so on.
- If you make a mistake after you started using markers, use masking tape to correct it.

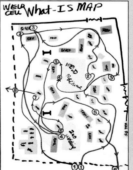

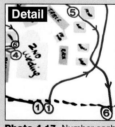

Photo 4.17 Number each step of the flow from when the material first enters your area until it leaves— and every stop in between.

9d. Estimate the total flow on your What-Is Map in terms of distance traveled and time that travel takes. Mark these numbers in an upper corner of your map. You have now completed your What-Is Map and can see why we say: Function + Location = Flow.

Photo 4.18 Multi-flow map.

Step 10. Prepare to share with others the insights your What-Is Map revealed about motion in your area caused by the current location of function. See the two complex What-Is Maps. (Photos 4.18 and 4.19).

If there's a second (or third) shift in the area, each shift does its own What-Is Map. Then both/all get posted and compared. If there are important differences, your trainer, supervisor and/or visual coach will help you work these out.

Photo 4.19 Mega multi-flow map.

Could-Be Map: Applying the Principles of Smart Placement

With the understanding and insights in hand from your study of your What-Is Map, you are now ready to apply the principles of smart placement explained in Chapters 5 and 6 to the Could-Be Map that stands ready. This work typically requires 3.0 to 3.5 hours. Your instructor may decide to split this work into two to three hour-long sessions (also a good way to keep people fresh.) Add another twenty minutes to an hour (depending on group size) for your all-important presentations to management (also explained in Chapter 6). Here are the four Could-Be Map steps.

Step 1. Put your Could-Be Map on the table. Tape your What-Is Map to a flip chart, chair back or nearby wall (Photo 4.20).

Step 2. Consider each smart placement principle, re-locating the blue, pink, and green sticky notes accordingly. Determine smart placement.

- Leave the yellow sticky notes alone for now (see below).
- Think about items you want to remove from the area in order to improve the flow. Just place those sticky notes in the margin of your map (red box, Photo 4.21).
- Think about items *not* on your map that you know you need. Make a sticky note for each and put a border around it so you can tell at-a-glance they are not yet in your area (Photo 4.22).

Photo 4.20
Keep your What-Is Map handy, on a nearby wall or chair back.

Photo 4.21 Put items you plan to remove in margin (red box).

Rolling Cart

Photo 4.22 Put border on notes for items you need.

More on This Step

a. Let everyone try out his/her ideas. That is: Individuals show what they imagine by picking up sticky notes and moving them around; that's how ideas gets shared when you use the maps.

b. Use the Four People Process Tools (Photo 4.23).

c. If you have ideas that interest only a few or no other people, develop your own Could-Be Map and create a minority report.

d. Later, all ideas/maps get presented to the larger group.

Now for the Yellows

When you have done a thorough job examining the blues, pinks, and greens, you may move on to the yellows—as long as you remember that yellows, by definition, are outside of your control to change; you will need approval and it might not come.

Photo 4.23 Respectful discussion.

Step 3. Trace and number the new flows of your Could-Be Map—in pencil first, then in marker.*

Step 4. Re-calculate the flow distance and flow time of your Could-Be Map; mark these in an upper corner of your map.

Step 5. Prepare a Change Chart (explained in Chapter 6) and get ready to present your improvement ideas (small and big) to your group and management.

* Steps 3, 4, and 5 are explained in more detail at the close of Chapter 6.

Leadership Task 10: Leaders Walk the Talk

Make sure enough training and improvement time is allotted so your employees can build their maps, work through the smart placement principles, and implement the improvements they discover there. As a manager, you'll get a better understanding of the time needed by mapping your own value field—desk or office.

This is exactly what Harris Corp. plant manager, Sue Osier, did in Quincy, Illinois. She not only put many improvements in place in her own work area, she also realized that the 15 minutes of improvement time she had allotted per person/per week were not nearly enough. So she upped the allotment to one hour and operator-led improvements soared in all five of the initial targeted areas.

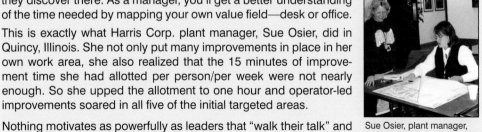

Sue Osier, plant manager, develops her Map. (Harris)

Nothing motivates as powerfully as leaders that "walk their talk" and lead by example. And there is no better way for you, as a supervisor or manager, to appreciate the value of Work That Makes Sense than to apply it yourself to your own work environment. Remember, waste in front office functions can run as high as 70%-80%. Lead improvement on all levels of your organization.

We'll discuss ways to organize and present your Could-Be Map improvements at the end of Chapter 5 and again at the end of Chapter 6 that will help guide and shape your Could-Be Map decisions. Now let's study the principles of smart placement.

> You can do anything
> but not everything.
>
> David Allen

Chapter | Five

Smart Placement Principles (1-7)

Going Visual
Principle 1: Locate Function at/near Point-of-Use
Principle 2: Nothing on the Floor/Nothing on Top
Principle 3: Capture the Full Function
Principle 4: No Doors/No Drawers
Principle 5: Put It on Wheels
Principle 6: Make It Ergonomically Sound
Principle 7: Make Function Appear or Disappear at Will

In smart placement we look for ways to take a bite out of the motion caused by the unintentional location of function—of things—in your area. When you apply the fourteen *Smart Placement Principles* (Figure 5.1), you discover ways to accelerate the flow of materials, people, and information in and through the work area simply by improving those locations.

These fourteen principles are divided into two sets, covered in two chapters. The seven principles discussed first target easy-to-make changes on a basic level (yellow box). The second set are more conceptual or abstract. Though these are not any harder to implement, it is sometimes more challenging to discover where they apply. As a result, your ability to think visually will increase.

As you walk through each principle and consider examples, look for ways to apply it in your own work area. You can do this solo or working in teams. In my experience, it is always better to sort through these principles with a Could-Be/Dream

	The Principles of Smart Placement
1	Locate Function at (near) Point-of-Use
2	Nothing on the Floor/Nothing on Top
3	Capture the Full Function
4	No Doors/No Drawers
5	Put It on Wheels
6	Make It Ergonomically Sound
7	Make Function Appear or Disappear at Will
8	Let Flow Do the Work
9	Do Major and Minor Sorts
10	Co-locate Like Items/Design to Task
11	Use the Existing Architecture
12	Store Things, Not Air
13	Double the Function
14	Use the Natural Flow Line

Figure 5.1 Principles of Smart Placement.

Map spread across the table—and a What-Is Map on a nearby wall to remind you where things/functions are right now. Remember: Smart placement begins with thinking. Only after you have considered all the principles will you decide which actual changes to undertake. Then you "go visual."

Going Visual

Smart placement is an early and indispensable step on the way to visuality. "Going visual" means: You add information to the functions you have smartly placed. That information is delivered visually—without speaking a word, as close to the point-of-use as possible—through visual devices. On the most complete level, the purpose of this visual information is to "show" you—at-a-glance—how to use a function safely, correctly, precisely, and entirely. In other words, visual devices help you do the right thing, the right way, at the right time, and safely—or prevents you from doing the opposite. We will begin the in-depth discussion of visual devices in Chapter 7 with the introduction of borders (the visual where).

Principle 1: Locate Function at/near Point-of-Use

Look at the things in your work area and think about how often you use each: Daily? Weekly? Monthly? Yearly? Based on your answer, determine how near to—or far from—its point-of-use that item (that function) should be located. In other words, how close to—or far from—your primary value field.

Daily or Hourly Use. Keep items you use daily or even hourly close—very close. It's called: *at point-of-use* (POU). The work light in Photo 5.1 is used all the time in this assembly area and so it is situated on the assembly fixture itself.

 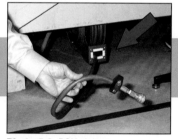 

Photo 5.1 POU work light.　　**Photo 5.2** POU air hose.　　**Photo 5.3** Air hose and outlet at POU.

Same with the air hose in Photo 5.2; it is located just under the fixture, at point-of-use and within easy reach. In Photo 5.3 the operator cleverly imbedded the air hose into the floor of the assembly mezzanine (under the metal plate), along with the electrical outlet. Perfect point-of-use thinking. The closer to the point-of-use we can position items that are used daily, the more safely and easily they can be used.

Look at Photo Series 5.4 for examples of weekly, monthly, and less-than-monthly use.

Photo Series 5.4 Other POU Applications.

 ◀**Weekly Use** Certain items may be needed, but only once a week. When so, keep them in the work area (in a cabinet, for example) so they are handy but out of your value field.

 ◀**Monthly Use** Items needed at least once a month get stored in a central location, close to but not in your immediate work area. The specialty dies you see here are used for products only periodically ordered.

 ◀**Less Than Monthly** Move items not used in the past month out of the immediate area and into temporary storage. In this company such items are put on a red pallet; then the supervisor decides if the item should be permanently removed.

Photo 5.4 shows another daily point-of-use function, installed directly into the value field: machine changeover tools on the face of the machine itself.

Take a moment right now and think: "Can I use this principle in my area?" If so, make a note of it. If you are working with a Could-Be Map, then target the blue, pink or green sticky notes—the changes under your control that you can make on your own or with a buddy. Leave the yellow notes alone (for now).

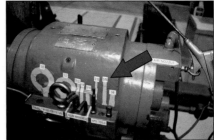

Photo 5.5 POU changeover tools on the machine.

Principle 2: Nothing on the Floor/ Nothing on Top

When you improve the flow of function in your area, you automatically improve safety. That's why smart placement always puts safety first. We see that as well in this next principle: *Nothing on the Floor/Nothing on Top*.

The Floor as Real Estate

Far too often, a company can fail to see the actual floor as an asset. Instead, floors are taken for granted and simply used to hold stuff. Viewed differently, floors can be elevated in importance to become partners of our work. In fact, in my experience, a company's floor is the single most valuable operational real estate a company has.

When I say "nothing on the floor," I do not mean to vacate the floor. I mean the floor must be properly and intentionally used—designed for use, designed to task. One of the first steps in getting maximum use out of the floor is to avoid putting items directly on it (Photo 5.6).

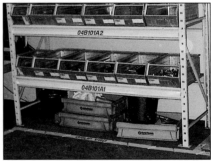

Photo 5.6 "Something" on the floor.

Doing this has four immediate pay backs. First, you can use the floor for actual work and work support. Second, when you do not put things directly on the floor, you automatically make moving them easier. Third, with no items directly on the floor, floor surfaces become much easier to clean and maintain. Fourth, when you target *nothing on the floor*, stumbling, stubbed toes, and other accidents are minimized.

Here are four of the several ways to achieve *nothing on the floor*.

Photo 5.7 The problem and its solution are side by side in this photo: boxes of parts under the metal rack, sitting directly on the floor; and boxes of parts on pallets in front of that rack.

1. Put it on a pallet or in a bin. Instead of putting an item directly on the floor, put it on a pallet or in a bin (see Photo 5.7 for the before and after). This is especially helpful for multiple items and heavy items—or both. Do this and you can also then change their location by simply moving that pallet or bin, instead of, one by one, moving the things they contain (Photo 5.8). Minimum motion, minimum time.

Photo 5.8 These large plastic containers protect what's inside while making the contents easy to access and move. Now put the containers on a pallet.

Photo 5.9 Airborne fan.

2. Make it airborne. Get an item off the floor completely and permanently when doing so does not impair its function.

A fan currently standing on the floor (or on your bench) functions just as well hanging from a bracket—with the added benefit of not taking up valuable surface area (Photo 5.9). Now you can use the space you liberated for something else—or leave it free for the unobstructed flow of other functions.

Photo Series 5.10 shows a sequence that began with making yellow part bins airborne and then led to the same for allen wrenches.

Photo Series 5.10 Make it Airborne.

The simple decision to move small yellow bins off the bench surface and onto the backboard is Principle 2 in action. The result? The value field is widened, cleared it for its true purpose: work.

These allen wrenches are smartly placed at point-of-use and anchored in the value field with a border and home address. But can we go further?

Yes: Clear the value field and make the wrenches even handier by making them airborne, positioned on the backboard. (See next paragraph on "Use the Wall.")

3. Use the wall. Dave Martin, head of Maintenance at Seton Name Plate (Connecticut), removed tools, coils, pulleys, and wiring from the floor and put them in the only available space in his shop—the wall (Photo 5.11). Then he added addresses (Photo 5.12)—and finally (Photo 5.13)—he installed automatic recoil (the visual where) for each item: border plus address (more on that in Chapters 7 and 8).

Photo 5.11 After Smart Placement.

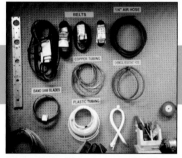

Photo 5.12 Addresses are added first instead of borders.

Photo 5.13 Borders came next and, with them, the visual where.

4. Build a Wall. No spare wall space? Build one. That is, find or create a partition or backboard; then invent ways to get things on it. Photo Series 5.14 shows five applications of this principle.

Photo Series 5.14 Build a Wall.

1. A small steel back plate is welded to a work bench so hand tools can be kept close to their point-of-use, yet off the bench surface.

2. This blue fixture for fixtures hooks onto the partition and keeps the surface of the work bench clear and available. Now there's room for actual work.

3. A metal peg board, fastened onto a wooden partition, smartly places many fixtures, tools, and consumables at—or very near—their point-of-use. (Red borders and home addresses were added later.)

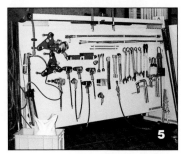

4. Reels of wire could have eaten up valuable floor space. Instead, a white partition with a blue fixture were built so that the reels could be made airborne.

5. Building this plain white partition was the answer to getting many tools and fixtures off work surfaces and off the floor.

Nothing on Top

The second part of Principle 2 tells us to put *nothing on top*. Have you noticed? The tops of cabinets and high shelves are like junk magnets (Photo 5.15). At some early point, that junked-up space had been vacant—and should have stayed that way.

When we store things up high, we usually forget they are there simply because we cannot see them—because we stored them out of sight. When we need them again, we can spend a lot of time searching before we remember to look up. That's motion enough!

But then when we reach for them, we learn yet another unfortunate result of "putting things on top:" the darn stuff comes crashing down on our heads. More motion. Ouch!

Photo 5.15 Everything on top.

The lesson is plain: Using remote out-of-reach/out-of-sight locations for storage is not smart. What to do? Here's one way: make that impossible (see next page).

Photo 5.16 Junk magnet.

The top of the shelving unit in Photo 5.16 was a junk magnet. So Anne, a night-shift operator at this Kansas facility, built a peaked roof out of scrap metal, secured it on top, and painted it all a pretty blue (Photo 5.17).

The result? No one had the slightest chance of storing anything on top! The principle of *nothing on top* got built into the real estate. Good visual thinking.

Photo 5.17 The solution.

Principle 3: Capture the Full Function

While you and your work are flowing into and through your work area, remember to consider each item's full function and take care not to build obstructions.

For example, look at Photo 5.18. Even though this corner looks orderly, those handsome yellow borders are not smartly placed.

As a result, we cannot access the cabinet without first moving the cart. (The borders are not the problem. The problem is the thinking that allowed them to be put there in the first place. When the thinking improves, your borders improve.)

Photo 5.18 Obstructed access.

In Principle 3: *Capture the Full Function*, we look for ways to release the flow of material and work by looking for unintentional blocks to that flow. The key is to capture each item's full function.

Photo 5.19 Access insurance.

For example, look at the cabinet in Photo 5.19. Its range-of-function goes beyond its flat sides, extending through the full swing of the two doors. This is captured in the red curved borders. But solid smart placement thinking came first. Without that thinking, vital access can get blocked and the flow halted. Instead, we see the full range of this item's function.

Can you use this principle in your area—on your bench? Think about it.

Principle 4: No Doors/No Drawers

Adding value is a physical event—it requires our bodies. In smart placement, we constantly think about what our physical bodies have to do in order to access function—arms, legs, hands. Anything you can do to minimize body movement is a step in the right direction.

One of the more hidden forms of motion—something we do so often it hardly seems like we are "doing" anything at all—is opening a door or drawer to retrieve something (Photos 5.20 and 5.21).

Photos 5.20 and 5.21 Hmmm, wonder what's in there? Guess I'll have to open those doors to find out...

The motion meter creeps up if, after we open that door or drawer, we discover that what we are looking for is not there and have to shut it and walk away empty-handed.

And that's just the start. We still haven't found what we set out to find. Information deficits abound, with lots of other drawers and doors banging open and shut in the aftermath. That's why we say that drawers and doors trigger the first moment of motion—and lots of other motion moments usually follow.

In Chapter 8 (home addresses), we talk about putting a table of contents on the face of every drawer and door so you don't need to open it to find out if what you are looking for is there. But that is not the point here. This smart placement principle questions the existence of doors and drawers in the first place: *no doors/no drawers*. This is surgery, not a band-aid: Get rid of doors; get rid of drawers. Here are two ways to do that.

Open-Air Storage

The first way is to store things out in the open. Günter at a Rolls-Royce machining site (Germany) removed his changeover tools from nearby drawers and cabinets and put them within easy reach on both sides of a foam-control A-frame panel (Photo 5.22). Next he wants to put the frame on a daisy wheel so he can rotate it and access either side, at will. Good smart placement thinking.

Photo 5.22 Open access to tools.

See-Thru Doors When Doors are Required

When you must have a door for security reasons or to protect contents against contamination, consider using see-thru material such as screening or acrylic, instead of opaque material. You still get the protection but you also get information sharing: You can see what is behind the barrier.

1. Use Screening.
Expensive tools on the inside required a door on the outside. Screening lets you know you've come to the right place.

2. Use Acrylic Doors.
See-thru doors protect items inside the cabinet and allow us to know at-a-glance, without opening the doors, if what we need is/is not there.

3. Use Acrylic Lids.
These bins hold many small look-alike parts, with acrylic lids that prevent us from dropping look-alike parts into other bins.

That's a Good One! Look at Photo 5.23. No, your eyes are not deceiving you. The door panels on this cabinet have been cut out—and, no, a set of acrylic panes is not on the way.

The guys in Final Assembly at Royal Nooteboom Trailers (Holland) proudly announced to me that they had finally found a way to eliminate the first moment of motion on their steel cabinet. I was excited; then they showed me what you see.

I laughed and laughed. They got me!

Photo 5.23 A *no-door* door.

Principle 5: Put It on Wheels

The wheel is one of the first tools invented by primitive man—and we can still get excited about its revolutionary capability. Here's why:

- Wheels make it easy to move just about anything.
- Wheels make it possible to turn heavy objects.
- Wheels make it easy to bring things closer to the point of use quickly and safely—and then get them out of the way just as fast and safely.
- Wheels allow us to maneuver around corners.
- Wheels make it handy to get what we want when we want it—the perfect smart placement partner!

Principle 5 tells us to put wheels to work in the name of smart placement.

70% Less Material Handling Because of Wheels

Fleet Engineers (Michigan) manufactures spring-loaded steel mud flap holders (Photo 5.24) for the trucking industry. At the time of this application, a single forklift driver serviced this non-union plant of about 110 employees.

With heavy bins of cast steel work-in-process (WIP), that driver was very busy—moving WIP between departments and from station to station within departments. Despite the forklift driver's best efforts, some person or department was always waiting for material handling, even when there was a mere ten feet to deal with between stations. Motion—and the habit of motion—was so deeply imbedded in the landscape of work that most Fleet employees simply accepted long waits as part of their work day, managers, supervisors, and associates alike. At the time of this story, the company had not yet embraced lean; it was, however, about to get visual.

Photo 5.24 Spring-loaded mud flap.

Photo 5.25 Piles of WIP.

The company's visual conversion began in the FB-27 Welding Cell. First, stacks of excess and out-of-date WIP were removed (Photo 5.25). Next, area associates cleaned up the area, invented many dirt-prevention devices, and addressed safety issues. Then it was time to tackle smart placement.

Photo 5.26 FB-27 cell after first cycle of improvement.

Photo 5.27 What a difference wheels made.

Using their What-Is and Could-Be Maps, FB-27 operators sorted out the flow of work and captured that in the crisp white borders shown in Photo 5.26. Productivity within the cell immediately improved despite the fact that material handling delays continued whenever a bin of WIP had to be moved—which was many times a day.

It was during one of those long delays that a light bulb went off: "Hey, why wait? Let's put the bins on wheels and move them from station to station ourselves!" And that is just what they did.

The FB-27 guys constructed metal pallet frames (an easy task for a welding cell), painted them a pretty blue, and fastened on the wheels (red arrow, Photo 5.27). WIP-on-Wheels came to Fleet!

The invention spread like wildfire through this hard-working plant. Material handling in the FB-27 was instantly reduced to zero inside the cell and to 70% for deliveries to the cell—because bins still had to be moved by forklift between departments. But with wheels in place, associates easily moved bins inside the cell themselves. No one was happier about this than the forklift driver.

Wheels for the Fixture for Fixtures

The heavy steel fixtures mounted on the black frame in Photo 5.28 used to lie in a heap on the machin-ing cell floor where Rick Ell, master machinist and ace visual thinker worked (Denison Hydraulics/Ohio). Rick used to spend a lot of time and effort heaving those tools around before he found the one he needed and lugged it to his machine.

When he learned about smart placement, Rick decided to build a fixture for his fixtures and put the whole thing on wheels. Now Rick rolls the dolly to the machine, uses the fixture he needs, and then rolls the dolly out of his way until the next machine changeover—safe, elegant, and inspiring.

Photo 5.28 A fixture for fixtures.

Photo 5.29 Orange box on wheels.

Box at Point-of-Use

The small orange box in Photo 5.29 contains specific tools and plastic clips needed to secure electrical wiring harnesses onto trailer frames that span 50-60 feet or more. "Why not put it on wheels," thought the three inventors, "since what's in the box gets used along the length of a trailer chassis?" (See the three inventors on the next page, Photo 5.30.)

Wheels allowed assemblers to make their way around the chassis with a kit of materials and tools always at the point-of-use.

Photo 5.30 The three Dutch inventors: Berry Vogt, Sven van Maanen, and Willie de Swart.

Notice the work instruction folder on the lid of the kit (white circle, Photo 5.31)—a great example of *use the existing architecture*, a smart placement principle you'll learn about in the next chapter. (Royal Nooteboom Trailer/Holland)

Photo 5.31 Work instructions on the lid.

Lazy Susan/Daisy Wheel

Lazy Susan-1. Yes, the humble lazy susan is also an example of *put it on wheels*—or, at least, on bearings —and can become a very smart part of your smart placement tool kit.

In Photo 5.32, a lazy susan for binders is mounted on the broad top of an old computer monitor, minimizing the clutter around the area and keeping this information within easy reach. (This is also an example of the smart placement principle *store things not air*, discussed in Chapter 6.)

Yes, we know…most companies have switched to flat screens. But don't throw this great idea away. Use it in principle—and send us a photo!

Photo 5.32 Binders on a daisy wheel.

Lazy Susan-2. The group of small dies (specialized machine tools) shown in Photo 5.33 used to be stored flat on this same deep shelf. But the dies in the back often got damaged when lifted over those in the front. What to do?

Photo 5.33 Dies on a wheel.

The brilliant Bob Comeau (United Electric Controls/Massachusetts) made a lazy susan to store them on, making it easier and safer to access the dies he needed simply with the turn of the wheel.

Reels-on-Wheels. In much the same way, the Cables Department at Lockheed Martin (Texas) mounted wire reels on a pipe rack and fixed the rack to a base also on wheels—

Photo 5.34 Reels on wheels.

reels-on-wheels (Photo 5.34). As a result, an assembler simply pulls the whole rack into her value field (the assembly bench itself), takes what's required, and then rolls the rack out of the way.

More Reels on Wheels

Many of our "teaching examples" in this book, including the next one, come from United Electric Controls (UE), a manufacturer of electrical switches and controls that won the Shingo Prize in 1989. UE has always had a strong improvement work culture. For example, they made it a point, early on, to involve associates in book study (see *Leadership Task 11*). This before/after story takes place in the department where Bob Comeau works. Bob is a long-time UE employee and, as you have already seen, a master visual thinker (his solutions are throughout this book).

Before, each time Bob had to cut wire (which was often), he had to search through the spools, lifting and moving many until he finally located the right one (Photo 5.35). Next he would haul that spool over to his bench and cut it to measure. Then, of course, he would haul it back—only to repeat the procedure the next time he needed wire.

Then Bob got smart about placement. He decided to put the entire system on wheels—and took it to the limit. Here's how.

First he assembled a metal frame and, instead of shelves, installed a series of cross pipes; then he loaded his wire spools on the pipes, taking advantage of the fact that spools are already "wheels." Look for these details in Photo 5.36.

Photo 5.35 Before: Lots of spools of electrical wire.

Notice that Bob decided to organize the spools by color (a customized company code) to represent such wire specifications as gauge, voltage, open/closed/common, and so on.

Once the spools were loaded on the racks, Bob never had to lift them again except for restocking—a very easy, safe, and smart system.

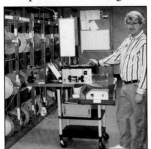

Photo 5.37 Bob Comeau, ace visual thinker!

But wait! Bob went further. Instead of having to carry a spool to his bench for cutting, he got rid of his bench completely when he installed his cutting machine on the small rolling cart you see in Photos 5.36 and 5.37. The result? Bob simply rolled his portable bench along the length of the shelving, stopped at the required spool, cut the wire lengths on the spot, and rolled away. Genius!

Photo 5.36 After: Everything is on wheels.

Leadership Task 11: Book Study

This book is an implementation manual. Put it to work for you and your company through regular book study groups. Invite area associates to meet to discuss this book chapter by chapter, usually once a week, possibly during lunch. Provide a quiet place and allow the group to discuss a chapter, share insights and questions, learn from other people's perspectives and experiences—and point to areas of possible application.

A group facilitator is a requirement in order to gate-keep, focus discussion, keep the reading schedule, and so on. A supervisor, manager or trainer usually takes on this role at first. Over time, area associates are invited to take the lead, usually on a rotating basis. This approach is also excellent for encouraging personal development. Many associates eagerly participate because of their own interest in learning and in seeing improvement happen in their areas—for their benefit and the benefit of the company.

As a manager, please consider book study as a powerful, low-cost option for capitalizing on your investment in this book.

Principle 6: Make It Ergonomically Sound

The sixth principle of smart placement is to make the area and everything in it ergonomically sound. Make it fit for us humans. That means we have to consider the body, its parts, and its range of function.

Here the addition of a small shelf to this workbench raises the packing function high enough that we do not have to bend down to fill the box. This small but useful addition can make all the difference in the world for repetitive work (Photos 5.38 and 5.39). Plus the small, knee-high shelf swivels out of the way when not in use (Photo 5.40)—which also demonstrates the next smart placement principle you will read about: *Make function appear or disappear at will.*

Photo 5.38 Retractable shelf.

Photo 5.39 At just the right height.

Photo 5.40 Now out of the way.

You see the same flexibility and attention to ergonomic detail in the assembly cell shown in Photo 5.41 (United Electric Controls, Massachusetts). First look at the slanted positioning of the wooden box in the foreground (arrow 1) to keep hand tools within easy and comfortable reach. The same principle is applied to the long, slanted, gravity-feed shelf above the bench (arrow 2) for component parts. They simply slide towards you as needed. Ditto for the drills; they are suspended above the bench on yellow cords (green box 3). You don't even have to pick up a drill; it is already in the air and ready to use.

The bottom shelf on the bench (arrow 4) reflects the same placement intelligence. It's constructed 10 inches off ground, making it just a bit easier to reach the items on it. "Just a bit easier" is the difference between a reach and a stretch.

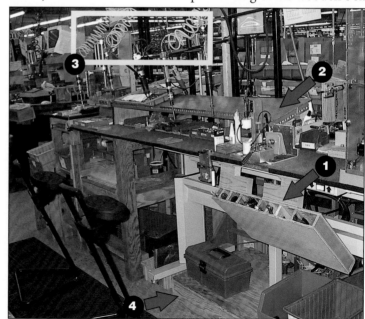
Photo 5.41 Ergonomically well-designed assembly cell.

Even the stools in this cell are ergonomically designed—flexible, with a small floor print, as easy to move as a briefcase, and yet they allow the body to be at ease and relaxed, even when active.

Photo 5.42 shows more gravity-feed positioning in the same cell: a first in/first out process. This puts sub-assemblies ready for packing within easy, comfortable reach (top red arrow). Notice that the same shelf keeps demand levels visible as well. Reverse gravity-feed on the lower shelf (lower red arrow) helps others retrieve empty boxes.

This cell is an excellent demonstration of many smart placement principles. Now it is ready to get visual—the next step in the visual conversion process.

Photo 5.42 Upper and lower gravity-feed shelves.

Principle 7: Make Function Appear or Disappear at Will

By now you know that a big part of smart placement is getting maximum flexibility out of your location choices. Principle 7: *Make Function Appear or Disappear at Will* asks us to figure out how to get function front and center when we need it—and make it invisible when we don't. Here are some examples, again from United Electric Controls.

United Electric Controls: Three Examples

Example 1. The 8-foot bench shown in Photo 5.43 is in the UE Machine Shop. This is where John Pacheco, master machinist and ace visual thinker, used to do paperwork. When he began to get visual, he got rid of all the things on that bench not related to paperwork. Only a few things were left—the logbook, some binders, masking tape. They took up so little room that John decided to get rid of the bench entirely—and with that, its 8-foot footprint.

In its place, he installed the 30-inch wide shelf you see in Photo 5.44—just room enough for the items John needed for the paperwork function. Notice also his use of vertical space—that small paper rack. But it's the fact that the whole function slides in and out, as needed, that makes this conversion especially noteworthy.

Thanks to the sliding brackets on each side of the shelf, John can draw his paperwork to him when he needs to do it—and push it out of the way when he does not. The "in-and-out" action of this shelf not

only puts function at his fingertips and saves space that John can now use for something else, it also lets him clear the other value field of obstructions when he is done—allowing easy access to the metal parts rack that existed long before John situated his paperwork function on it. After he figured out this excellent application, he spruced it up with paint and a host of helpful visual devices (Photo 5.45).

Two other smart placement principles are seen here and in the next two examples: *Use the existing architecture* and *Store things, not air*; both are discussed in Chapter 6.

Example 2. In Photo 5.46, we see the same "appear/disappear" principle used on this sliding shelf for a small punch press. Why buy another workbench when all you have to do is remove a spare shelf from an already existing rack and turn it into mini-value field?

Photo 5.46 Pull-out machine.

Photo 5.47 Pull-out coils.

Example 3. In another department at United Electric (Photo 5.47), the vacant space under a work bench was converted so it could also contribute to the company's bottom line. This sliding drawer holds coils of steel ribbon used in switch assemblies. Operators simply pull the drawer out to access the coils—and when done, push it back and out of the way.

Scania Trucks

Scania Trucks manufactures what many consider the best truck engines and cabs on the planet (Photo 5.48). We visit the Scania facility (Holland) and find an excellent application of the appear/disappear principle.

On its takt-time driven assembly line, Scania operators need some of their tools some of the time—but not all of their tools all of the time.

Because of that, sets of tools are located at specific points along Scania's indexed assembly line. But operators do not go to their tool boxes or a bench to get them. The tools are mounted on extendable metal arms so operators can pull tool sets to them, at will—and, at will, clear them out of the way (See yellow boxes in Photos 5.49 and 50). This is precisely Principle 7 in action.

Photo 5.48 A Scania-built engine in a Scania-built cab.

Photos 5.49 and 5.50 Exactly the right tools on this Scania assembly line are instantly available at every station along the way.

Next Steps

As we walked through this first set of smart placement principles, I hope lots of possibilities occurred to you. "Gee, I could use that. Gee, I think I might try that out." This is exactly what is supposed to happen—the realization that there are things you can do by yourself (or with a buddy) to improve the flow of materials, information, and people in and through your area.

Through the examples, you saw that you can accelerate the flow in ways that are simple and yet also powerful.

If you are also using the mapping process described in the last chapter, then you've been moving sticky notes around as well and seeing the changes both on the Could-Be Map and in your mind's eye. That is an excellent place to start.

Your Change Chart

Before you move on to the second set of principles, take a moment right now to take stock. List out your current thinking—what you intend to change. If such changes affect only your own work, then you can probably undertake them right away. But you may not change *anything* in common or shared areas unless and until everyone accepts that change. (And you already know: There is no such thing as improvement that is unsafe.)

You'll add to this list as you examine the smart placement principles in the next chapter.

To help that along, set up a simple change chart that shows your thinking and your list. Below are three chart formats that others have used (Photo Series 5.51). Choose the one you like, combine elements or create a format that is uniquely your own. Just make sure to get your thinking clear before you move on.

Photo Series 5.51

This chart separates ideas needing approval from those that do not.

This chart uses the four colors of sticky notes as an organizer.

This chart separates items based on cost/no cost.

If you are working with others on this list, it may prove an ideal time to apply the *Four People Process Tools* you learned in the last chapter: brainstorming, appoint a gatekeeper, talking stick, and consensus making. All thinking is valuable. Keep the listening, sharing, and learning open.

In keeping with our definition of consensus (Figure 5.2), you want to surface areas of enduring differences as well as areas of easy agreement. If that process stalls, do not hesitate to create a "minority" list—one that satisfies you but perhaps no one else. And when you are ready, move on to Chapter 6 and the second set of smart placement principles.

Consensus

The active search for disagreement . . .

Until enough agreement is reached for us to move forward together.

Figure 5.2 Definition of True Consensus.

Whether you think you can or think you can't, you are right.

Henry Ford

Chapter | Six

Smart Placement Principles (8-14)

Principle 8: Let Flow Do the Work
Principle 9: Do Major and Minor Sorts
Principle 10: Co-locate Like Items/Design to Task
Principle 11: Use the Existing Architecture
Principle 12: Store Things, Not Air
Principle 13: Double the Function
Principle 14: Use the Natural Flow Line
Next Steps

In the last chapter, you studied and applied the first seven of smart placement's fourteen principles—and discovered ways to accelerate the flow of material, information, and/or people in and through the work area by improving the location of function. You reduced motion caused by the unintentional layout of function. In this chapter, you'll consider and apply the second set of seven principles (Figure 6.1).

I believe you will easily notice the difference between these two sets. The first set of principles targets improvements on a micro—or very detailed—level related to safety, comfort, and ease of access. You looked at clearing the floor and the tops of things, showing the range of function, minimizing motion caused by doors and drawers, using wheels, slides, and other ergonomic elements to ease handling and retrieval—and ultimately to accelerate the flow.

Principles 8 through 14 look at larger conceptual matters, including the overall design of space and flow in your area. While we will look at a number of detailed applications for these, we will also take the opportunity to branch out with these new principles for wider applications, perhaps even impacting the flow in your entire area.

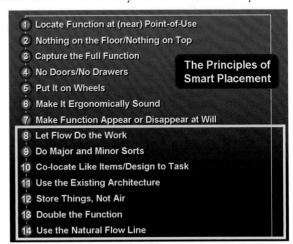

1 Locate Function at (near) Point-of-Use
2 Nothing on the Floor/Nothing on Top
3 Capture the Full Function
4 No Doors/No Drawers
5 Put It on Wheels
6 Make It Ergonomically Sound
7 Make Function Appear or Disappear at Will
8 Let Flow Do the Work
9 Do Major and Minor Sorts
10 Co-locate Like Items/Design to Task
11 Use the Existing Architecture
12 Store Things, Not Air
13 Double the Function
14 Use the Natural Flow Line

The Principles of Smart Placement

Figure 6.1 Second set of smart placement principles (yellow box).

As you walk through these principles, again consider where you might apply each—actually, really, physically. If you are using a Could-Be Map, do your experimentation directly on that map, moving your sticky notes around and developing alternatives. And remember to create your own separate map if you have a burning vision and others don't quite get or support it—create a minority report.

Principle 8: Let Flow Do the Work

As mentioned, we addressed many micro applications in the previous chapter. Now we change the scale and talk about something big—really big—Principle 8: *Let Flow Do the Work.*

That single word—flow—captures the big picture of what we want and get from smart placement: a flow of value that moves through the area with a minimum of obstructions or surprises, one that allows us to move through our work day not just without struggle but with ease, safety, precision, and completeness.

Think about this in terms of your own individual work as well as the work undertaken by your entire department. Think about flow (Photo 6.1).

To help do this, step back from the principles we covered in the previous chapter with their tight focus on the detailed placement of things and look at the overall layout. Look at the path—the flow line—that material, people, and information follow as each makes its way through your department. How would you describe it? Does it move along at a self-pace or does it get stalled? Does it flow freely as streams do, skirting around rocks, boulders, and tree limbs—keeping the pace, flowing no matter what gets in its way? Or does it pool and get stalled in the nooks and crannies of your department?

How would you describe the flow of work into and through your area? Do this now and, if you are with others, share your impressions and insights.

Photo 6.1 The flow working.

If you are working with a Could-Be Map, survey its surface and the sticky notes that populate it and consider the flow you see there. (You may get added insights if you back up and study your What-Is Map.) As you do, certain ideas or notions may occur to you. Talk about these with your colleagues.

If you are not using a map, go directly to your area and watch the flow there, just as it is.

Flow, Pull, and the Yellows

Here's something else to consider: flow paves the way for pull; flow is pull's foundation. They are allies. Pull is flow under demand. Pull is flow driven by time. And time is driven by your customer. That makes pull—and the flow that comes first—an indispensable part of enterprise excellence. Think about this and discuss it with others.

As you study the flow in this way, you may be tempted to consider moving the yellow sticky notes, representing those items that are hard or impossible to move by yourself or without authorization. Not only is there nothing wrong with that, there is everything right with it—as long as you recognize and accept that: a) Just because you thought of it doesn't mean it has to happen; and b) Just because it doesn't happen doesn't mean your idea was dismissed or not considered worthy.

By definition, yellow sticky notes are under the command and control of management, not yours. Before committing to changing any yellows, company managers need to consider a range of factors (some public, some private)—one or more of which may prevent your idea from getting implemented.

Rest easy with that. Your job is to show up, tell the truth, and stay open. After that, let the cards fall where they must and keep going forward.

Two Mini Case Studies in Yellow. Here are instances of area associates, such as yourself, developing powerful solutions involving yellow sticky notes that were implemented.

Study 1: Drop Line Ceiling Grid. The company in our first study specializes in engine overhaul and repair in the aerospace industry and was on its visual-lean journey for nearly a decade at the time of this story. Continuous improvement at the site had long become a habit, eagerly exercised by associates, supervisors, and managers alike. The enterprise fairly hummed with new thinking.

Over the years, many area layout changes were made, but always with some reluctance, since moving the electrical wiring for benches and air lines for pneumatic tools was so costly. Then one day, a group of associates had a breakthrough. They decided that instead of thinking about improving the flow of material through the area, they should focus on improving *the flow of improvement*. Yes, you read that right. Since the cost of moving wiring and air lines slowed down the improvement rate, they focused on eliminating that cost.

Photo 6.2 Ceiling Grid.

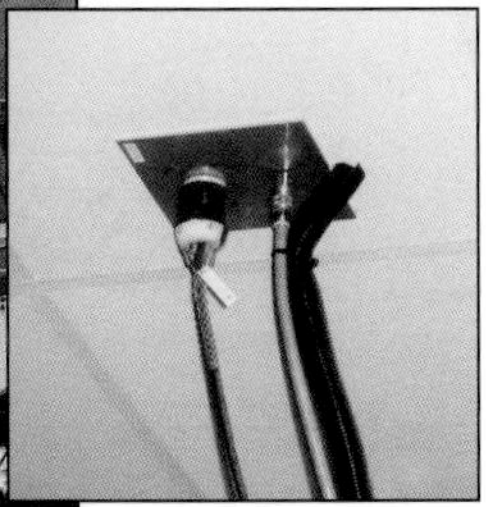

Photo 6.3 Close up of drop lines.

Here's how. They recommended that a set of drop-lines be installed in the department's ceiling at ten-foot square intervals (Photos 6.2 and 6.3). The result is a ceiling grid that allows the location of benches to be changed at will, with little lost production time. Now whenever the team wants to improve the flow (or when the model mix is changed over), drop lines over benches in the existing layout are disconnected, the benches (all of them already on wheels) are then moved and connected to drop lines in their new locations.

Company management embraced this solution wholeheartedly and with speed. A victory for smart placement thinking and the shrewd pursuit of the yellows.

Study 2: Test Clinic Transformation. Hitchcock Industries (Minnesota) provides precision aluminum and magnesium products for commercial and military aircraft and engines. The Test Clinic, or rework area, discovered many small smart placement improvements when they studied their Could-Be Map.

Photo 6.4 Before: Test Booth, blocked by WIP.

But they also saw a way to improve the entire flow of rework in and through their department. Specifically, the main test booth had become a major bottleneck, situated at the end of a narrow corridor that was always crammed with units waiting for test (Photo 6.4).

Photo 6.5 (next page) is the Clinic's What-Is Map; the yellow box on the lower left indicated the location of the main test booth; the blue box that surrounds it shows the waiting WIP.

After the Clinic team had presented improvements within their control to general manager Ronn Page, they shared their Big Idea: moving the main test booth out into the open area to the far right, and create a second test booth (Photo 6.6). The red box surrounds the area where the two booths are now; the red arrow points to where the single booth used to be). The icing on the cake was to replace the back wall of the newly moved test booth with heavy plastic curtains. Similar to a grocery store check-out counter, units then flowed into the booth from the left, got tested, and flowed out on the right (again red box in Photo 6.6). It was the perfect solution for speed, quality, ease, and convenience.

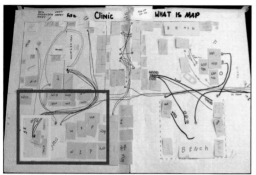

Photo 6.5 What-Is Map of the Clinic department (blue=WIP).

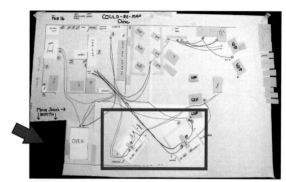

Photo 6.6 The Clinic Could-Be Map: the main test booth was moved in the open area and split in two.

This change made so much sense, it got instant approval. With all the wiring, air hosing, and partitioning, the change took nearly five weeks. Area associates used that time to put their many powerful small improvements in place.

You may discover similar opportunities with your yellow sticky notes. Just remember: No matter how elegant and worthy an idea may be, other factors can impact management's response: safety, cost, timing, organizational structure, misalignment with future changes not yet announced, and so on. The result? That idea may not get implemented.

Principle 8: *Let Flow Do the Work* is a powerful organizing concept in smart placement because its application benefits everyone—in your area, throughout the company, up and down your supply chain, and throughout your customer base. That's why it's important for you to continue to keep it in the forefront of your thinking. Notice flow, consider it, target it—improve it.

Principle 9: Do Major and Minor Sorts

"Piles of things" is a classic trigger of massive motion. Just because a set of things passes the first point-of-use test (you are certain you need them on a daily or weekly basis) doesn't mean it will be easy to access the exact "thing" you need when you need it. This is especially true of things that come in many sizes, like drill bits, inserts, packaging materials, fasteners, needles, material types, grades, and shapes, and on and on.

One of the simplest and most powerful ways to handle "lots of things" is to determine their sub-sets or categories. I have several names for this: doing major and minor sorts, sorting the universe, and finding the buckets (Photos 6.7 and 6.8). They mean the same thing: find the sub-sets so

Photo 6.7 Nesting Bowls: Sorting the universe. (Courtesy of www.chefs-resource.com)

you can see the differences in things that appear to be identical but are not. Once you see that, you will be better able to figure out how to locate them accordingly—smartly.

Sorting the universe is particularly important when we feel overwhelmed by the amount of "stuff"—the universe. "How can I get my arms round all this? How can I handle it?" There is simply too much of whatever "it" is.

Photo 6.8 Sorting the universe: Finding the buckets.

How to Sort

Begin your sorting by noticing what's different about that "stuff" (that universe) and what's the same. For example, what's standard and regular *versus* what's special and occasional?

- That will give you your first two categories or chunks.
- Now look at those two chunks and see if you can make them into four chunks (or categories).
- Then see if you can sub-set those four into eight and, after that, into sixteen.

Start with a major category and then sort down into minor ones. That's the idea behind the many colors and sizes of the nested kitchen bowls shown in Photo 6.7; all the bowls have the same overall function

Photo 6.9 Inserts in family groups.

but noticing their sub-categories helps us locate (and use) them more exactly. We notice the differences.

Inserts Example. The same principle applies to the rack of machine inserts in Photo 6.9. Instead of having all the inserts in a single huge tray, they are grouped in so-called families and smartly placed in separate trays. More precise locations = faster retrieval. You have sorted the universe.

International Example. Another brilliant application of this sorting principle is found at Seton Name Plate, a Connecticut catalogue company that sells and ships thousands of ID products every day to locations around the world. But a category called "shipments" was too broad for the Pack & Ship Team to handle with precision. So the Team sorted the universe into two major buckets: domestic shipments and international shipments. Then, because a finer focus was still required, the team sorted the international category into countries—Germany, Australia, Canada—as shown in Photo 6.10. Later, this very smart placement was captured by the splendid colorcoded borders and crystal clear home addresses you see here. But the thinking and planning came first.

Photo 6.10 International vs. domestic sorting.

Scania Example. To picture the *do major and minor sorts* principle on a large scale, we go back to Scania and its facility in Zwolle, Holland where engines and cabs are manufactured (Photo 6.11).

Photo 6.11 Scania-built engine.

Scania is a master at driving out costs through modularization—standardizing as many vehicle components as possible and then making sub-assemblies that are interchangeable between engine models. Yet the company also had a strong market for custom-made vehicles.

Previously, standard and customized vehicles were made on the same assembly line in Zwolle. But the Zwolle site needed 30% more capacity for its growing business. At first, Scania contemplated constructing a second plant. Then it applied the principle of sorting (finding the buckets) and separated its operations into two assembly lines—one for standard, highly repetitive vehicles and the other for specialty orders.

The result was the brilliant nested layout that you see in Figure 6.2 (Scania dubbed this design *Castor & Pollux*, famous twins in Greek mythology). The green U-shaped assembly line on the outside is for standard models (notice it is longer) and the red inside U-line is for specialty models.

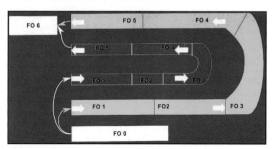

Figure 6.2 Nested layout: green is for standard models and red is for customized models.

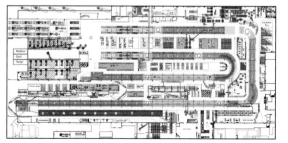

Figure 6.3 Castor & Pollux: architectural detail of the same nested layout.

Scania achieved the 30% increase in capacity it needed by nesting the custom line within the standard line and enjoyed the added benefit of enabling the same supervisors to oversee both lines in parallel. Figure 6.3 provides a more detailed layout drawing.

Principle 10: Co-locate Like Items/Design to Task

At first, this next principle, *Co-location/Design to Task*, may look the same as the previous principle of sorting into buckets. But it isn't. Here's why.

Principle 10 is about putting like items in the same place. We co-locate them. We do this not in order to organize them into families, as we did a moment ago with inserts and parts. We co-locate in order to have the different items needed for the same task in the same location.

Photo 6.12 All belts in the same location.

In the example in Photo 6.12, press operators at Fleet Engineers (Michigan) searched the area around their 500-ton Bliss Stamping machine, collected all associated conveyor belts, and stored them on the blue standing rack you see here, which stands not three feet away from the press. They did the same with dies for that press: located them smartly in the bordered area in Photo 6.13. Both are excellent applications of the co-location principle.

Photo 6.13 Machine tools (dies) are situated in the same location.

Design-to-Task: Type 1

The next level or dimension of the co-location principle is *design to task;* it focuses co-location squarely on a precise activity. In a manner of speaking: we kit.

You saw the orange box in Photo 6.14 before when we discussed the *put it on wheels* principle. This time we look beyond the wheels to inside the box. Here associates pre-gathered in a box the tools and clips they need to secure electrical wiring harnesses onto trailer frames. The box is designed for that specific task—and no other. Every item in the box shares the same purpose: some aspect of fastening harnesses onto the trailer chassis (Royal Nooteboom Trailers/Holland).

Photo 6.14 Design-to-task assembly kit.

Lockheed Martin Aerospace (LM-Aero) set the pace in its use of the *design-to-task* principle when the Fort Worth Logistics Team wanted a better way to deliver assembly parts. Up until then, sets of parts were stuffed—or kitted—into plastic bags; but those bags were often missing parts or the parts got damaged in transport. So the team devised a series of stiff-foam delivery boxes (Photo 6.15). Each box held all the components for a specific sub-assembly. Here's more on how this intelligent delivery system works:

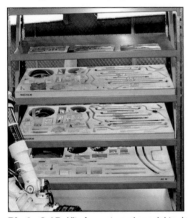

Photo 6.15 Kits for parts and special tools.

- The system is comprised of four elements: a) the assembly parts; b) a carrying box; c) a stiff white foam insert the size of the box; and d) heavy stencil paper the size of the top surface of the box.

- First the parts are laid so they fit on the stencil paper. Then each part's profile is traced. Next the paper is laid, with the ends taped down, on the stiff foam; then the shapes are cut into the foam with a sharp knife. Finally, each assembly part gets inserted into its corresponding foam cut-out. The box is ready for delivery.

Not long after LM-Aero started using this approach, someone had the bright idea of enlarging the box so special tools could be included as well. That means you get all the parts and all the tools for a specific assembly in a single box. Fantastic! This design-to-task delivery system became a Visual Best Practice across all seven LM-Aero sites and became especially important in areas where foreign object damage (FOD) was a concern (Photo 6.16). For an important design-to-task material innovation for anti-FOD and clean rooms see Inset 6.1 on the next page.

Photo 6.16 Happy anti-FOD customer.

Photo 6.17 Design-to-Task Took Kit.

A variation on this is a design-to-task box for tools only, shown in Photo 6.17. Here you see the exact set of tools needed to assemble (or disassemble) a specific product in this overhaul and repair facility. The stiff foam cut-outs act as borders to the tools and also control their positioning. The yellow lining makes it easy to see, at-a-glance, when a tool is not there.

Take a moment and study both blue boxes. Does anything catch your eye or surprise you? Yes, that's right! Each contains some of the same tools—needle-nose pliers, mallets. And yet these boxes are side by side. (Note: those two mallets differ in weight; each is for the specific task its box supports.) Costly tool redundancy? But this company populated by highly-skilled assemblers finds it more productive and less expensive to provide complete tool sets in design-to-task boxes than to chance anyone having to search for or share these tools. As with a missing part, if you can't find the tool you need when you need it, work stops.

Inset 6.1 Special Material for Design-To-Task Kits in Clean and Anti-FOD Areas

HDPE plastic in action.

The design-to-task principle was deployed for nearly a decade before companies noticed that the high density foam used in these customized systems broke down (particulated), leaving many tiny contaminants.

At first, aerospace, anti-FOD assembly areas, and clean rooms had to avoid these applications due to the deteriorating foam. Then technology caught up. Long-lasting, highly durable HDPE (high-density polyethylene) plastic is now available in a foam-like format for these applications. For more information, contact **The 5S Store** in this book's Resource Section.

Design-to-Task: Type 2

In Photo 6.18, we see an ingenious application of the *design to task* principle, created again by the LM-Aero workforce—a motion-buster of the first order thanks to the brilliant location of function.

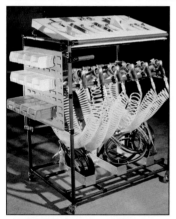

Photo 6.18 Six-pack assembly bench.

Called the *Six-Pack* because of the six pre-set pneumatic drills it holds, this lightweight assembly bench is specifically designed to assemble the parts in the foam cut-out box sitting on the top of the bench. The top of the bench is actually the parts box itself, ergonomically positioned for ease of use.

At hip-level are six pneumatic drills, identical except for their bits; each bit is set for a specific assembly task related to the same parts box—another example of the design-to-task principle.

The bench's bottom tier holds three identical air hoses, each pre-set with a different PSI value (pounds per square inch)—again to reduce the motion called "adjustments."

Principle 11: Use the Existing Architecture

Buying stuff for a company is not unlike buying items for your home. "Things" cost money and buying one thing usually means some other purchase has to wait. That's why making one item serve two (or several) functions means you save money on two fronts: (1) you don't buy the second thing; and (2) you don't need to find additional space or real estate or use up the existing real estate to accommodate something new.

Use the existing architecture is a doubling-up principle. That means simply this: Attach one function to another. That is, you locate an additional function on a structure that has an existing function. When you do, you double up on that structure so new space or new items do not need to be acquired.

This powerful principle has a wide range of uses, many perhaps put into place before you learned that it was part of smart placement thinking. Now you can exploit this principle on purpose.

104 WORK THAT MAKES SENSE

Applications

I-Beam Application. A simple application of this smart placement principle is shown in Photo 6.19. The primary purpose of the I-beam is to bear weight, keeping the ceiling up and the building intact. We get more mileage out of that I-beam by fastening an air hose reel onto it; and that does not subtract from the beam's first function. (Also notice that since the reel is airborne, it does not eat up valuable floor real estate: no footprint.)

Photo 6.19 Let's maximize the use of this I-beam.

Photo 6.20 The end of this shelving unit now holds three additional functions—a thrifty use of space.

End Cap Application. Tall shelves like those shown in Photo 6.20 are used to store inventory. That's their primary or main purpose. But their usefulness is increased when a notice board—a second function—is added to the shelving unit. Though the primary purpose of these shelves is storage, posting that notice board gets double-duty out of them and also saves us from having to find (or buy) a new way to post announcements.

We used the existing item—the existing architecture—for a second purpose. In this example, two more functions were added: a place for outgoing mail (on the low blue shelf to the right) and a place to hang hard hats (the red one is for visitors).

Forklift Innovation. Frank Mulder, a material handler at Royal Nooteboom Trailers (Holland), is well-trained in workplace visuality and an innovative visual thinker in his own right (Photo 6.21). He cleverly and safely applied the existing architecture principle to his forklift in four ways (Photo Cluster 6.22): (1) He fastened his red paperwork bin to the forklift door; (2) He kept his schedule in a plastic sheet he taped to the door; (3) He wrote notes and reminders directly on his side window; and (4) He marked his route on his windshield at the exact point of use.

Photo Cluster 6.22 Use the Existing Forklift Architecture

Photo 6.21 Frank Mulder and his prize forklift.

Tool Cabinet Application. Look at the doors of the tool cabinet in Photos 6.23 and 6.24. Before, they served one purpose—to enclose and protect the tools inside. Now they have a second purpose, a double function. One door holds a set of metric wrenches. The other door holds allen wrenches, an adjustable wrench, and an oil gun. Very compact!

Photos 6.23-6.24 Even the doors of this tool cabinet are put to use.

Photo 6.25 Belt storage on back of bench.

Backboard Application. In Photo 6.25, the back of this assembly bench doubles as a storage location for crane belts at point of use (the yellow crane column is to the right). This is a small and handy way to maximize your real estate.

Tool Box Application. Photo Cluster 6.26 presents a little masterpiece of *use the existing architecture*, created by a Boston operator. He started with a common red toolbox (on wheels); added a slab of wood to extend the top surface; fastened a white board and cork board to the back; hung two wire bins for paperwork, plus a hook for hoses; fixed his drill bits to the top; and added a chair to rest his weary bones on. Since the entire unit is designed for a specific set of tasks, this is also an example of the *design-to-task* principle.

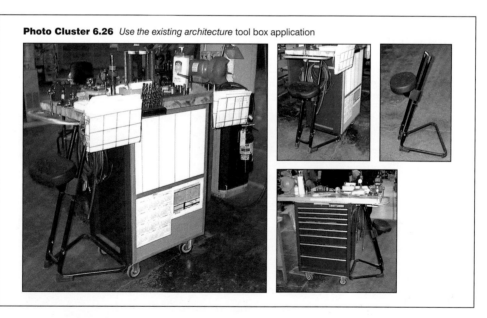

Photo Cluster 6.26 *Use the existing architecture* tool box application

Principle 12: Store Things, Not Air

What maintenance department ever has enough room? Not many. But if we look closer, we might notice unused space in some unexpected places.

When the visual thinkers in maintenance at Denison Hydraulics (Ohio) noticed a wide-open white wall above the entry way, they thought: "Why not use that space for something—instead of for nothing? Why not apply the *store things, not air* principle of smart placement?" So they gathered up the pulleys and coils piled up here and there in corners—and made a home for them on the wall (Photo 6.27).

The result was excellent on every level. The empty space above the entrance way used to cost the company money and never gave anything back. It was underused—what I call "negative" space. Afterwards, when it became home to all those coils and pulleys, the same wall space made a positive contribution to the company's bottom line. And I call that "positive space." The company pays for this wall whether or not it is used. Now there's a return on that investment. The red arrow points to a clipboard with location numbers.

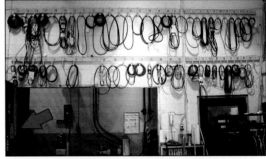

Photo 6.27 This wall now pays for itself.

Photo Series 6.28 shows a wide variety of applications for the *store things, not air* principle.

Photo Series 6.28
Store Things Not Air

1. Not only does this cabinet not have doors, the inside space is maximized by replacing deep shelves with metal peg board panels at a slant, positioning tools for easy access.

2. Pallets, stored high off the warehouse floor, makes excellent use of otherwise un-used and un-noticed air real estate.

3. A modest application of store things/not air, the bucket fits perfectly under this small stool and the company is the better for it.

There is a second aspect of the *store things, not air* principle. It's called: *squeeze the air out*. These are both in action at Delphi Deltronicos (Mexico) in the hazardous materials (HazMat) cabinet shown in Photo 6.29 (below) and 6.30 (next page).

A. Store Things, Not Air. In Photo 6.29, notice the use of vertical space on the upper left where the two yellow tubs of grease-off are stored (see red arrows). If you are not thinking about "air" as an asset, you might only think about storing one.

Applying this principle requires a form of reverse thinking: You have to see what is not there in order to spot the opportunity that unused air provides as you seek to maximize the use of space through smart placement.

Photo 6.29 Turning negative space into positive space.

This kind of out-of-the box thinking can lead to first-rate improvements. Develop an appetite for it.

B. Squeeze the Air Out (I). You can see the *squeeze the air out* dimension of this principle on the bottom shelf of the cabinet (red arrow 1, Photo 6.30). The air has been squeezed out so only the three containers that are supposed to be on it can fit.

Photo 6.30 Behind the yellow doors of this HazMat cabinet is an expert level of smart placement—and the visual where.

How did they do that? They raised the base of the cabinet by welding in an 12-inch metal plate that squeezed out the excess air. Now that shelf can be used exclusively for the purpose for which it was designed.

The middle shelf for grease guns shows the same principle in action (red arrow 2, Photo 6.30). We could have just laid the grease guns down on the shelf. But the extra space around the guns might invite the arrival of more stuff, with the shelf getting so cluttered we might fail to see the grease guns at all.

Instead, that middle shelf was tilted up and pushed forward, with the result that the air got squeezed out. Then the grease guns were affixed to what became a back plate. In doing this, not only did the air "disappear," but the shelf itself was designed for a single task—and the grease guns were situated ergonomically for easy, safe retrieval. Three smart placement principles in one application. Fantastic smart placement thinking.

C. Squeeze the Air Out (II). Susan Heater and Lucy Manley, assembly experts at Vibco Vibrators (Rhode Island), wanted to go further in their 5S efforts so they (rightly) added smart placement principles. Photo 6.31 shows one of their many innovative applications—in this case, for store-things-not-air. Instead of loading up a ten-inch deep shelving unit with supplies they did not need or leave it unoccupied to collect what did not belong, Lucy and Susan backfilled each shelf with empty packing boxes so only the wanted quantity could fit. Photo 6.32 shows you the telling detail. Great visual thinking. (See Inset 6.2 for more on combining smart placement principles and 5S, a perfect partnership; page 114.)

Photo 6.31. Vibco Innovators Lucy (left) and Susan (right).

Photo 6.32 Smart placement plus a great use of borders, addresses, and arrows.

D. Squeeze the Air Out (III). If you can't physically reduce the air footage, then at least prevent air from acting as a "junk magnet."

The blue shelving unit in Photo 6.33 is a case in point (next page). You saw this unit before in Chapter 5 when we discussed *nothing on top*. Remember? The operator put the metal cap on the top of the shelving to prevent stuff from landing there.

When the same operator began to identify the use for each of the unit's 25 cubbies, she realized she did not need them all. Instead of risking that all those unneeded cubbies would get filled up with "junk," she squeezed the air out, making it impossible for anything but the right items (in the right amounts) to be stored there. She created a junk barrier, blocking off 16 other cubbies and leaving her the nine she needed (Photo 6.34). Later, a colleague added a pipe on the side for yellow bungee cords (Photo 6.35), adding yet another smart placement principle. Can you name which one? (Yes: *use the exiting architecture*.)

Photo 6.33 Twenty five chances to collect stuff.

Photo 6.34 Since nine is all that's needed, barricade the rest.

Photo 6.35 The pipe that holds the yellow bungees swings out for easy access.

Principle 13: Double the Function

Question: What is to stop us from using the same "thing" for two purposes, for two functions—the same real estate, the same device?

Answer: Nothing but our imagination!

In smart placement, we call this *double the function*. We'll examine three examples for starters; you'll see many more throughout this book.

Application 1: The Original Double-the-Function Application

Photo 6.36 Double-function borders (with the addresses removed to make you think).

It was the first year of the visual conversion at Fleet Engineers (discussed in *put it on wheels* in Chapter 5). The transformation began in the FB-27 Cell, where mudflaps were welded by a smart, energetic, determined and—as you will see yet again—remarkably innovative team. At the far end of the area was the floor device you see in Photo 6.36.

At first, I looked but could not make out what it was. Then I saw two borders that seemed to overlap. But why? What reason would there be for two borders in the same location? That would defy the law of physics we all learned at school: "Two physical objects cannot occupy the same physical spot." But that is exactly what we see here. What could it mean? Time for a Pop Quiz.

Pop Quiz. What could it mean? What is your answer? Why do you think there were two overlapping borders? Speculate, guess, imagine—because unless you've actually been in Fleet's FB-27 cell, there's little way for you to know for sure.

Take some educated guesses and come up with the possibilities, as many as you and your imagination can conjure. At last count, people just like you came up with eleven. See how many you can find. Just be assured that this double border means something. It must: it's visual!

The answer is: model A vs. model B (Photo 6.37). Here's the story. This double border was situated at the top of the FB-27 cell (green X, Photo 6.38), put there by Gary, who worked at the far end of the cell (red arrow). Gary wanted a way to know what mud flap model was coming through the line next and when, so he could get the right set of tools ready (he wanted to be prepared). And he wanted

> Here's a short list:
> 1. Good Parts vs. Bad Parts
> 2. Process A vs. Process B
> 3. Model A vs. Model B
> 4. Ready vs. Not Ready
> 5. Incoming vs. Outgoing
> 6. Left-hand vs. Right-hand

a way to tell that at a distance so he didn't have to ask questions or walk over and read the work order. He wanted a way to know visually—without any motion.

The double border told him at-a-glance and at-a-distance whether model A or B model was next. (Notice that Gary's own need to know—his "I"— drove this solution.)

It is also worth noting that Gary's need was for very precise information. His other informational needs had been addressed.

Photo 6.37 Answer revealed.

As far as he was concerned, being able to tell at a distance if model A or model B was next was all that was left for him to know. Are there places where a double-border could help you in your work?

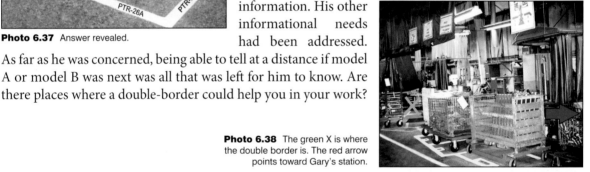

Photo 6.38 The green X is where the double border is. The red arrow points toward Gary's station.

Application 2. A Lot and a Little in the Same Spot

Photo 6.39 Same space, two uses.

Since I first discovered the FB-27 double-border function in 1995, I have shown it to thousands of people all over the world, including the workforce at Royal Nooteboom Trailers (Holland). When they saw it, lots of new thinking was triggered. Here are two examples.

See the large solid outside orange border in Photo 6.39? See the smaller dashed orange border inside? Both mark out real estate but for two separate sets of materials. Right now, there's a delivery of bogies (wheel/axle sub-assemblies) in the small border inset. The larger area is not in use.

And that's the point. Sometimes operators in this area need a lot of space for materials. Sometimes they need a little space. But they never need a lot and a little at the same time. So they can use the same floor location for both. Because that use is dictated by the sequence of work, there is never a conflict in using the same physical location for each.

This is splendid visual thinking—splendid smart placement. Here's why: This application uses the same real estate for stacked purposes—not for just one thing. Why is that important? Think of the impact of this principle on scarce floor space. Why rent or buy, borrow or steal more space if just thinking differently means you already have enough? That's what you see here. "Sometimes we have a lot. Sometimes we have a little. But we never have a lot and a little at the same time." Wonderful!

Application 3. Work Sequence Borders

The group in Final Assembly at Royal Nooteboom Trailers used the double-up on borders concept in yet

another way (Photo 6.40). They mapped out smart locations for the sequence of operations in each trailer work bay. At the moment of this photograph, work utilizing the area bordered in orange had already been completed. The next operation is now underway, covering the space previously utilized.

Smart placement thinking came first, followed by the smart location of function; and then they made it visual through borders. The floor became a true partner in the important work done in this area.

Photo 6.40 Sequence-related borders.

Principle 14: Follow the Natural Flow Line

We opened this chapter, stating that flow rules smart placement. Our final principle, 14, echoes the theme: *Follow the Natural Flow Line.*

You and I both know that very little in life happens at right angles. In the same way, right angles are not a requirement of a sound layout design at work. And right angles are certainly not required for smart

Photo 6.41 Natural positioning.

placement. The truth is: Right angles can often cause motion instead of removing it. Instead, follow the natural flow line.

The positioning shown in Photo 6.41 is a good example of the natural angle of relationship between parts in process on the left and completed parts on the right. The white borders reflect that. But those borders came second—only after the correct link between those two functions was figured out—that is, only after smart placement had been determined.

Here is a mini-case study that tells you more about this powerful final smart placement principle.

Mini-Case Study

Denison Hydraulics (DH) in Ohio is a union-based manufacturer of high precision hydraulic pumps. When DH began its improvement journey, piles of WIP (work-in-process) covered the production floor (Photo 6.42). Since the company had not yet begun to implement lean practices, those piles did not go away. Instead people learned how to make them visible by implementing floor borders. Suddenly they could see the WIP and the categories of WIP.

Photo 6.42 Piles of WIP everywhere.

You see the first generation of floor borders in Photos 6.43 and 6.44. Pallets of work-in-process are organized into grids, neat, straight, and orderly—everything at right angles.

Photo 6.43 This grid looks neat and orderly —but it masks a big problem.

Photo 6.44 More of the same.

Though these grids looked crisp and beautiful, they held a surprise problem—they triggered motion. Can you see why?

Frankly, none of us saw it at first—not the operators, managers, supervisors, engineers, and not me.

▲ **Photo 6.45** Bill Podolski.

▲ **Photo 6.46** Another right-angle grid.

▲ **Photo 6.47** The brilliant solution.

It was Bill Podolski (Photo 6.45), the first shift forklift driver, who opened our eyes—though he didn't call it a *problem*. He simply asked for a favor about a bit of struggle he was having.

Bill's Struggle. Bill is a man who puts a high premium on civility; he is by nature polite and respectful. About a month after beautiful, crisp grids were implemented in the CNC cell (Photo 6.46), Bill visited Dorothy and Sheila who worked there. He asked if they would mind if he cut across the grid when he turned that corner in his forklift.

"No, we wouldn't mind," they said. "But, Bill, why would you want to do that?" Dorothy and Sheila had tremendous respect for Bill but were curious about his request. "Well," said Bill, "It's pretty hard for me to make that 90° right angle turn in my forklift. I have to back up quite a few times to do it. It just seems like a lot of motion…. If I could just cut the corner a little, I'd be OK. Would you mind?"

"Oh sure, Bill," they replied, "No problem. Just go ahead and cut the corner. We'll make sure not to put any pallets in that square."

Bill hesitated. "What's wrong?" Dorothy asked. "Well," replied Bill, "Errr, if people see me cutting across that beautiful grid, they might not understand. They might think I am disrespecting you—and I wouldn't want to do it in that case."

Dorothy and Michael understood. The three of them thought about how to handle this…and came up with a brilliant solution—a visual solution: implement a cross-cut on the border to indicate that Bill (and the other forklift drivers) were supposed to cut the corner (red arrow, Photo 6.47). Bill felt good about that and the motion caused by that particular right-angle turn disappeared. And there's more to this story. Read one….

When the DH Macro-Visual Team (Doorway 9) heard about Bill's worry and saw the solution, they probed further and realized a lot of motion was caused by the other right angles across the facility. They observed that each time a driver picked up or delivered a pallet, it took three or four maneuvers to get a 12-foot forklift in and out of position. Those right angles were crisp and neat—but they were frustrating the forklift drivers and slowing down material movement throughout the plant. The solution? Another DH innovation: slanted borders that soon became a Visual Best Practice.

Slanted Borders. Slanted borders are simply borders at an angle that permits forklift drivers to make easy in/easy out stops. Photo Series 6.48 shows what happened next. And remember, this brilliant solution resulted from smart placement thinking; the borders came second.

1. Operator, Mel Foreman and engineer, Paul Baker, measure out slanted borders.

2. Bill Podolski (bent over) joins them, tape measure in hand.

Photo Series 6.48 Slated Borders Help Us Follow the Natural Flow Line.

Having discovered the immense positive impact of an angled pick&put approach, the Denison team applied the principle throughout the facility. Remember, at the time, Denison was a high WIP site. Inventory was everywhere. Smart placement allowed the company to optimize its traditional/non-lean manufacturing approach.

All levels of management actively supported this and many other operator-led visual innovations. Look through this series to get a better understanding.

3. The result was splendid to look at and very effective!

4. This new system of angled borders spread—yes, you guessed it—like wildfire through the facility.

5. The little floor footage lost due to slanted borders is made up for in speed, time, safety, and efficiency.

Next Steps

Over the past three chapters, you have learned a great deal about smart placement and its fourteen principles. Hopefully, you are now convinced that the location of function matters—a lot. Smart placement thinking goes a long way to ensure that those locations are first-rate.

By now, you and your colleagues have discovered many ways to do that—from moving "stuff" off cabinet tops to squeezing the air out of the physical layout of your area. Many of these are easy to do (the blues, pinks, and greens). Others (the yellows) require management review and, at its option, approval.

Now let's look at the several next steps needed to deliver on the smart placement promise.

1. If you have developed a Could-Be Map and if time permits, trace and number the new flows (in pencil first, then in color marker). Re-calculate the new flow distance and flow time; mark these in an upper corner of your map.

2. Add your improvement proposals to the change chart you started at the end of Chapter 5. Here is a reminder (Photo Cluster 6.49).

Our Changes				
Easy-To-Move	WIP	Consumables	Hard-To-Move Needs Authorization	By When

Photo Cluster 6.49
Reminder of three types of Change Charts—or design your own format.

Then it is time for you and your team to get ready to present your ideas, big and small. If you and your mates have developed the two maps, use them to show and share your thinking as you present. If you created a minority report, you'll present that right after your team.

Inset 6.2 Smart Placement and 5S

Here's something I haven't talked about that may be very important for you and your company: smart placement is a process that can help every 5S team before a single border is put into place. In fact, that is exactly why I first developed the smart placement process. The companies I was working with on 5S were not getting enough benefit from their efforts. For one thing, borders were thought of as nothing more than lines; as a result, in such a company, they rarely served any function beyond being a simple boundary.

That is why smart placement was added to my version of 5S. I call it: *5S+1: Visual Order®*. Here are the steps:

S1: Sort Through/Sort Out (remember: the first *S* is for Spirit)
S2: Scrub the Workplace (focus on dirt prevention)
S3: Secure Safety (reduce risk in your area)
S4: Select Locations (function+location=flow)
S5: Set Locations (install automatic recoil/visual where)
+1: Sustain (make visual order a way of life in the company)

Keep this in mind if you are about to implement 5S or are well on your way. For more, see my book, *Visual Systems: Harnessing the Power of a Visual Workplace*.

Your Presentation

If at all possible, the presentation session directly follows the completion of your change chart and/or Could-Be Map, after a break. Your supervisor, trainer and/or coordinator facilitates the session. They help you get ready, and then welcome and introduce the managers invited to sit in (including, I hope, the ranking site executive, members of your maintenance department, and, as applies, representatives of your union leadership). Your facilitators will help set up a flip chart with team names and the order of presentations.

These presentations are an important opportunity for you and your colleagues to present your thinking to senior management. But remember, you do not need permission to make improvements based on the blues, pinks, and greens. These are "Just-Do-Its." Only the yellows require authorization and approval. As we have discussed many times, present these with an attitude of openness. Expect appreciation for your thinking and your efforts to innovate. Expect nothing beyond that—though it may indeed come. And if it does, smile and say "thank you."

When it's your team's turn to present, I like to see all members stand (or sit) up front together, taking turns at presenting, two or three minutes each. It's that simple and people will definitely love your ideas. See Photo Cluster 6.50.

· If you are certain that you do not want to present, just tell the facilitators; they will probably still invite you to "stand" with your team. I hope you say *yes*.

Photo Cluster 6.50
Hitchcock Teams present their smart placement thinking to COO Ronn Page.

More Presentation Detail. Here's how presentations usually run when maps have been developed.

1. You (or a buddy) walk us through the What-Is Map, sharing insights and understandings about the causes and extent of motion.

2. Your facilitator asks the audience for any clarifying questions—questions about what you meant by what you just said (but not about what you are going to do about it).

3. You (or a buddy) walk us through the Could-Be Map, sharing insights, understandings, and improvement ideas about reducing the causes and extent of motion through smart placement. You tell or show us what you want to move (or remove) and why, stepping us through your Change Chart.

4. Once again, your facilitator asks for clarifying questions from the audience. Then he/she asks the larger group something new: to name a minimum of three—maximum of five—things they really liked about your thinking and recommendations.

5. Your response to everything that is offered from here on out is "Thank you"—or "Wow, that's so interesting. Thank you"—unless you ask a clarifying question back.

6. Then your facilitator asks for constructive feedback—ways that audience members think you could strengthen your improvement ideas or adjust them in some way. Once again, respond to everything with a *thank you* unless you need something cleared up. Sometimes an open exchange with the whole group happens at this point. Your facilitator will continue to facilitate—and then ask for things to wrap up when time runs out.

7. And finally, everyone gets their photos taken. Well done! (No problem if you don't want your photo taken; just make sure to say so.)

Adding to Your Hit List

After the formal presentations, the tasks you are going to tackle get posted on your Area Hit List. Because there are almost always things that people outside your group must undertake, your supervisor and maintenance group also develop a hit list with those tasks on it. I call this the *punch list* or Management Hit List (Figure 6.4). Some groups use a special two-color Smart Placement Hit List, similar to the one in Figure 6.5—blue for associate tasks and yellow for management tasks.

Figure 6.4

			Lead Team Punch List: Smart Placement	090804					
Sequence	Associate Name	Lead Team Name	Action Item	Date	Due Date	Estimated Time to Complete in Hours	Associate Assistance Required Yes or No	Lead Team Member Required Yes or No	Maintenance Person Required Yes or No
1	TOM / JOE	Wes	ONE HOSE SYSTEM OF AIR TOOLS	27-Aug			Joe Sanacono	No	No
2	TOM / JOE	Wes	AIR FEED DRILLS	27-Aug			No	No	Yes
3	TOM / JOE	Wes	AIR HOSE REELS ON WALL	27-Aug			No	No	Yes
4	TOM / JOE	Wes	DOOR LOCK CHANGED.	27-Aug			Yes	Yes	No
5	TOM / JOE	Wes	063 / 1308 FIXTURES NEED NEW WHEELS	27-Aug			Yes	No	No
6	TOM / JOE	Wes	804 FIXTURE NEEDS NEW BASE	27-Aug			Yes	No	No
7	TOM / JOE	Wes	COMPUTER IN ROOM	27-Aug			Yes	No	No
8	Dave/Chuck/Mr. Harpo	Melanie	Clean Ceiling	27-Aug			Yes	Yes/No	No
9	Dave/Chuck/Mr. Harpo	Melanie	Clean Walls	27-Aug			Yes	Yes/No	No
10	Dave/Chuck/Mr. Harpo	Melanie	Repair cracks in floor	27-Aug			Yes	Yes/No	Yes
11	Dave/Chuck/Mr. Harpo	Melanie	Paint floor	27-Aug			Yes	No	Yes
12	Dave/Chuck/Mr. Harpo	Melanie	Clean shelves - excess alloys	27-Aug			Yes	Yes	No
13	Chuck	Melanie	Build Chucks Workbench	27-Aug			Yes	No	No
14	Dave	Melanie	Build Dave's Workbench	27-Aug			Yes	No	No
15	Dave/Chuck/Mr. Harpo	Melanie	Build Shelving for Pressure and Milling Fixtures	27-Aug			Yes	Yes	Yes
16	Dave/Chuck/Mr. Harpo	Melanie	Build Pressure Tank Lid.	27-Aug			Yes	Yes	Yes
17	Dave/Chuck/Mr. Harpo	Melanie	Remove Dust Collector	27-Aug			Yes	Yes	Yes
18	Dave/Chuck/Mr. Harpo	Melanie	Clean Lights	27-Aug			Yes	Yes	No
19	Dave/Chuck/Mr. Harpo	Melanie	Clean Air Vent	27-Aug			Yes	Yes	No
20	Dave	Melanie	Fixture Rack (workorder submitted)	27-Aug			Yes	No	Yes
21	Dave	Melanie	Dirt Prevention - Hand Saw Area.	27-Aug			Yes	No	No
22	Dave	Melanie	Make decision on need for table at hand saw.	27-Aug			Yes	Yes	No
23	Mike / Tim	Ken	Remove crucible pot cleaning Cabinet	8/27/2004	9/9/2004	4.00	Yes	No	Yes
24	Mike / Tim	Ken	New Lights Mixer Room	8/27/2004	9/9/2004	2.00	Yes	No	Yes
25	Mike / Tim	Ken	Remove gas reel from ceiling	8/27/2004	9/9/2004	0.50	Yes	No	Yes
26	Mike / Tim	Ken	Remove Swing Arm	8/27/2004	9/9/2004	0.50	Yes	No	Yes
27	Mike / Tim	Ken	Remove Flood Light	8/27/2004	9/9/2004	0.50	Yes	No	Yes
28	Mike / Tim	Ken	Build New Pegger	8/27/2004	9/9/2004	36.00	Yes	No	Yes
29	Mike / Tim	Ken	Run Computer lines to office	8/27/2004	9/3/2004	2.00	Yes	No	Yes

Figure 6.4 An actual *smart placement management punch list* from Hitchcock Industries (Minnesota).

Figure 6.5

	SMART PLACEMENT HIT LIST		DEPARTMENT: NORTH WAREHOUSE	EASY-TO-MOVE NEEDS EXTRA HELP OR AUTHORIZATION		START DATE: NOVEMBER 1, 2009		VISUAL COACH: KENNY + DAVE
	SMART PLACEMENT TASK DESCRIBE IT IN A FEW WORDS	WHO IS POINT PERSON? (+ BUDDY)	START DATE	TARGET DATE	STARTED	HALF – WAY	FINISHED	COMMENTS/PROBLEMS/SPECIAL NEEDS
Operator-Led Tasks	1. Locate filters at each work station.	Bob	11-1	11-9	X			Wrong filters were ordered again.
	2. Install new lines from west hall.	Vern Jo	11-1	11-15	X	X		
	3. Locate gap board at each tank fill tank.	Vern Les	11-5	11-25	X	X		We need more wood and green paint.
	4. Connect high pressure water on Tote Line.	Mary	11-3	11-12	X	X	X	That works great.
	5. Move Flow Aid closer to point-of-use.							
	6.							
	7.							
	8.							
Management-Led Tasks	1. Move manifold 1 to left corner.	Bud Frank	11-8	11-8	X	X	X	That was easy. Let us know how it works.
	2. Rotate manifold 2.	Cindy Merle	11-8	11-20	X			This has to wait til next week. Compliance issues.
	3. Move Test Booth to the Packing Line.	Frank Cindy	11-3	11-19	X	X		We need another three days for the wiring. Almost there!
	4. Build new entrance at KH Rover.	Merle Bud	11-9	11-12	X			We're with a long wait. Harry had a baby.
	5.							
	6.							
	7.							

Figure 6.5 This special to-color hit list separates associate tasks (blue top section) from management task (yellow bottom section).

These special hit lists get posted—along with your What-Is and Could-Be Maps—on or near your area's visual workplace bulletin board. In that way, everyone continues to think about the changes that are on the way and keeps his or her eye on what is or isn't happening. This is critically important when you have multiple shifts the way many organizations do (having five to eight shifts is not unusual anymore).

What to Expect

What should you expect from all this great smart placement thinking? If you and your colleagues came up with a lot of ideas, count on it taking two or three weeks to get them in place. Maybe longer. This is not just a question of management follow-through (see *Leadership Task 12*). It is often also a matter of time availability. In organizations that adopt improvement time as a measure, that will mean how much time your supervisor can afford to release for improvement activity.

One further point. Some companies committed to continuous improvement can nevertheless go through a period where things seem to get a bit rocky. That is usually because people are learning to balance improvement goals with production demands. It can take extra time before improvement gets steady and the production schedule does not suffer. With patience and a strong resolve, the tide usually turns and good progress is made.

One More Thing: The Paper Doll Layout

If you have big plans for changing the current area layout, you and your group may want to do a *Paper Doll Layout*. First make full-size cardboard cutouts of all floor items (benches, machines, WIP, cabinets, chairs, etc.) in as close to their actual size and shape as possible. Then lay out the cardboard pieces in a large, vacated space, such as the parking lot (weather permitting), some warehouse area or the cafeteria when not in use.

In that way, you can check out your thinking and discover if you, for example, over-estimated or under-estimated the distance between value fields, the direction and complexity of the flow—or got it just right. The paper doll layout allows you to validate your "dream" and to edit it. Your supervisor will help.

Leadership Task 12: Smart Placement Follow Up and Follow Through

Leaders, there is no way to over-emphasize the importance of your responding to people's improvement ideas with speedy support, in this case smart placement ideas.

For easy-to-move items (blue, pinks, and greens) that means releasing improvement time so associates can get those tasks done; making sure they have the required supplies; using the hit list to help people focus and target their next activity; scheduling blitzes as time permits; staying positive; giving lots of compliments (*specific praise* is better than general thanks); checking in through open-ended questions; and before, during, and after, taking lots of photos of things and people (as permitted).

Your active involvement and support are key to ensuring that your company reaps the many benefits smart placement can produce.

Of equal important is your follow-through on the tasks on your Management Punch List—the yellows. Walk the talk. Nothing dampens the interest and excitement that smart placement can trigger more than lukewarm or non-existent follow-through on your own commitments and those of your peers. As a rule, this is a 3-week window. If something doesn't happen during that time, associates start dropping out, first in their minds and then in their hearts. You may never get them back.

By the same token, if a management task gets legitimately stuck, you need to communicate that. "I know we planned to move that bench by Friday—but Jerry is out ill; we plan to do it as soon as he gets back. Sorry guys." The "guys" will usually understand—because they have something to understand. I know this may sound overly simplistic. But in fact, we cannot over-estimate the importance of communicating, communicating, communicating. There is truth in the adage: The biggest mistake in communication is thinking that it has happened. Don't let that happen to you.

So follow-up and follow-through. Reap the benefit of all the splendid smart placement thinking.

What lies behind us and what lies before us are
tiny matters compared to what lies within us.

Oliver Wendell Homes

The Visual Where

Once you have applied the principles of smart placement and made the physical changes, you are ready to nail those new locations down—to anchor them—into the landscape of work. You are ready for the *visual where*, the topic of this section.

As you will learn, the visual where—or *automatic recoil* as it is also called—is made of three types of visual devices: borders, addresses, and ID labels.

You begin with a thorough introduction to borders, the first step in the process of installing the visual where. Over 70 examples of visual solutions show you the breadth and depth of the border function and inventive ways to reduce information deficits through them, along with the motion those deficits trigger.

Then, you learn about addresses and ID labels that makes it crystal clear what lives in those borders—unless of course it makes more sense to use non-specific addresses. You'll see brilliant examples of both. In fact, you'll study over 70 visual devices in action, including color-code solutions.

By the time you finish this section, you will understand the power of the visual where and how to implement it in your area.

Chapter | Seven

Visual Where: Begin with Borders

Now that you have improved the current location of function in your area through the principles of smart placement, you are ready to "nail" those locations in place through visual location information—visual devices that imbed the visual where. At the heart of the visual where is *Automatic Recoil*. We'll begin there.

Automatic Recoil

Automatic recoil is the ability of a work item to find its own way back home—to its proper and designated location—based solely on the visual location information captured in its border, address, and ID label. (See Photo 7.1)

As such, it gets applied to everything in the work area that casts a shadow. Said another way, everything that casts a shadow in your work area gets a border, home address, and, if possible, an ID label. And that's everything.

As you will soon discover, this "everything" requirement is a powerful driver of the level of visual excellence that in many companies results in a 15% to 30% improvement in productivity.

Remember Cycle Hub in Portland, Oregon? The back room was mayhem (Photo 7.2)—except for one spot that was carefully laid out: a panel of tools (Photo 7.3). That makes sense, doesn't it? The

Photo 7.1 The three elements of automatic recoil: border + address + ID label.

owners (Mr. & Mrs. Majhor) use their tools many times every day. Because of their vital importance, the Majhors took steps to ensure the tools were always handy. In visuality we say that the tools were smartly placed. But we also observe that automatic recoil is not yet in place; there is no visual where. As a result, when the Majhors finish using their tools, they

Photo 7.2 Cycle Hub back room.

Photo 7.3 Tools are smartly placed but there's no automatic recoil.

will have to think about where the tools go on the board. Information deficits (and a ton of motion) stand between them and a simple return process. Why? Because that information is not built into the board itself—visually.

The same thing applies to the stamping cell at Greene Rubber where area associates applied smart placement principles in the case study in Chapter 4. They moved work items into the physical locations they had chosen, and motion (the spaghetti) was hugely reduced (Figures 7.1 and 7.2). Then they nailed those locations in place through a border, home address and, if possible, an ID label. They implemented automatic recoil— the visual where—the topic of this chapter and the next (Figure 7.3).

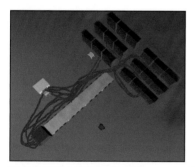
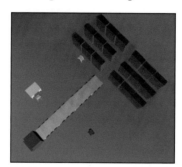
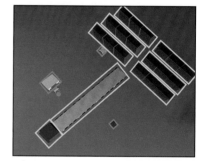

Figures 7.1 and 7.2 Smart placement at Greene Rubber meant a lot less spaghetti.

Figure 7.3 Borders are the next logical step.

Begin with Borders

Automatic recoil begins with borders—starting from the floor up; they are the foundation. Floor borders are implemented for every item that has a footprint—that casts a shadow on the floor. That applies to items that are moveable, like the buckets in Photo 7.4—and items that are *not* moveable, like the large CNC machine in Photo 7.5.

Photo 7.4 Buckets, easily moved.

Photo 7.5 CNC, not easily moved.

Borders For the Floor

When we commit to borders as a regular and required part of our visual conversion, they become like words in a book to use—an operational vocabulary. And the more specific the application, the more borders become a language for us—a visual language. Photos 7.6 to 7.8 show three classic examples.

Photo 7.6 The simple placement of two trash cans on red squares and the trim yellow border that surrounds the blue cabinet create a geometry that defines the pattern of work. You can feel it in your bones.

Photo 7.7 The pattern of work is well defined in this machining cell—for everything that casts a shadow, from the rolling fixture to the blue machine behind it to the WIP locations in front of it, complete with person-width borders.

Photo 7.8 This double orange/white border allows operators to precisely position large cable reels for feeding into the machine so when the first reel (top right) is empty, the second reel can get threaded in fast and production resumes.

Borders on Benches

Just as borders help us understand work by capturing its pattern on floors, borders are equally useful on work surfaces—on top, underneath, and inside. On work surfaces, borders help a lot with little things. It can be as simple as bordering the location of workplace items, as you see in Photo 7.9 (left), in a sup-

Photo 7.9

porting value field for the electron microscope in the top of that photo. (This is an anti-static area; red was the only antistatic tape color available at the time.) The bench top is covered with blue paper that is then covered with plexiglass, keeping borders from fraying and dust to a minimum. (Alpha Industries/Massachusetts).

Photo 7.10

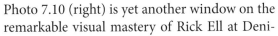

Photo 7.10 (right) is yet another window on the remarkable visual mastery of Rick Ell at Denison Hydraulics, whose work you see throughout this book. Here is the backboard to a side bench, home to assorted gauges, with borders cut to shape from yellow contact paper.

Borders On the Inside

Some people only think of borders on floor and work surfaces. Borders are useful everywhere, including when they are hidden behind doors and drawers. We'll look at three examples in Photos 7.11 to 7.13—and they are a rare three because few companies can be convinced to install borders on the inside. See those three examples on the next page.

Borders on the Inside

Photo 7.11

Photo 7.12

Photo 7.13

Borders In the Office

We've already said it: Borders on work surfaces help a lot with little things. Here are two good examples in office settings—and a third for a laugh. Photo 7.14 shows a paperwork station, with borders for a paper cutter and a small office machine; the hatched area permanently claims the space where we temporarily lay paper to 3-hole punch (hole puncher on left). Photo 7.15 show us a computer station with a blue square for the work that is being done now. Photo 7.16 shows the same boundary concept but with a twist(see red arrow). Can you guess what it

Photo 7.14

Photo 7.15

Photo 7.16

says? "Rich, keep your stuff on your side!" (As if that would help!)

Border Worries

Laying down borders can trigger strong and logical opinions in favor of borders and often some hesitations that sound like this:

> *"Isn't it better not to lay down floor borders in the first place—if we are just going to change our minds about where they go? If we skip borders, we won't ever have to change them!"*

This is a faulty perspective, based on the faulty belief that borders take so much time to apply and remove, they are not worth putting down in the first place. Based on more than 25 years of research, I have three responses:

1. Borders and the time needed to implement them are well worth it because of their positive and significant impact on safety, quality, productivity, and on-time delivery—often on a micro level.

2. Borders do not take any longer to implement than any other safety, quality, productivity or cost-saving tool.

3. Changing your borders can become a routine and fluid part of your improvement process— when you have a procedure for pulling them up overnight and laying them down to last a year. Once you do, you will want your borders to get smarter—to continually improve. (For more on border materials, see Inset 7.2 on page 146.)

The Logic of Borders: Six Reasons

Yes, there are many reasons why borders make sense. So far, we've collected a list of twelve—and counting. We'll examine six in some detail. (See Inset 7.1 for all twelve reasons.)

Reason 1: Meaning to the word "empty." Without borders, the real estate called the workplace (floor/desk/bench) remains un-designated—not selected. As a result, when an item is elsewhere, the space it is supposed to occupy looks unclaimed, available, and "up for grabs." Walk through the barrel sequence in Figure 7.4 for the impeccable logic of borders.

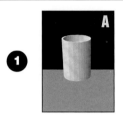

Figure 7.4. The Impeccable Logic of Borders. Frame A shows a barrel sitting in its spot. But when it is not sitting in its spot (when it is elsewhere), we don't know that this spot is its home (Frame B). The spot has no meaning; it simply looks unclaimed. Put a border around the barrel as it sits in its little spot (Frame C) and suddenly, the floor has meaning. It sends the message: "This is an item's home—even when (especially when) that item is elsewhere" (Frame D). Add a home address (discussed in the next chapter) and you make this border even more powerful.

Reason 2: Out-of-place. With borders in place, you can tell at-a-glance when an item is out-of place and simply shift it back. If always out-of-place, we may learn it's in the way of something else, a nearly impossible discovery in a non-bordered work area (Photo 7.17).

Photo 7.17

Reason 3: Something Missing. With borders in place, you can tell at-a-glance when something is missing. Combine that border with a home address and you can also tell exactly what is missing—at-a-glance (Photo 7.18).

Photo 7.18

Reason 4: Intruders. With borders in place, you can spot intruders at-a-glance: Items that don't belong in your area. The cart in Photo 7.19 does not belong in this work area—and everybody knows it. (If it had an ID label, you could send it right back home.)

Photo 7.19

Reason 5: Room-No Room. With borders in place, you can tell at-a-glance what part of the real estate is still available for use. In the case of the machining cell in Photo 7.20, barely any is. And you know it at-a-glance—thanks to the excellent system of borders that capture the floor print of everything that occupies the cell (everything that casts a shadow).

Photo 7.20 Jimmy's machining cell —every inch is making money for the company.

Reason 6: Seeing the Flow. Starting to apply borders from the bottom or floor up is for a specific purpose. That purpose is to make the flow or pattern of work plain and obvious—the course or pathway that materials, people, and information follow into and through your work area (and your company). That pathway is extremely important; you want to be able to know it at-a-glance. Without borders, that pathway is hidden beneath the surface of things.

Many of us have worked in departments like that—where the flow of work is anybody's guess because it is not apparent. It is not visual. No borders, no nothing. In such an area, we still manage to manage.

But we pay a price in motion, morale, and performance; and so does the company. Over time, we may memorize the flow and the sequence of work it contains. But many telling details remain beyond our reach. The absence of those reference points wears on us. We get irritated and feel unsafe; and our true work— adding value—suffers.

What do I mean by the flow of work? You already know that, too. It is the flow of function (materials, people, and information) in and through your work area—the smart placement formula: *Function + Location = Flow*. Work gets done, one way or the other, flow or no flow. But work flows better, faster, and safer when smart placement is imbedded. It is that flow that you will now make plain to see and follow, first through borders and later through home addresses and ID labels.

> **Inset 7.1 12 Reasons for Borders**
>
> 1. Borders reveal the pattern of work
> 2. Borders give meaning to the word *empty*
>
> ***Borders allow us instantly to see:***
>
> 3. When an item is out-of-place
> 4. When an item is missing
> 5. Intruders
> 6. What space is available
> 7. What space is not available
> 8. Where we are supposed to walk
> 9. Where we are not supposed to walk
> 10. The extent (or range) of function
> 11. Where we are supposed to work
> 12. Where we are not supposed to work

The Mind and The Pattern of Work

Here is how I discovered the concept of the pattern of work and its powerful link to borders. I had just begun helping Denison Hydraulics implement visual order. Incoming Inspection (called the Incoming Team) was one of the areas targeted for a visual conversion. The men who worked there were, at best, skeptical. They were grumbling because material handlers kept dropping overflow parts anywhere in the department when the proper lanes were full (Photo 7.21).

Then the group learned about and began to get visual—smart placement, automatic recoil. You see the result in Photo 7.22—crisp color-coded borders (in order from the bottom): red for on-hold; orange for incoming (with a blue inset for the tow-motor); and, at the top, green for ready to go. I was happy. The Incoming Team wasn't.

Materials handlers were still leaving pallets of overflow parts in every unoccupied space, including the aisles. The team asked me how to stop this behavior. I told them it was my job to teach them visual principles and practices and their job to figure out how to apply them until they got the behavior they wanted—from themselves and from others. "You are great visual thinkers-in-the-making," I said. "Keep going!" And they did. In their next version, they added a big yellow **X** across each aisle in their effort to communicate that this space is "Off Limits!!" (Photo 7.23)

It didn't work. Materials handlers simply took boxes off pallets and placed them in the four vacant spaces within the **X**. Clever humans, Denison's forklift drivers found a way to do the wrong thing despite the best improvement efforts of the Incoming Team.

Fuming by now, the team again asked me what to do. I told them to keep thinking, and keep going. (The truth was, I was also surprised by the "craftiness" of the material handlers. But I could not have thought of a better solution than the **X**s—which clearly were not powerful enough to change the behavior of the forklift. I was just as mystified as the Incoming Team.)

What the Incoming Team did next worked superbly well and instantly (Photo Cluster 7.24).

They painted the entire width of each aisle a bright solid yellow. And the behavior stopped. *Instantly.* No material handler (or anyone else for that matter) ever put overflow parts in the aisles again. Why? How? That, dear reader, is the question: What made them stop? (I didn't have an explanation either.)

Photo 7.21 *Before*: Incoming Inspection.

Photo 7.22 *After-1*: Color-coded borders were handsome but did not help.

Photo 7.23 *After-2*: The clever addition of **X** did nothing to change the behavior.

The drivers had not undergone special training. Nor had they suddenly decided to "obey" the request of the Incoming Team to "deliver materials to the proper lanes only!" Their behavior simply changed from wrong to right, overnight. Could it have been the power of bright yellow paint? Perhaps. But I sensed there was something else to this. And then I remembered!

Photo Cluster 7.24 New incoming borders at Denison Hydraulics that capture the pattern of work.

The Mind is a Pattern-Seeking Mechanism

I remembered an incident that happened 25 years earlier when I lived in New York City in a fifth-floor walk-up on the Lower East Side, holding down four different jobs to make ends meet, and basically going nuts from the pressure. I was tense. I was unhappy. A friend noticed and said I should learn to meditate. "What's that?" I asked. My friend handed me an address. Miserable and ready to try anything, I went. It was a meditation center and the teacher told me to close my eyes and not think of anything. I closed my eyes—and I thought of everything. The drive-in movies came on! In fact, I couldn't stop thinking. I went back to the teacher with my complaint; and he then said something I suppose he thought would help. He said: "Don't you understand, Gwendolyn, the mind is a pattern seeking mechanism." Huh?

Twenty-five years later, staring at those intensely yellow person-width borders, I remembered his words, "the mind is a pattern-seeking mechanism" and suddenly realized that the drivers had simply recognized the pattern of that layout—now that it was undeniably visible—and accepted it. As a result, their behavior changed, as it were, overnight. This was a staggering insight for me. In a flash, it led me to a whole new set of understandings. I will share these now so you understand as I did why borders are so important to you—and to the full, reliable, predictable, and excellent functioning of your work area as well as to your company's journey to excellence.

Seeking the Pattern. When we say the mind is a pattern-seeking mechanism, we mean that your mind—when faced with a puzzle, mystery or challenge—will seek to make sense of it. It will seek to find the pattern. Why? Because that is what the mind does: It seeks patterns. That is its nature.

All of us have had the experience of our mind not letting go. It latches on to a thought and churns. This can happen at work when we are trying to puzzle out a new procedure. It can happen at school when we are tangling with a new concept. It can happen in personal relationships when we are trying to figure out what the heck our spouse/girlfriend/boyfriend is trying to communicate as the cause of her/his unhappiness. In all three cases, we are trying to make sense of them, trying to—understand. And we won't let go until we do!

> ### Inset 7.2 FLOOR-Mark™ Borders: Thinner is Better
>
> Recent developments in floor tape have revolutionized thinking on how to get borders to last.
>
> Before, the focus was on making tape thicker and therefore stronger. But thick tape often gives way to forklifts and can cause tripping. It's usually guaranteed for years... except if hit from the side.
>
> The new FLOOR-Mark™ brand is backed by a strong adhesive but purposely designed to be "thin." Instead of getting snagged or torn up when hit by a forklift from the side, it just gets scratched.
>
> So thinner is better. The result is: your FLOOR-Mark borders may have many small scratches over time—but they will still function as borders until you apply heat to peel them up.
>
> **FLOOR-Mark in Action**
>
> For more, see **Visual Workplace Inc.** in this book's Resource Section.

That's our mind, determined to complete its function: Find the pattern. And it usually succeeds. Our minds are very bright. And when our mind does "get it," it can be very satisfying. But then what happens? What happens after the mind finds the pattern it was seeking? It seeks the next pattern. And the next and the next and the next. Cats chase mice. Minds seek patterns.

The focus of this reaches far beyond borders—and includes them. Here's what I mean.

Continuous Improvement, Naturally. If our mind is a pattern-seeking mechanism, what happens if we can't find the pattern? Yes, that's right: our mind continues searching for it. But what if we still can't find the pattern, say, after a couple of weeks? The search simply moves to a back burner but it doesn't leave the stove. Your mind will keep at it but in the background now. We experience this as a small dose of stress.

When this happens a lot, when there are lots of unresolved searches, there are also lots of small doses of stress. The pressure builds. But the mind does not stop—because that is not its nature. The mind continues to search even if we aren't aware of it. If this goes on for an extended period, the mind can simply check out from the effort (go numb) or go ballistic.

And what happens in the reverse? What happens when your mind seeks the pattern and finds it? The mind pauses a moment to absorb and savor its victory—and then it seeks the next level of pattern. There is a term for this recurrent, relentless seeking and finding, seeking and finding, seeking and finding. It is a term important for our discussion, for this book, and for your company. That term is: *continuous improvement*.

Continuous improvement. Do you see? That means continuous improvement is a natural condition of our mind. We were made to seek improvement, level by level—to improve our surroundings and ourselves, our work and our lives, our work area and our company. It's our nature.

Finally, I understood what that meditation teacher had told me 25 years before. I also understood why those yellow person-width borders at Denison worked so superbly well! I understood this: When the Incoming Team laid down those person-width borders, they unknowingly put a powerful pattern in place that the forklift drivers simply recognized and accepted. With that in place, they could continue layering in more and more advanced pattern levels as they visually transformed their area. And that brought me to another big realization: Borders support a fundamental need of the mind—the need for pattern, for harmony, for balance, for a sense of unity (Photo 7.25).

Photo 7.25 When you see borders, see function.

Smarter Borders: Adding Dimensions of Meaning

The more we understand our work and the motion that keeps us from it, the more fully we recognize how borders can help us create work that makes sense. That means the borders change as our understanding of the work flow and content changes—as our visual intelligence grows. As we get smarter, our borders will as well.

Think about it: When you improve the flow of your work (your value stream), your borders must char in response because borders inscribe that flow into the physical landscape of work. A simple appli of this powerful understanding of borders evolving for safety's sake is shown in Photos 7.26 a

Photo 7.26 This yellow border marks a busy forklift traffic lane. But the lane had a second function: doorway access. One day, a forklift driver rolled by when the door opened suddenly. Wham! Some vital information was missing.

Photo 7.27 Then people got smarter and made the border smarter—that yellow notch alerting the driver of the possibility of a pedestrian as well as providing a safer place to walk. See the trace of the border's previous location (red arrow).

Because visuality is a form of language, we can use visual devices to communicate broad concepts and intentions as well as less obvious ones. I call this "adding dimensions of meaning." And that's just another way of saying smarter borders.

In this section, we look at eight dimensions that make your borders smarter:

1. Extending the Border Function
2. Borders as Visual Controls
3. Dots and Commas
4. Person-width Borders
5. Dashed Borders
6. Photocopied Borders
7. Slanted Borders
8. Double Borders

Extending the Border Function. As you learned in smart placement, borders reflect your understanding of the function of workplace item it surrounds. We don't merely focus on putting a fat line around the hard edges of the physical item. We first determine that thing's range of function— and border that. You saw this early in this chapter when we discussed the machine in Photo 7.28, though you may not have noticed it at the time.

Look at the yellow floor border around the machine, on the far right end (red arrow 1); it does not hug the machine. It stands, instead, about three feet from the machine base. Why? Because that is the extent of the machine's full function—and that includes the narrow aluminum conveyor on the right end (red arrow 2). The border captures and defines the machine's full function (smart placement principle 3)—and the shadow that function casts. Borders make that range of function visual.

Photo 7.28 Borders and range of function.

You see that logic again (Photo 7.29) in the rolling rack in the Screen Department at Seton Name Plate that stores the silk screens the first shift prepares for the second shift to process. But the rack's true function is not restricted to the rack alone; if we put a border around just the rack, we miss what the rack is really for: silk screens. That's why the white-dot border extends more than a foot beyond the physical rack, enclosing both the rack and the screens stored there. The border now encompasses the rack's full range of function.

Note: At Seton, white dots are used to border items that are moveable or portable—carts, trash bins, racks like this, and so on.

Photo 7.29 Silk screen rack.

Borders as Visual Controls. A colleague once said to me: Borders are just fences that haven't yet realized their full potential. He thought he was joking but I think he had a point. By building size, number or volume into our borders, we can use them to direct, limit or even control behavior—our own or that of others. In that way, borders can do double-duty as visual controls (a visual control controls by restricting our choices). Here is a series of visual control border solutions.

Solution 1 (Photo 7.30): With the orderliness of borders and the precision of controls, this storage corner does its own counting. Boxes of vinyl are stacked one high, three deep, and, if you could see the entire section, five across: fifteen boxes at-a-glance, minus any that are not there. Counting has never been easier.

Photo 7.30

Photo 7.31

Solution 2 (Photo 7.31): The lower shelf of this bench is another case of combining the border and control functions: fastener boxes two rows deep by five rows long— only and just enough room for ten boxes. We are in control of the details.

Solution 3 (Figure 7.5): The same control principle is at work in this spool storage illustration. Exactly 75 empty spools are held in this bordered location (5 wide/5 high/3 deep). When that quantity is reached, the spools are sent back to the supplier. That standard is built directly into the physical environment so we can tell, merely by looking.

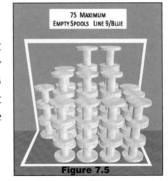
Figure 7.5

Foam/HDPE Control Materials. There are ways other than tape or paint to achieve the combined border and control function—for example, stiff foam (Photo 7.32). Stiff foam and more recently HDPE (high-density polyethylene) are used extensively in the aerospace and medical industries for parts delivery (discussed in Chapter 6) due to its powerful control capability. Your supervisor can contract out this work; but, regulations permitting, you can also do it yourself. The steps are easy:

1. Cut a piece of stiff foam to the size of the box, drawer or cart.
2. Cut a piece of brown paper to the same size.
3. Lay out your tools on the paper (remember to squeeze out the "air").
4. Trace around each tool with a dark marker.
5. Lay the paper on the stiff foam and, very carefully, cut your shapes into the foam through the paper.

Photo 7.32 Foam serving as both borders and visual control.

Presto Chango! The visual where, plus—thanks to foam or foam-like material—we also get visual control. Photos 7.33 to 7.35 show three levels of foam solutions.

Photo 7.33 The foam is cut by an outside contractor.

Photo 7.34 The foam is rough-cut by hand.

Photo 7.35 The foam is not cut, just pierced by the tool.

Dots and Commas. Photo 7.36 shows yellow commas that take the place of full borders. Commas can provide enough border information to capture the real estate and at less cost. If a comma gets torn, you replace it instead of an entire border. Commas, however, have no place for an address—the subject of our next chapter—vital to a well-functioning workplace. So use them sparingly. (See this book's Resource Section for suppliers who sell ready-made borders.)

Photo 7.36

Inset 7.3 You & Your Visual Supplier.

5S Task Board from **5S Supply**.

You'll need supplies as you implement visuality whether border materials, containers, bins, andon lights, toll organization systems, and much more.

5S Supply in this book's Resource Section has these and more—as do the other vendors listed.

Your best bet is to build a relationship with your vendor, whomever you choose. Let them know what you need and also what you want. Many fine innovations in visual supplies have come from the interaction between customers and vendors.

Photo 7.37

A red dot of paint or plastic is home enough for the bucket in Photo 7.37. But a worry applies here as well: While there is room to apply an address, the item that resides on that dot will hide that address. There are ways around this and I am sure you can figure it out. But here are two hints: Think about using nearby architecture and think about the air.

Photo 7.38 at right shows you an innovative use of dots. The red circle makes it easy for us to find the fire extinguisher with a minimum of motion. Because when we need an extinguisher, even the tiniest bit of motion (time) can be disastrous. "Look for the red dot!" That's the safety standard in this facility.

Photo 7.38

Person-Width Borders. Person-width borders is another highly innovative adaptation of borders that has many valuable applications, especially in companies that have not yet gone lean—the ones that still have lots of WIP, especially in the warehouse. Here's a learning sequence that shows how person-width borders can help (Photo Series 7.39).

Here is a far too typical loading dock (Photo 7.39). Miles of piles. Tons of motion. Zero visual information. Let's improve the area and our performance first by installing the visual where, beginning with borders.

Photo 7.39 Tons of stuff/tons of motion.

That's better! A loading dock with three designated lanes, the exact volume needed to fill up an 18-wheeler (Photo 7.40). That's a start. But, though improved, these borders need to get smarter.

Photo 7.40 The basics of visual order.

Stacked high and wide, there's no easy way to access the pallets to, for example, verify we packed the J-190s (Photo 7.41). We ask Joe, the move man. He moves it all out; we find the J-190s; Joe moves it all back again. We need a better way.

Photo 7.41 But more is needed.

What can we do instead? We can install person-width borders, as shown in Photo 7.42. Person-width borders allow me, you or Joe to find out if the J-190s are on the dock, without moving a single pallet.

Photo 7.42 A better way. **Photo 7.43** Look closely here for a clue. **Photo 7.44** See it?

There's more to discover in this interesting example. Study the floor itself, the close-up in the middle gives a good view (Photo 7.43). Notice anything? See the scraps of yellow in-between the borders? What are they? Think. (*Hint:* Notice the yellow paint scraps are at a right angle to the wide yellow borders.)

That's right! They are leftovers from a previous set of person-width borders that were laid at right angles to where they are now. Because the old borders were not removed completely, they left us a kind of archeological record of the previous border logic.

And what was that previous logic? What were they like before and why? The answer is in front of your eyes, at the tip of your nose. Look. Sharpen your visual thinking. (*Hint:* Look at the red arrow at the far end of Photo 7.44. Look at the far end of the existing personal-width aisle. What is there at the end?)

"Oh my gosh," you say, "That's the dock door!"

That's right! The previous lane layout ran counter to the dock doors; it blocked them. That meant each pallet had to be handled twice: once when it was delivered to the dock area and again to move it around directly in front of the loading doors. The new layout lines up with the dock doors precisely, allowing pallets to flow directly onto trucks.

> *Note:* The previous person-width borders had been laid out so forklifts could easily deposit pallets directly from the main warehouse floor, a straight shot that seemed easier at the time. That logic was eventually set aside for the new one (above), with pallets ready for loading from the get-go.

The company got smarter so its borders got smarter, too.

Here's another *Before-and-After* example that shows you how practical person-width borders are for any area.

> **Before:** Pallets of WIP were constantly delivered to this spot because it was empty and therefore looked available. But it turned out the pallets always blocked one of the entrances to the cell directly behind the WIP (Photo 7.45).

> **After:** So the operator worked with Maintenance to install: 1) a person-width border, allowing her easy entry and exit; and 2) an official bordered location for WIP pallets (red arrow) since that spot was going to get used anyway (Photo 7.46).

In Photo Cluster 7.47 you will see a selection of person-width borders at Denison Hydraulics (Ohio) before the company went lean.

Dashed Borders. Dashed borders allow us to designate locations that are only sometimes used. Photo 7.48 shows a corner of the production floor that is in use—only sometimes. But because it houses an important function when it is used (customized materials for only certain orders), we provide a designated location. (Royal Nooteboom Trailers/ Holland)

Photo 7.48 A temporary location, vitally needed from time to time.

Photo 7.49 Photo-copied borders.

Photo-Copied Borders. Bench-top borders can be as innovative as the ones on the floor. Bob Comeau, resident visual genius at United Electric Controls, had been working at UE for 20 years when he started looking for a shortcut to laying borders down. That's when he invented the photocopied kind (Photo 7.49).

Bob simply carried his hand tools over to the photo copier, laid them on the glass (very gently), and pressed the button—instant borders! Then he cut them out, arranged and glued them onto heavy paper, and covered them with plexiglass. Bob's innovation spread like wildfire through UE and across the world.

By the way, which tools are missing right now? That's right: the scissors, level block, and two spring screwdrivers (lower right). But it's a bit tricky to tell, creating another form of motion, unintentional though it was.

That small dilemma was addressed when Grace in the shipping department of Alpha Industries (Massachusetts) adapted Bob's photo-copy invention for her calculator and tape measure, two items she used

a lot. Great idea—except the likeness was too exact. As a result, from time to time, she'd get mixed up, thinking one of the items was in place when it was only its photo (Photo 7.50).

What to do? She added a telling detail: red marks on the face of the two real items so she could tell the difference between there and not there—at-a-glance (Photo 7.51).

Photo 7.50 There or not there?

Photo 7.51 Now I can tell.

Slanted Borders. We introduced slanted or angled borders in Chapter 6 when we discussed the smart placement principle: *Use the natural flow line.* Remember we said: very little in life happens at right angles—and why should life at work? Borders set at a slight angle allow forklift drivers an easy put-and-pick when moving material. Photo Series 7.52 (next page) provides more examples. As you examine these, remember that these splendid borders are the result of smart placement thinking—and that the thinking came first.

Photo Series 7.52 Slanted Borders at Denison Hydraulics (Ohio).

Bill Podolski, day-shift move man triggered the invention of slanted borders with the famous words: "Gee, those right-angled lines make it awfully hard for me to maneuver my forklift.... Would you mind if I cut the corner?"

This slanted border in Jimmy's area is on the main aisle, letting material handlers pickup and deliver with ease. Notice how he used borders to squeeze every inch from his cell real estate.

LEFT: Slanted borders for material pick/put on the main aisle.
MIDDLE: A long, broad yellow person-width border allows easy access.
RIGHT: A grid of squares for pallets in long term storage.

Double Borders. Remember the double-border function shown in Photo 7.53 (also discussed in Chapter 6)? Gary in the FB-27 Cell invented it so that he could tell, merely by looking, which model was in production. This is a highly innovative and economical use of floor real estate. Called "double borders," they helped Gary be ready for his next changeover (discussed in Chapter 6). Now discover your own applications of double borders in your area.

Here's another double border story. Photo 7.54 shows you a desk piled so high with debris, the value field looks like it has moved to the chair.

You and I know that as soon as the chair fills up, the value field will shift again—this time to the floor. Who's desk is this anyway? We want to know!

Photo 7.55 shows a better way to handle a desktop: Francis's desk. She was the visual workplace coordinator for a GM plant in Indiana. See how Francis identified her value-field with a simple black border. This was her way of reminding herself to keep that area free of clutter—because that's where her actual work happened (her primary value field).

This example makes some people worry that their boss will ask them to implement, as a standard, the same bordered layout on their desks. This would be the boss's mistake. First, it would be a weak use of the power of standardization (see *Leadership Task 8* in Chapter 3). Second, desk layout is a fairly personal segment of the operational real estate; cookie-cutter imitations are rarely effective.

Here's a better desk standard: Set up a single drawer in every desk (say, the upper left) with a basic set of supplies (pen, paper, etc.) and allow anyone away from their own desk to pick up an incoming call there and access those supplies. United Electric Controls implemented this as a standard in its Purchasing Department, improved their customer responsiveness while saving a ton of motion.

Photo 7.55 Francis's desk at a level of visual order that she found useful and pleasing.

For right now: Watch the phone. Francis put a border around it (Photo 7.56). But then she added a second border (Photo 7.57). Question: Why? Why did she add that second border? Look. Think. Consider.

Photo 7.56 Close up of her phone.

Photo 7.57 Francis added a second border, but why?

Photo 7.58 A courteous visual solution. Thanks!

Did she make a location for her pencil, perhaps? That would be clever; but that is not why she did it. Think some more. Here's a hint: I discovered that second border—and its purpose—when I sat in the side chair at Francis's desk and asked to use her phone (her office, deep inside the plant, was a dead zone for cell phones).

Get it? Yes! She gave the phone a second border; then when someone in the side chair asked to use the phone, kaboom, she turned it (Photo 7.58). As a result, the phone was never out of visual order. Automatic recoil/visual where is imbedded.

· Again, just because Francis decided to go this far does not mean you must. She put a double border down because it made sense to her; she didn't share her desk with anyone so she implemented as she saw fit.

Next question: Where did Francis get her idea? Yes: Gary's double border function in the FB-27 cell at Fleet, the one we just looked at.

Does it surprise you that someone in an office should learn from the shop floor? In fact, it happens all the time—and vice-versa as well. We also see manufacturing employees learning from hospitals—and vice versa.

Contrary to popular belief, seeing examples from other industries can actually help us better understand the principles of visuality than if we restrict ourselves to same-industry solutions. Bear this in mind when you start thinking about expanding your visual conversion. It's the principles that teach—and they are found in all great examples.

See Photo Cluster 7.59 as a reminder of the many double-border applications shared earlier in this book, plus a few new ones. All but the airport solution were inspired by Gary's invention.

Photo Cluster 7.59 Double Borders.

Color-Coded Borders

We color-code borders in order to strengthen or reinforce the address portion of the visual where (Photo 7.60). But these colors are not addresses in themselves despite some companies' attempt to treat them as such. As a result, the borders fail to contribute what they are capable of to operational excellence. Because color coding is a form of address, you'll find more about it when we discuss addresses in Chapter 8.

In the meantime, bear the following in mind when combining color coding with borders.

Photo 7.60 Visuality allows us to tell the difference merely by looking. This border system identifies international packages, sub-divided by country address, enhanced by color coding. The colors let us see from a distance that there is difference. But color coding is shorthand—it requires an address for the telling detail. (Seton Name Plate/Connecticut)

High-contrast, double-colored borders

Set two high-contrast colors side-by-side and the colors vibrate, each color competing for our eye's full attention: white/black, yellow/black, red/black, magenta/black, and so on. ANSI and OSHA, federal agencies for workplace health and safety, have standards (requirements) governing the use of such color combinations for borders in high-risk situations—and guidelines for their use elsewhere (guidelines, not requirements).

Some companies, however, use double striped borders everything. And that's a bit of a problem.

Look at the hand truck in Photo 7.61. It's in perfect visual order, with: a border that surrounds it, a home address that identifies it, and an ID label on the thing itself. The only problem is the use of high-contrast yellow/black tape for the border material. OSHA federal register regulation 1910.144 requires its use to mark hazardous areas. The yellow/black combination is purposely engineered to warn us. But what is the danger here? Will that hand truck jump up and throttle us if we walk too close to it? I doubt it.

Photo 7.61 Overuse of high contrast, double-colored tape can give us the jitters—or worse.

Photo 7.62 Aaaah, that's better. We no longer harbor the suspicion that this hand truck might ambush us. Nice hand truck.

"Well, it's just overused," you may say. "What's the harm?" The harm is this: when the eye lands on high-contrast colors, the eye is not able to settle and when the eye cannot settle, the brain cannot settle. That is why those colors are used in situations of risk: disturb the eye, disturb the mind, get our attention so we pay attention.

But when these combinations are overused in a factory (as in aisle after aisle of yellow/black or white/black borders), our eye and mind are continually disturbed. As a result, we enter into a state of hyper-vigilance or alarm, a condition that our bodies register as stress. Just use solid yellow instead (Photo 7.62).

So let OSHA and ANSI regulations guide you—but knowingly. See Photo Series 7.63 for more.

Photo Series 7.63 Correct Use of High Contrast Borders

Right Use This white/red bordering tape alerts us to an emergency exit.

Over Use Why use black/white tape? This solid wood work bench and supplies pose no danger.

Right Use A plain yellow border serves this location and its contents very well.

Applying Borders: Follow a Process

You know that borders are powerful and will anchor the operational functions in your area and make them knowable to everyone. And you know borders will make your area look terrific—operationally and cosmetically beautiful.

Now you have to get them physically into place. I call it: "Laying down the lines. Laying down the law."

Leadership Task 13: Company Color-Code System for Borders

Long before the first border is laid down, management must define and finalize a company-wide color code system. This eight-step procedure works well for a team of 5-7 knowledge-able individuals, working in teams of two to three. I recommend you undertake this process, even if you already have a color system—if only to vet it.

1. Each team lists all items that have a floor or wall print.
2. Each team clusters the items into like categories.
3. The teams get together, compare notes, and create a combined cluster.
4. Each team separately attempts to whittle the clusters down to not less than five and not more than seven, if at all possible.
5. Discuss the thinking as a group.
6. Separate into teams and assign colors.
7. Come together and compare. Develop a final draft.
8. Post or distribute for feedback, including from associates. *Wait a week*, then finalize.

See the next page for an example of a color-code border system template (Figure 7.6).

So much of what one needs to know about laying down borders is linked to your specific area and company, plus the kind of floor—epoxy, concrete, stone, wood. Plus border material—paint (oil or latex); paint plus sealant; striping paint; vinyl tape; electrostatic tape; FLOOR-Mark; DuraStripe; and so on. There are many choices and many decisions. Before you decide on an approach or buy anything, contact a reputable supplier and get educated. (See *Leadership Task 14* for more, next page.)

Floor Border Color Code System: Examples*

We suggest a color-code system with between five and seven colors.

Color	Part Number for Tape**	Part Number for Paint**
	2R276	
	2R266	
	2R677	
	2R731	
	2R332	
	5E312	
	5G688	

1. YELLOW: For transportation and forklift lanes; for walkways for people walking between departments; for parking places.

2. GREEN: For outgoing material or finished goods; could also be for WIP location when ready to move internally from one area/operation to another).

3. ORANGE: For incoming material, supplies, consumables, parts.

4. BLUE:*** Around machines (all sections); for machine-associated carts & racks, such as change over carts; for dies and tooling racks and cabinets.

5. WHITE:*** For racks/return racks and pallets; for desks, filing cabinets, and other workplace furniture; for lockers and break areas; for trash cans.

6. RED: For inspection, rework, scrap, defects, on-hold items, and red-tag area/pallet locations.

7. YELLOW/BLACK (or red/black): For hazardous areas or items; for indicating that caution is required when entering or working in a given zone; for chemicals and chemical zone, Fire Zone, fire extinguishers and fire equipment, used rag cans. (Use high-contrast borders appropriately. They are designed to create optical stress as a means of catching our attention; overuse can be tiring.)

* There will always be a close corollary between colors for floor borders and those for work surfaces (such as work benches).

** As a rule, borders around and outside the department are 4 inches wide; borders within departments are 2-3 inches wide. (The numbers you see here are examples of part numbers in one particular company.) Also, if you end with paint, begin with paint. If you end with tape, don't forget to wax.

*** You may find the distinctions between blue items and white items too refined for your environment. In that case, they can be collapsed into a single border color: either white or blue)

Other Border Considerations

Purple is a useful next color.   Light gray works on some surfaces. Dark gray is better for others.

Brown is hard to see on dark floors.   For long-lasting easy on/easy off floor borders, check out Floor-Mark and DuraStripe.

Here are two ways you can use two colors on borders to make more differentiation. Think about it.

At this company, this stripe approach identifies structure, pipes, air lines, electrical lines that cross overhead an aisle way, walkway, etc. Used as a *heads up* for personnel transporting items that a structure is overhead. 4" black and 4" white alternating stripes.

Figure 7.6 One company's Color-Code System for Borders.

Guidelines and Tips

Laying down borders is work and almost always a two-person job. Make sure you are prepared.

1. Make sure to think about what type of borders you want. Confer with your supervisor and Maintenance; you can't move forward without their involvement, agreement or direct help.

2. If your is a union company, learn about and abide by the same established levels, requirements, and procedures as you would in any improvement initiative. Confer with your supervisor about this and to see if certain requirements have been relaxed for the visual conversion.

3. Many areas begin by testing out their border placement in plain masking tape (or, in some settings, chalk); then they move to more permanent materials (as above).

4. Some areas decide to use a striping machine to lay down borders because it is so quick and easy to apply: Just fill the machine with paint and walk, pushing it ahead (Photo 7.64). Because the paint must be thin enough to flow through the machine, it takes less time to apply and to dry than paint applied by roller. But those borders rarely last a month and have to be refreshed often. Some people see this as an advantage since they might get smarter during that time and will not have to remove the old borders before applying new ones. Wait a week, this thinking goes, and the old layout will be gone.

Photo 7.64 The striping machine.

5. If you decide to use paint, make sure to consult with your Maintenance or facilities department for tips and expert advice. Your supervisor will either gather the knowledge for you or hook you and a buddy up with the right people. If you are on your own in this, consult with a reputable floor and paint supplier.

6. If your company has a color-code system for borders, find out about it. There may be part of the existing system you'd like to see revised, including the colors themselves; in most companies, this will be beyond your reach. But again, your supervisor can provide an invaluable assist, along with your Maintenance Department, visual coordinator, trainer, lead team and/or coach, if you have such helpers in your organization. (See *Leadership Task 14* on page 144 for more.)

Now here are nine tips that relate to almost any bordering situation.

Tip 1. Before you lay down your borders, make sure the floor is clean, dry and dust free. Remove the old tape. If you have a stone floor, you may have to grind off the old borders or mask them with paint matching the color of your floor.

Tip 2. Whether paint or tape, it's worth taking time with this. Precision is a key to outstanding results. Use a tape measure, straight edge or chalk line to make your borders straight and true, especially if a border is free-standing (not close to a structural edge like a wall or machine).

Tip 3. Leave a margin between the item and its border—breathing room. That is, do not lay a border flush against the item itself. If you do, you may spend far too much time getting the item situated within that tight border. Instead—and as a general rule—leave 2.0-3.0 inches between the item and its border; and 0.5-1.0 for work surface items.

Tip 4. If you decide to use paint, map out the width and length of your borders in masking tape. Here you see Tommy making his way around a machining complex, measuring out the tape width and length. Maintenance followed with the paint.

Tip 5. Circular borders (for bins and floor fans, for example) can be tricky. Try using a trash bin lid to get a nice round shape; then work your way around with small strips of masking tape. The circular shapes in the photo got filled entirely with paint—as compared to simply a border.

Tip 6. Mark the color for each border on cardboard or, as applies, on the masking tape itself so that painters (usually Maintenance on an off-shift or over the weekends) will know at-a-glance what has been decided. Or, if you are doing your own painting, so you don't forget.

Tip 7. Extend the life of your newly-painted borders with a double coat of sealant—especially in heavy forklift traffic. When you seal, use a roller wide enough to get 1-2 inches of overlap on both sides. Check with your paint supplier first!

Tip 8. If you are using plastic tape, remember not to stretch the tape as you lay it. If you do, it will curl and never adhere properly. Instead, lay it gently off the roll; this is typically a two person job. Also: Regular waxing is essential to keep tape edges sealed. Once dust gets under an edge, the tape will start to loosen.

Tip 9. Remember: Borders are meant to change as the flow of work changes. Set aside thoughts of laying down borders once and only once. Borders are dynamic—as dynamic as your own improvement thinking. The same goes for waiting to get the flow *just right* before borders get implemented. Borders are far too important to delay. Instead, learn how to lay them down and remove them quickly.

Next Steps

You just learned a lot about borders. Now it's time to bring your visual workplace hit list up to speed on your new thinking (Figure 7.7).

Working alone or with a buddy, think about the opportunities for borders in your area. Make a list of them and think through the ones you want to tackle—alone or with a buddy. When you meet with your supervisor, you post those on the hit list. Don't forget to post the ones you are excited about but don't plan to tackle yourself. Remember: just because you thought of it, doesn't mean you have to do it. And just because no one is interested in a certain project, doesn't mean it should not get done.

Figure 7.7 A hit list keeps track.

And finally…. The men and women at Denison Hydraulics were big fans of borders. Highly inventive and thorough, they also had a lot of fun. Because this is a union plant, Maintenance lays down the paint, based on the notes that associates left the night shift. Junior was the person—and, as you will see next, he had quite a sense of humor.

Look at Photo 7.65 for an example of a border that made me laugh right out loud. What happened? Bill

Jones left a note for Maintenance to paint the border you see in the photo yellow—but he neglected to move his coat tree. Maintenance, always ready for a laugh, decided to take Bill's request literally and painted everything along the way. Everybody in the area enjoyed the joke (Photo 7.66).

Photo 7.66 Bill's neighbors enjoyed the joke, too.

Here's another great joke at the expense of the border requirement: "for everything that casts a shadow."

Photo 7.65 *Everything* in the line of fire got a yellow border.

Late one afternoon, the guys from Assembly Test came running over to get me. Lloyd, they said, had finally gotten on board with borders. They went on to state that he had decided to begin by putting a border around his red tool box. "At last!," I thought. As I arrived in Lloyd's area, a crowd had gathered. When Lloyd showed me his red tool box and crisp yellow border, I expressed delight. Then, with the words "My tool box is never out of visual order," he moved the rolling box—and the border went with it! We fell over laughing (Photos 7.67 and 7.68).

Photos 7.67 and 7.68 This red tool-box is never without its border—and that was the point of Lloyd's joke.

Leadership Task 14: Maintenance Gets on Board

The role of Maintenance is crucial to the success of your visual conversion. While still in the planning stages, you as a leader need to meet with your Maintenance Department for at least four reasons.

1. To learn about the company's color-code system for borders, if there is one. If there isn't one, make sure Maintenance participates in creating one (*Leadership Task 13*). Maintenance will prefer to keep to a few colors to keep supplies to a minimum—and you need to convince them to support more.

2. To obtain Maintenance's involvement in developing (or validating) a standard procedure for laying down borders efficiently—and for removing them fast. This will go a long way in easing people's worries about changing the layout.

3. To work out with Maintenance how much time (or percentage of time) it can provide the visual conversion effort on a weekly or monthly basis. The goal is 5% minimum; 10% would accelerate the improvement process handsomely. This is the time that Maintenance assigns, for example, to help on smart placement tasks, building fixtures, laying down borders, and so on. Improvement activity is usually slow for the first month or two of a conversion; then it steadily builds. Prepare for this now.

4. To work with Maintenance to develop a special work order form just for the targeted areas. Make the form a different color, preferably bright. Work out a simple system for submitting and tracking orders. And get all this done before you launch. Then pilot the new system and work out the bugs.

> # Discipline is remembering what you love.
>
> Albert Einstein

Chapter | Eight

Visual Where: Address and ID Label

Address Basics

We now move to the second element of automatic recoil: addresses. In this chapter, you will learn about the waste—motion—that gets triggered when addresses are inaccurate, unreadable, incomplete, weak, or simply absent from the workplace.

In far too many companies, addresses are overlooked or merely given lip service. It is not enough, for example, to throw some parts on a shelf, hang a sign that says "parts storage," and leave the rest for other people to figure out. This non-approach is not just inadequate but a sure prescription for accidents, mix-ups, defects, long downtime, long lead time, unhappy employees, unhappy customers, and plummeting profit margins. Like a road map without names on it, shelves, racks, benches, cabinets, drawers, walls, and floors may hold items we vitally need—but without excellent addresses we have no clear way of finding them.

You are about to see dozens of addresses that work—some highly specific, others very general. All of them are adequate, many excellent, and some brilliant and unsurpassed. In every case, each address serves us until the next incident of motion informs us the address needs to be upgraded and improved.

As you read these pages, take the opportunity to expand your understanding of what makes addresses work and how to make them even more effective. What's that we hear? "I already know everything there is to know about addresses. I mean how much can there be anyway? It's just a label with a name on it!"

Photo 8.1 The three elements of automatic recoil: border+address+ID label.

If that is you speaking, then hear this: You are wrong. Despite over twenty-five years (at this writing) of researching and implementing visuality all over the world, I learn more about addresses all the time.

Over seventy addresses are discussed in this chapter and they merely scratch the surface of what is possible. I include them in order to ignite your thinking and trigger your inventiveness so you can create addresses that go even further and serve you precisely and completely. In fact, there are many types of addresses I do not discuss here—either because of space constraints or because premier examples have not yet been created. This is especially true for offices and hospitals where deep visuality has only begun to be developed.

Pattern Recognition

The necessity of addresses goes beyond our ongoing need to know where things are in a fixed and reliable way—that is to say, visually. In a larger way, addresses support our earlier discussion about the mind as a pattern-seeking mechanism. Addresses help us find and recognize the full pattern of work— and feel a new level of psychological and physical safety as that happens. Without addresses, the pattern is incomplete. To underscore the mind's remarkable ability to find and recognize patterns, read Figure 8.1.

Aoccdrnig to a rscheearch at Cmabrigde Uinervtisy, it deosn't mttaer in

waht oredr the ltteers in a wrod are, the olny iprmoatnt tihng is taht the

frist and lsat ltteer be at the rghit pclae. The rset can be a ttoal mses

and you can sitll raed it wouthit porbelm. Tihs is bcuseae the huamn mnid

deos not raed ervey lteter by istlef, but the wrod as a wlohe.

Amzanig huh?

Figure 8.1 The mind will always seek a pattern.

At first, the letters look garbled. Then we find we can read them. Even though every word longer than three letters is spelled incorrectly, we still recognize each of them and understand each sentence. We could even read the text aloud despite its many typos. Pettry amzanig huh?

How is that possible? It is possible because your mind—which is fully linked with your eyes—does not read letters; it recognizes patterns or profiles. In this case, it recognizes the word's profile or shape as defined by the first and last letter.

In a similar way, this powerful ability of our mind allows us to know the time on an analog clock (Figure 8.2) nanoseconds faster than on a digital readout (Figure 8.3). That is because an analog clock allows us to recognize the whole and its meaning in order to tell the time—instead of reading each number, as we must on a digital

Figure 8.2
Analog Clock.

Figure 8.3 Digital Clock.

clock. Both types of clocks (analog and digital) are installed in the high-risk environment of a fighter jet's cockpit for the sake of redundancy—but it is analog instrumentation that allows for decisive responses that are nanoseconds faster in that high-risk location.

We harness that same power of the mind for the benefit of our company when we lay down borders—and then apply its operational partner: addresses. So let's begin to create work that makes (more) sense by understanding and applying addresses—for everything that casts a shadow.

Border + Address

The premise behind an address in the workplace is the same as an address on your home. In one case, "you" are the resident. In the other, the work item or material is. But at work we can go one step further in making this link crystal clear: an item's address tells us what belongs in the "real estate" you claim through borders.

Photo 8.2 A good address means you don't have to ask.

Photo 8.2 shows the home for Completed Parts—and you know it because of the address. Without the address, you would have to guess, remember or ask someone—all forms of motion. A border without an address only works when the item is in that location—only then can we know what "lives" there.

Photo 8.3 Occupant unknown.

In the case of Photo 8.3, it's anybody's guess what "lives" in the yellow bordered area. Only habit (or what we call *tribal knowledge*) can help you; but it can't help newcomers or visitors. The purpose of borders is to surround and visually organize material, tools, machines, furniture—and any other items that occupy real estate in your area, whether on a floor, wall, bench or shelf. The purpose of addresses is to name those occupants.

Addresses can be fixed to a range of locations: 1) imbedded in the border itself, 2) fixed on a wall surface, 3) posted on a standing sign, 4) behind the border, 5) over the border (airborne), and so on. See Photo Cluster 8.4. The one place an address can't be is "nowhere."

Photo Cluster 8.4
A range of innovative addresses.

In my years of hands-on implementation and coaching, I have found only one situation where an address for border location is not required: traffic lanes and pedestrian aisles (Photo 8.5). Because the aisle or traffic function is continuous and cuts across the entire production site, it does not require addresses. Some companies address this acceptable gap by embossing a forklift or pedestrian icon (Photo 8.6). But mostly, these lanes just snake their way through the facility.

Photo 8.5 Traffic lanes and aisles.

For Everything That Casts a Shadow. With that single exception, the visual where requires a border plus address for every thing that casts a shadow (more about ID labels later). That is

Photo 8.6 Pedestrian walkway.

the hard-and-fast definition. And it serves your business purposes exceptionally well, not just at the outset as order begins to emerge visually, but also later when your focus shifts to sustaining and extending the important visual functionality already achieved. When you adopt the everything-that-casts-a-shadow rule, you are in a position to use that rule both as a tool and as a standard for self-examination, self-audit, and continuous improvement.

This is where you can use the laminated map discussed in Chapter 3 to register, with a yellow dot, when the visual where is strongly in place in each area. When that is so, you have already reaped a 15% to 30% increase in throughput in that locale. See Photo Series 8.7 for three more examples.

Photo Series 8.7

Without an address on the bright yellow border of this blue paperwork desk, we would not know its specific purpose: *Hold and Ship.*

Without the address on the border, we don't know what belongs here when the cart is in use, where to return the cart—or if the wrong cart (an intruder) is in this location.

Eight air hoses "live" in this wall system. Make it more exact: Number each circle—and put a matching ID label on each hose. Then you know the number of hoses, without counting.

On All Surfaces. As with borders, begin to apply addresses on the floor and work your way up—to the walls, work surfaces, and then on to short shelves and tall ones, and into cabinets and drawers.

The Rules for Addressing

When you apply addresses, keep the following rules in mind so they are effective from the outset.

Rule 1: Large Enough. Make each address large enough for us to easily read—easily grasp—at a distance. The basic rule is: perfectly readable at two feet when on foot; and perfectly readable at four feet when on a cart or forklift. Your addresses will then be "right-sized"—at a scale and proportion that fits the setting. You can rarely make an address that is too big. Always avoid "too small." If an address is small, we work too hard to see it. Then the address (which is supposed to be a motion-buster) ends up a motion-producer.

Rule 2: Upper and Lower Case. Whenever possible, use upper case and lower case letters in your addresses. Avoid the popular but problematic ALL UPPER CASE (ALL CAPS) address. Using all caps prevents the mind from identifying the pattern. Why? Because all caps create an undifferentiated block; they flatten the pattern profile. As a result, the pattern of the word disappears and we are forced to read, rather than recognize, the words. (See Figure 8.4 and Photo 8.8.)

Figure 8.4 Upper/lower case rules.

A word in all CAPS—as in this very sentence—stands out when (and only when) the words on either side of it are not in all caps. Why? Because the upper/lower case words that surround it create a profile that makes the caps stand out. BUT WHEN WE CAPITALIZE ALL THE LETTERS OF ALL THE WORDS IN A SENTENCE, THE PROFILE IS LOST—and our quick understanding with it.

Photo 8.8 Easy to read address.

When given a choice, use upper and lower case letters. You may be challenged to find this in stencils. Last time I checked, most came in all caps only. Label-making machines, however, now offer a choice of upper/lower and all caps. Brady Corp. puts out a fine array that work well with your computer and make effective addresses that are also affordable (Photo 8.9). For more, check this book's Resource Section, under Brady Corp.

Rule 3: High-Contrast. Another common address error is in the use of color. Just because black appears to be the opposite of white does not make *black and white* the best color combination for addresses. In fact, black letters (and numbers) tend to fuse on a white background into a nearly unreadable grayness. Black-on-white is the least easily seen as an address and yet the most commonly used.

Photo 8.9 Brady BMP 71 Label Maker Printer for upper/lower case and ALL CAPS addresses. Also in the preferred black-on-yellow color combination. (See **Brady Corp.** in Resource Section.)

What does work? Uncle Sam has already done the research for us: bold black letters (or numbers) on a dense crayon-yellow background. In a field of colors, the human eye is drawn first to yellow. When given a choice, create high-contrast, easy-to-read addresses in that yellow-black or black-yellow color combination. (See again, Photo 8.9.)

Look around the community and you will see that combination everywhere: from crime scene tape to crayon-yellow school buses (a vehicle color reserved by U.S. Law for the school bus) to many airport terminals where vital customer signage is often black-on-yellow (or yellow-on-black). Most license plates in the England use that combination. (Note: White-on-black can work well, especially when large black margins surround the letters or numbers.) Let's take a lesson from all of these applications and use high-contrast colors to make our addresses more readable. See Photo Cluster 8.10.

Photo Cluster 8.10 Black-on-yellow is the most readable color combination. Yellow-on-black is next.

Rule 4: Color-Coding. You may think that color coding is a border function. It is not. Technically speaking, color coding is a form of home address (that is sometimes imbedded in borders). Colors let us quickly sort (at-a-glance)—but addresses provide the telling detail.

The look-alike fixtures on the lower cabinet shelf in Photo 8.11 are each clearly addressed—and the color coding makes it even easier select the correct one. After all, we are human and lead busy, often compressed lives, especially nowadays. And we forget. And then we forget that we forgot…and by then we can get into big trouble.

Photo 8.11 The three elements of automatic recoil: border + address + ID label.

Photo 8.12 These collar gauges need more.

Look at the handsome color-coded drawer in Photo 8.12. Attractive though it is, can you see what's wrong? Yes, there are no addresses for the two collar gauges. The purpose of color coding is to enhance an address, not replace it. Don't make the mistake I have seen in many companies new to visuality: they use color coding instead of addresses—as a substitute. Though that seems to be a time saver, this "shortcut" can turn into a long cut, leading to mix-ups, accidents, defects, long lead times, and unhappy customers.

There's another reason we combine color coding with words (or numbers): Some of us are color blind. Studies show that 8%-12% of all men (and 1% of women) are some degree of color blind, usually in the ranges of green and red. So words and numbers come first—then add color coding.

Rule 5: Surround Addresses. It is always better to put an address on all sides of a floor item—rather than on just one side—especially if the item is large. In Photo 8.13, three of the four sides of border that surround that tool dolly are plainly addressed. This becomes critical for items with a large floor foot-

Photo 8.13 Surround address for a fixture for fixtures.

print, such as monument machines (Photo 8.14). In that case, locate the machine address on all sides (whether airborne or border-imbedded or both) and vital address information can be seen and known, whatever the angle of approach.

Photo 8.14 Surround address on a machining center.

Rule 6: Standardize Names (Nomenclature). You and your colleagues have to agree on a common set of names for the things in your work area. This often requires a pause prior to assigning addresses so everyone can settle on a single name; for example, for the machine you refer to as the "JTM-1," others refer to as the "2-Axis CNC," and still others, "Big Blue." Your supervisors, engineers, and managers may want to weigh in on names that have cross-departmental impact.

In visuality, we refer to this as: determining a standard nomenclature—a common name for things. This is an important activity not just for things within your department but for items, materials, machines, and processes that are shared across departments. Your supervisor can, will, and must help—and, as visuality spreads, the added assistance of the Macro-Visual Team (discussed in Chapter 3) may apply.

> ## Leadership Task 15: Naming by Consensus
>
> Supervisors & Managers: Finding common names for the things within your area is an excellent opportunity for you to practice helping associates reach a balance between I-driven and group preferences—in other words: true consensus.
>
> Don't be tempted to use your position as "boss" to shortcut the process, save time, and get your favorite names adopted. Instead of gaining time, the I-driven process will grind to a halt. People who report to you will simply let you have your way—and you will have short-circuited the spirited associate engagement you have worked so long and sincerely to cultivate. I can almost guarantee it.

Make Your Address More Effective: Tips

Many companies casually undertake the mighty opportunity that well-developed addresses offer. This is usually because they have not yet realized how powerfully addresses can contribute to the bottom line. In many such facilities, white addresses (with black letters or numbers) are plastered on everything, cookie-cutter fashion—usually under a 5S umbrella—in the mistaken belief that this fulfils the requirement.

It does not. Small wonder the very people asked to put such dull addresses in place lose the will to maintain them and the heart to look for ways to make them more robust. The standard has already been set; it was called "good enough," a sworn enemy of excellence.

Let's do something other than that. Let's begin with the premise that: 1) addresses are indispensable to operational excellence; and 2) addresses should improve, just as borders do—because as we get smarter, our addresses should get smarter.

Here are five tips to keep in mind as you seek to make your addresses as effective as possible. By "effective" I mean: easy-to-see, easy-to-read, accurate, complete, and related to the task-at-hand.

Tip 1: Use Arrows

When you start applying addressing to racks and shelves, don't subtract from your efforts by not making it clear which address applies to what shelf.

The positive impact of the bold yellow + black shelf addresses in Photo 8.15 is reduced as we hesitate and wonder if CD30C applies to material above it—or below it. Add arrows and the question is never asked; any hint of that form of micro-motion evaporates.

Photo 8.15 Better, but …

Arrows + Barcoding. More and more, product barcoding is an operational necessity for asset tracking, inventory control, unique identification, and automatic data collection or RFID (Radio Frequency Identification Data)—a technology developed in World War II as an IFF (Identify Friend or Foe) tool for aircraft. Tall warehouse shelving is a key application opportunity (Photo 8.16).

For the purposes of workplace visuality, however, barcode addresses weaken visual viability because the tag is white, only inches small, and filled with equal-

ly small black letters, numbers, and bars unknowable without a reader. Plus, many companies apply the barcode strip directly onto the shelving units. If the shelves are beige (Photo 8.17), the barcode tag is even harder to locate, far away or close up.

But barcodes are so widely used, we better not ignore the problem or complain about it too long. Instead, let's use visual principles to make barcodes more user friendly. Here are two ways:

1. Add a contrasting background. Using paint, colored cardboard, or a colored magnetic strip, add backing to the barcode tags. Then secure that to the shelf, as shown in dark green in Photo 8.18.

Photo 8.16 Tall shelves.

2. Add arrows. As mentioned earlier, a hidden motion (hidden question) with many shelf addresses is this: Which shelf does that address apply to: the shelf above the address? Or the shelf below the address? Add arrows and clear up the mystery (Photo 8.19).

Photo 8.17 White gets lost on beige.

Photo 8.18 A dark backing helps.

Photo 8.19 Arrows clear up the mystery.

Gwenie's Rant on Arrows. In my view, arrows on all shelving should be mandatory (made a standard)—not just in the warehouse but everywhere. "Why?" says the newcomer to visuality. "After all, the time lost in figuring out which shelf the address applies to can be measured in nanoseconds. The motion is tiny." But the visual thinker knows better. The visual thinker knows to add up the nanoseconds of motion triggered by a single vague address—in this case, one without arrows—over the course of a single day, then a week, and then a month. That's when the cost of the absence of arrows becomes screamingly apparent. Go a level higher and multiply those now-thousands of nanoseconds per month by the number of individuals who go to that same shelf, day after day, month after month, year after year…and the screams grow louder.

I don't believe anyone has ever had the internal fortitude to go to the next level—multiplying all that by the number of products on that shelving unit, and then the number of shelving units in the department, company, and corporation. Why torment yourself? Better to just get arrows going and watch them spread as the intelligent, forward thinking people who work with you get the message. As inevitably as the sunrise.

Tip 2: Use Driver-License Level Addresses

Unless you make the decision to use a purely generic address (Photo 8.20; discussed further in a mo-

ment), your aim is to add telling detail to each address, making them ever more specific. In that way, you and others will have sufficient information to act immediately, independently, and correctly, without questions or hesitation—that is, with minimal motion. Said another way: The address must anticipate people's need-to-know. When an address does that, I call it a *driver-license level address.*

Your driver's license shares: your name, photo, home address, birth date, height, vehicle restrictions, driving restrictions, the license number—and what you want us to do with your vital organs should you get into a fatal accident. In short, it contains the information needed for us to make positive identification, make correct and timely value-add decisions, and take effective, timely action.

Photo 8.20 Generic addresses.

In the same way, a good workplace address shares many levels of information about its resident. The more complicated or look-alike an item, the more specifics get included in the address in order for us to put or pick that item quickly, without the slightest hesitation or possibility of mix-up.

Examine the four-address system in Photo 8.21 that John Pacheco developed (United Electric Controls/Massachusetts). It was the first address of its kind I had ever seen; I named it a driver-license level address. John's addresses made us see the difference between the four sets of look-alike rods to which they applied. The rods were identical in length but not in material; they had identical ODs (outer diameter) but different IDs (inner diameter).

John wanted an address approach that minimized mix-ups across these look-alike rods. Here's how he did it:

1. John alternated the location of rods by material: stainless steel-copper-stainless steel-copper.

2. He placed the ID specification of each rod type at the top of the address to make it easy to spot the telling at tribute.

3. John paired similarities: *ID .015* together and *ID .021* together.

4. He colored the copper addresses yellow to break the seeming symmetry a tad further.

Photo 8.21 John Pacheco's first driver-license level address.

This exceptional address system perfectly demonstrates the principle of how to tell the difference merely by looking, a principle of all workplace visuality. Providing driver-license level information can be so useful and satisfying. Effectively implemented, this elegant address approach has the capacity, in the manufacturing sector for example, to reduce picking errors, speed up material handling, and prevent stock-outs. In hospital and medical settings the benefits are even more pronounced. Look for ways to adapt and apply this principle to all situations that need a crystal clear, detailed address.

Tip 3: Use Generic Addresses

With addresses, begin with the intention of creating the most accurate, precise, and complete address possible (driver-license level). But be prepared to change your mind because sometimes the polar opposite is required. That polar opposite is called a generic address. Generic (or general) addresses have many applications. Typically, they are used when items located together are so different they cannot be defined by a single address.

Photo 8.22 Now we can find that pizza!

Here's the story of a generic address (Photo 8.22), triggered by a uncommon form of motion: searching for a lost pizza. The night shift at Greene Rubber (Massachusetts) phoned in for a pizza. Expecting the delivery within 30 minutes, people continued working and were surprised an hour later when the pizza still hadn't show up. They called to inquire. "But we delivered it 40 minutes ago," was the response. "No, you didn't!" "Yes, we did." "No! You didn't!" "YES! WE DID!!"

A team member went to night reception and asked. The reply was: "Sure it came. I took it back to your department ages ago." "Well, where did you put it?" "In your department!" went the response.

The pizza was eventually found, needless to say, cold and hard. That was when the night shift decided that this would never happen again. They designated a location they simply called "Drop Zone." Everything and anything delivered to the department was put there—parts, cardboard, tools, and piping hot pizza.

Tip 4: Avoid Meaningless Addresses

Look at the addresses in Photo 8.23 (and Detail). They are: 12089499, 12065401, etc.—part numbers of the components you see here in bins in an automotive assembly area. Lots of numbers but no meaning.

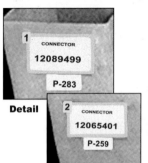

Photo 8.23 Lots of numbers but no meaning.

We do not doubt that this address system was developed with care and a desire to be of help. It *is* of help and certainly far better than nothing. It is something. It is a beginning.

But if we sit and observe the micro-activity triggered by such addresses, we see a lot of earnest, hard-working employees engaged in a lot of micro-motion. First, we see operators bent over, maybe kneeling, straining to see the numbers. If we keep watching, we observe the strain that this almost-good-enough system also visits on the material handler, re-stock person or water spider—the person responsible for keeping the bins filled. Lean close and you might hear her muttering: "Hmmm, does this box of parts match the bin number? Well, almost, I think…gosh, maybe not. Wait a minute let me double check. Darn, where are my glasses?" We would see a ton of motion.

What's the remedy? No, not a better pair of glasses. The remedy is to think visually—first by recognizing that that woman is struggling, not working. And then start improving this set of addresses, with her active involvement.

And how can we improve it? Not by removing those long part numbers but by adding to them—by adding what I call *handles*.

Tip 5: Add Address Handles

Adding handles to an address clarifies and strengthens it. A handle is an equivalent or amplification of the existing address that purposely creates redundancy. Handles provide different and distinct ways to ensure that communication happens—completely, precisely, accurately, and on time. Here are some handles to add to long part number addresses in order to accomplish this:

- Trade name
- Photograph
- Drawing
- Whom to call when the part is low or out
- That phone number

Look at the blue parts holder in Photo 8.24. Each blue pocket holds the specific part whose number is indicated directly above it. Pocket 3 holds part number 12064171. Directly above that is a drawing (a handle) of that part to make the match (see Detail).

Detail.

And in case we forget exactly how to assemble that part, the number of the standard operating procedure is included in the address as well: SOP 19. Fully and visually informed, we move forward with confidence and go home satisfied that we contributed to our company today and earned our keep.

This is a blistering great address! Visible, accurate, correct, specific, precise, complete, and very effective.

Photo 8.24 So many visual devices to help assemble correctly.

That concludes the five tips for developing highly-effective addresses in your area. Next we look at innovations that make addresses more and more powerful.

Making Your Address More Powerful: Innovations

Addresses are a major part of the operational language you imbed into the workplace through visuality. Sometimes it seems that there are nearly as many ways to apply effective addresses as there are words to put on them. Here are some innovative ones.

Stacked Address. What happens when you combine a floor border with stacked bins? You get stacked addresses (or, at least, that is an option). In Photo 8.25, two large stacked bins are home to three part numbers, shared visually through the three-level address on the border itself. (Fleet Engineers/Michigan)

Detail.

Photo 8.25 Stacked Addresses.

Photocopied Address. Do you remember Bob Comeau's invention of photocopied borders discussed in the last chapter? Never to be outdone (even by himself), Bob proceeded to develop another layer of

innovation on this innovation. You see it in Photo 8.26: a photo of the tools needed to changeover the Nichifu machine (to the left). That tool photo acts as an address—not a border—because it tells us what tools reside in the blue bin above it, a type of Bill of Tools. (United Electric Controls/Massachusetts)

3D-Tab Address. A powerful yet largely under-used address option is 3D tabs—addresses that stick out into space so that you do not need to stand in front of the address to know what is located there. One of the most useful applications of 3D tabs is in rows of racks. The challenge with rows, especially if there are a lot of them, is that you rarely discover if what you need is in a row until you walk down it. With 3D tabs (Photos 8.27 and 8.28), you can tell at a distance, from either end of the row.

Photo 8.26 Photocopied address for changeover tools.

Smart retail stores use 3D tabs to improve the customer experience while keeping floor staff to a minimum. Empowered consumers, we can be self-regulating because the retail environment is self-explaining, as shown in the splendid end caps in Photo 8.29.

Photo 8.27 We get to know what we need to know from a distance.

Photo 8.28 The closer we get, the more value-add information we get.

Photo 8.29 Blue endcaps are 3D tabs. Notice: 1) generic addresses combined with words. 2) the use of yellow; and 3) major and minor sorts in the airborne addresses.

More 3D-Tab Addresses. Melody Sparrow's bench was located near five rows of hard-to-find diodes, resistors, and transistors. Though not her area, nearly everyone who went to those rows assumed, since she was close by, that she knew where things were. They were wrong. But that did not stop them from repeatedly asking for her help.

By default, their information deficits rapidly became hers and that translated into the endless motion of interruptions and searching. Melody took the situation in hand and created the system of 3D-tab addresses you see in Photos 8.30 and 8.31. She further improved that visual solution by adding a second color to the already color-coded borders, surrounding the tall racks (Photo 8.32). In that photo, you see the yellow for resistors running the length of the associated resistor inventory. Brilliant visual thinking. (Harris Corp./Illinois)

Photo 8.30 3D tabs along the row.

Photo 8.31 Yellow 3D tab for resistors.

Photo 8.32 Yellow border defines the resistor inventory.

While Melody's addresses needed to be very specific, the tall shelves you see in Photo 8.33 need to accommodate a constant flow of ever-changing parts. Generic 3D tabs allow the same spaces to be used for

Photo 8.33 Generic 3D tabs.

different products and still retain their visual logic. The tabs remained stable (B1, B2, B3…) while the product mix changes—and often. (Delphi/Mexico)

Can you find opportunities to apply 3D-tab addresses in your own work area?

Number Address. Complexity in human interaction is one of the primary reasons that visuality is vital in human endeavors. That is also why we often discover excellent visual solutions in community places: so many people…so many opportunities for mistakes.

As you just saw in the Delphi 3D-tab solution, numbers can help when variation (difference) becomes

Photo 8.34 Number addresses match the phone books to the county map.

too great for specific addresses. Because there were too many phone numbers in a seven-county area to fit in one book, a set of seven phone books was developed (Photo 8.34), organized by numbers one through seven instead of by county name. The match between book and county is made without titles, thanks to the color-coded map on the backboard. Can you see the next step in making this solution even smarter? Yes, color-match the numbers on each book to the map.

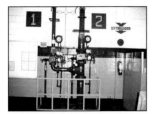

Photo 8.35 Numbered pipes, a tiny detail that results in big savings.

Another example of using a number as an address is the pipe system in Photo 8.35. When you see a company that bothers to differentiate the pipes in the facility, you are among advanced visual thinkers—those who look ahead into the repair and maintenance function and take steps, in advance, to reduce the associated downtime. Picking up the money lying on the floor is another way to say this.

Metric vs. Standard. Numbers are often able to make addresses more specific than words can, as in the case of the two types of rod stock shown in Photos 8.36 to 8.38.

The rods are identical materials—but one set is cut in metric units (for European customers) while the other is cut in standard units (for US clients). Bill Jones made sure each address captured that key difference by using numbers—not words—and he spelled out the distinction further through color-coding (yellow for metric/red for standard). As we saw earlier in John Pacheco's driver-license level address, by alternating the color, Bill minimized mix-ups. (Denison Hydraulics/Ohio)

Our final number-as-address solution belongs to the world of cams—tools used for machining complicated parts such as screw threading in our example case.

Photo 8.36 Metric rod stock in yellow.

Photo 8.37 Standard rod stock in red.

Photo 8.38 Rack from a distance.

Cam Storage. The shocking *Before* in Photo 8.39 shows how cams used to be stored. The equally astonishing *After* (Photo 8.40) gives you a sense of the hundreds of cams this company utilized across more than 30 screw-making machines—and why creating a visually coherent system for them was an operational requirement.

Photo 8.39 Cam storage—*Before.*

Notice how the two operators who created this visual solution situated the cams on a backboard, using cam size as the address (Photo 8.41). Though they did not realize it at the time, when these operators painted the board with white and blue bands, they automatically made finding specific cams—as well as returning them—faster, more accurate, and easier. Why? Because of the now-familiar principle of harnessing the mind's power to recognize and make meaning of patterns. The blue and white bands created enough of a pattern for people to key into (Curtis Screw/New York). CNC machining has since replaced the role of cams but the visual principles reflected in this address solution are well worth your study.

Photo 8.40 Bands of color make it easier to remember.

Photo 8.41 The address is the cam size.

Address By Function

Visuality is a form of operational language. Addresses can do more than simply tell us where things are and where they go. Used innovatively, they can support day-to-day operations specifically and admirably well. We'll look at four such address categories now:

- Tool Checkout
- Process Sequencing
- Departmental Addresses
- Material Handling

1. Tool Checkout-A: Magnetic Address. New magnetic materials bring useful options to the address function. The department in this next example (Photo 8.42) has manual processes, requiring small but highly specialized tools and fixtures. These tools are too costly for each associate to have an individual set. Instead of chasing down tools all the time, the area invented a simple checkout system for maximum tool sharing and traceability. Here's how it works:

- Tools and fixtures are placed on a low metal rack in visual order. (This is an electrostatic area and the only available bordering tape was red.)

- The name of each associate is marked on a magnetic tag. The tags are lined up on the rack front. A sixth tag is marked *Repair* for tools that leave the area for that reason.

- When an associate needs a tool or fixture, he takes it from the rack and leaves, in its place, a name magnet. If the tool needs repair or calibration, he turns it in and leaves that magnet in its place.

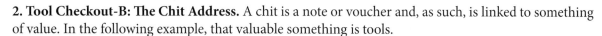

Photo 8.42 Magnetic address system for specialized tools.

- In this way, if someone else needs that tool, they know where it is and either wait or find the current user and ask for it next. Minimum wondering. Minimum wandering. Minimum motion. (Alpha Industries/Massachusetts)

2. Tool Checkout-B: The Chit Address. A chit is a note or voucher and, as such, is linked to something of value. In the following example, that valuable something is tools.

Photo 8.43 Tool checkout system.

The system in Photos 8.43 and 8.44 uses chits for tool checkout and traceability in the Warranty Department at Volgren, a bus manufacturer in Australia.

Notice that this system tackles two separate outcomes: 1) checking out a tool so the person who takes it can be held accountable for returning it; and 2) providing a colleague that needs an unavailable tool a way to find the current user and schedule a turn.

Before this chit system, repair operators spent a great deal of time chasing down highly-prized tools or were simply forced to wait for people to return from lunch/rest room/meeting/etc. in

Photo 8.44 Special tool corner. See yellow circle for the chit check out system.

the hope that they knew a tool's whereabouts. The layers upon layers of motion triggered by the lack of a system defies quantification.

Here's detail on how the chit checkout worked:

1. Specialized tools are co-located on a stand on the production floor.
2. Each operator is provided with six chits in a given color, with their respective name on them.
3. When the operator takes a tool, he leaves the chit in place.

The aerospace industry makes good use of chit checkout systems. Typically, each operator carries individualized chits on a large key ring, with a personal photo and barcode that is scanned when a tool is taken.

3. Process Sequencing Address. I never fully realized how much an innovative address can silently, reliably, and precisely reveal process sequence until I saw the following series at Curtis Screw in 1994.

Notice the four addresses in Photo 8.45 have the same top-level information: M8219. But they are not repeat addresses.

The information below the M8219 address maps out the process sequence—the stages of production. This is the part that is brilliant. Look.

Photo 8.45 Four addresses that only seem identical.

Photo 8.46 Stage 1 address.

In Photo 8.46, the stage detail reads: "AFTER WASH/COUNT/WAITING FOR TUMBLE."

In Photo 8.47, the stage is: "AFTER TUMBLE/WAITING FOR HEAT TREAT."

Photo 8.47 Stage 2 address.

This makes so much sense. It is often very difficult to see the difference between parts at various stages, by sight alone. For Curtis operators, that was exactly the point: They were not able to reliably tell the difference merely by looking at M8219 parts as those parts went through a four-stage process. Parts that had already gone through heat treat looked almost identical to those that had not.

Lots of mix-ups resulted, followed by lots of scrap. The solution was to set up the address system here, and place parts under the address that reflected their current process stage. This address sequence is a remarkably simple and effective visual solution that combines smart placement principles with highly functional addresses.

4. Departmental Addresses. We already discussed that addresses are not only about retrieval. They can also have other important purposes. The IN-and-OUT function and departmental addresses are two such cases.

a. IN-and-OUT Address (when not to standardize). Many people rightly link standardization with the journey to excellence. But far too many think this means making everything the same, uniform, and identical. Here, they are mistaken. Take addresses, for example. People who say they want everything "same/uniform/identical" almost always want addresses to be like that: the same size, shape, and color.

That's not a move towards standardization. That's cutting cookies (Photo 8.48).

As far as visuality and addresses are concerned, cookie-cutter standardization is no standardization at all. It is death by sameness, robbing the enterprise of high-performance excellence and its employees of the satisfaction that comes from genuine inventive engagement—aka, thinking—and the robust, creative solutions that derive from that. For me, one of the hallmarks of a spirited and engaged workforce and a genuinely effective visual conversion is what I call the "weird" factor—or, in polite company, the "local" factor.

Photo 8.48 Cookies anyone?

If a company's array of visual devices looks suspiciously similar and appears to occur on the same level of mind or imagination, something's not right with the rollout. Usually that means two things. First, the "good enough" bar is set too low; as a result, the company standardizes on visual improvements too soon and too quickly. Second, no time or not enough time is set aside for improvement activity; as a result, people simply do not have the time or the quiet to think and do—to test their own ideas, to experiment. In either case, the visual improvement process is short-circuited.

Instead of standardizing on a specific outcome (for example, requiring a specific type of address), companies are better served by requiring that a specific function be put into place—not a specific way to express that function. For instance, a company can require that each area have IN-and-OUT addresses—but should not mandate what those address need to look like, cookie-cutter fashion.

There are dozens of ways of creating such a set of addresses. Let the experimentation begin! Managers, don't seek to control that. Seek to make sure each department has: 1) a highly visual location for newly delivered goods and materials; and 2) a separate, highly-visual location for goods and materials that ready for removal or pick up.

Now that's a smart standard. What those addresses look like is not the point at this stage. What is the point is that each department has a pair.

You may have seen better in your lifetime—or imagined better in your mind—but for me the IN-and-

Photo 8.49 Incoming.

OUT locations shown in Photos 8.49 and 8.50 are simply delightful—though I would love to see a border define the limits of OUT. Why not widen the scope: apply the same IN-and-OUT requirement to workbenches as well; that could go a long way toward ending senseless mix-ups from picking up material that is not yet ready.

Photo 8.50 Outgoing.

The department next door may go about this another way. And the department next to that yet another. Let each area go through a period of trial and error as it discovers what works for it. At some point, your company will want to adopt a more or less uniform format for the IN-and-OUT function—a so-to-speak "standardized practice."

But that comes later, after people who use those locations many times a day have a chance to explore the possibilities and experiment with, for example, location, look, and feel (form, fit, and function). That is how inventive visual solutions can transform into true Visual Best Practices.

b. Addressing the "Entrance." In much the same way, your company can (I think *should*) require each department to visually indicate or show its name, as you see in Photo 8.51, Rear Headers Department.

Now go further. When you designate your area's name, identify its entrance or the "top" of the stream. In many departments there are no actual doors or threshold so it's not so easy to tell where the area actually begins. Yet it is important to know flow-in and flow-out points, at least for the sake of materials (WIP). Begin that process by selecting your department's "main entrance;" now designate it—give it an address. Most departments at Trailmobile/Canada had no walls. The site manager made naming the entrance to every area a requirement and saw many unspoken questions immediately answered. Motion of a deeply hidden form was reduced.

Photo 8.51 The Rear Headers team built their departmental sign into the floor at the "top" of their area (red arrow). (Trailmobile/Canada)

Big Challenge. The big challenge in creating an area address and locating it at the so-called "entrance" is that many departments cover a vast amount of floor space (Photo 8.52). When there's that much undifferentiated square footage, you can hardly find the perimeter (the outside edge), let alone the top of the stream—the entrance. The department in Photo 8.53 attempted to solve this by plastering signage high in the heavens of this very large space. Despite their best intentions, they have substituted one confusing universe with another.

Photo 8.52
Nothing.

Photo 8.53
Not much more.

To tell you the truth, in 25 years, I have never seen this handled in a way that makes sense. As a result, I have no benchmark. But I do suspect why: Area addresses tend to have the same cookie-cutter look and the same cookie-cutter failure because the task of departmental signage is almost always given to busy engineers or an equally busy HR department—usually triggered by a visit from corporate. "Get some darn signs up!" cries the CEO, "Corporate will be here in three weeks!" A list of departments is compiled, sent to an outside contractor, and two weeks later three dozen look alike signs are hung.

While usually well-made ("to last the ages"), such signs rarely offer a way for us to see—to discern—the difference between departments. The signs themselves do not help; they do not show a difference in shape or color or information. Only the departmental name is different. As a result, we remain uninformed, despite the sizable investment in professional signage. Many of us might prefer the previous absence of an approach because at least we had a reason to ask questions—instead of wandering around with our heads bent upward, looking for clues amidst the new population of vinyl.

A week later, the corporate team arrives, sees the mob of airborne signage, and declares the "darn signs" a best practice because they are identical in look and feel to the signage the corporate team saw in the showcase/best practice plant they toured last month.

So much more is possible.

Bribe. At the moment I have nothing to contribute to this sorry situation except my complaints—and a bribe. Will you help find a better way—a way in which departmental addresses can make a genuine visual contribution to the operational excellence of the company?

If you develop one—a practical and functional visual approach to departmental addresses in large spaces, send it to me with an explanation. And if I agree that it works and moves the thinking along, I will present my one-day visual workplace/visual thinking seminar at your company for expenses only, as my schedule permits. And I won't restrict this to one satisfactory approach—or the first one. Send them all.

I am happy to recognize multiple approaches from different companies. This is untested ground. I'll keep this offer open through this book's first printing. I'll bet we'll have an array of splendid approaches by the time we get to the second print run.

c. *Homemade Address vs. Commercial Address.* While I realize departmental addresses for large companies are usually made by an outside contractor, I favor homemade addresses when volume is not a factor; Photo Series 8.54 provides an assortment.

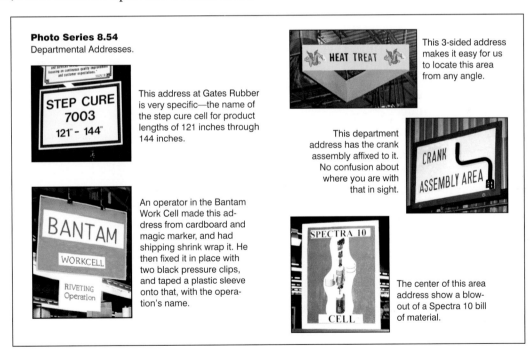

Photo Series 8.54
Departmental Addresses.

STEP CURE
7003
121" - 144"

This address at Gates Rubber is very specific—the name of the step cure cell for product lengths of 121 inches through 144 inches.

BANTAM
WORKCELL
RIVETING
Operation

An operator in the Bantam Work Cell made this address from cardboard and magic marker, and had shipping shrink wrap it. He then fixed it in place with two black pressure clips, and taped a plastic sleeve onto that, with the operation's name.

HEAT TREAT

This 3-sided address makes it easy for us to locate this area from any angle.

This department address has the crank assembly affixed to it. No confusion about where you are with that in sight.

CRANK ASSEMBLY AREA

SPECTRA 10
CELL

The center of this area address show a blowout of a Spectra 10 bill of material.

Museum Quality Addresses at Fleet. Fleet Engineers (Michigan) had two goals in mind when it decided to go visual: 1) reduce the mountains of waste that were choking the company at that time, and 2) awaken the workforce to a greater sense of ownership and accountability. The surprise came by just how much and how quickly both goals were met.

Business-wise, for example, materials handling was reduced by 70% within the first year, quality improved by over 50%, and overall manufacturing lead time shrank by a third (and the facility was still four years away from tackling lean). Employee-wise, operators didn't just take ownership; they got ignited, even about something as ordinary as meeting the new requirement that each department prominently display its address. Photo Series 8.55 shows you two superb contributions. Who knew such talent existed?

Photo Series 8.55 Museum Quality area addresses.

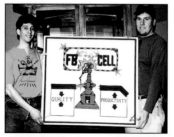

Jeff Hamm and Gary White wanted the departmental address they created for the FB-27 Cell to communicate the team's commitment to quality and productivity.

The FB-27 address hung high over the welding booth for everyone to see and admire (red arrow).

The area address for Fleet's Cut-Off Department featured a green cutting machine and a superhero competing for supremacy. Robert Oldaker (inset), the artist, titled his work, *Man against Machine.*

---

5. Material Handling Addresses. Wikipedia defines material handling as:

The movement, storage, control, and protection of materials, goods, and products throughout the process of manufacturing, distribution, consumption and disposal. The focus is on the methods, mechanical equipment, systems and related controls used to achieve these functions.

Let's see how visuality makes a powerful contribution through addresses for this core function in (Photo Series 8.56) below.

a. Variable (Temporary) Addresses. A temporary address is home to items that are variable; they can change in type and/or quantity. Because of this, the address mechanism has to be flexible but also complete, accurate, precise, and readable. Here are five good examples.

Address Solution 1. The excellent example on the left (Photo 1 of Series 8.56) is a standing sign for components in short-term storage. As soon as the pallet is moved, the standing sign is removed—unless or until a pallet of the exact same part number occupies that floor space again.

Detail. Notice the three handles that amplify the address: a) exact part number; b) common name, and c) a photo of the part itself. the potential motion of mix-ups is minimized.

Address Solution 2. In Photo 2, you see a different type of temporary standing sign—this one provides the temperature and duration for a batch of units already in the oven for an epoxy cure cycle. This address (that's what it is, strictly speaking) represents a temporary location for that material—and we have only one place to look for accurate timely information: this standing sign near Oven 2.

The information on the white sheet of paper changes from shift to shift. Why not laminate it, then wipe it clean for new use? Notice the mix of bold/non-bold letters and upper/lower case. In this case, the mix forces us to read each word to get the meaning—a smart idea in this venue.

Address Solution 3. Here's another address challenge, solved through a temporary address. Freudenberg-NOK manufactures a wide range of elastomeric seals and custom-molded products, with over 30 sites worldwide. That translates into a large variety of dies (tooling) at each site. The Georgia facility tackled the challenge of dies complexity by developing this flexible storage system, built on two key visual principles: temporary address and point-of-use.

The aim was to make sure only the dies for a given week of work were brought to the production floor. The solution hinged on two factors.

First, the dies rack had to be large enough to hold a week's worth of dies—but small enough to prevent unneeded dies from accumulating. Once the right-sized rack was chosen (Photo 3a), it was moved closer to the production floor (point-of-use) and the machines it served. (The dies not in weekly use were stored nearby but out of the main value field.)

Second, the approach needed to be flexible but accurate and complete; magnetic addresses were the solution. A magnetic tag was made for each die in the inventory and stored at the end of the dies rack in a type of physical table of contents (Photo 3b—a great example of *use the existing architecture.*)

Yes, we'd love to see these black-on-white addresses upgraded to black-on-yellow—but this is still an excellent example of the permanent power of temporary addresses!

Address Solution 4. Innovation—the use of our imagination in the workplace—is sometimes our only chance at developing a solution to unusual operational challenges, at Fleet Engineers for example.

We already know the Fleet team is a wildly creative group. Here's what they did when faced with sheets of steel with specs so similar, they were nearly impossible to tell apart without special instruments and a lot of time. As a result, material handlers would "eyeball" the sheets, make a best guess—and often be wrong. What to do?

Only a highly-specific address for each steel type would work. But where to post it? People experimented and finally hit upon using the hollow supports in the rack structure itself (Photo 4). They made blocks of wood to fit the slots (see red arrow), marked part numbers on them, and inserted and removed them as needed. Challenge met!

Address Solution 5. Our final example of a temporary address solution is one of the most innovative I've seen, brought to us by those brilliant operators at Denison Hydraulics (Ohio). As you will see, their visual answer reflects many address principles discussed in this section and previously.

The challenge is familiar: a high variety of parts (this time on pallets) that move in and out of the same physical area—in this case the Test Cell—all needing to be found quickly, accurately, and easily. Each pallet (Photo 8.56) holds an array of part numbers, with new pallets replacing the previous as testing is completed. The upshot: There was no way to post specific addresses on those beautiful yellow borders.

Photo 8.56 Test Pallet: *Before.*

Photo 8.57 Yellow Temporary Addresses: *After.*

Knowing this, the Denison Test team created a set of yellow laminated cards with all current part numbers on them and stored them in a nearby bin. When a pallet is delivered, the material handler matches the part numbers on the move order to the correct yellow card and places that card on the part (Photo 8.57). Presto Change-o! Highly accurate temporary addresses and exceptional material handling.

Please note that because these cards are lightweight and not anchored down, drafts could scatter them (Detail). Can you think of some further innovations to deal with this issue?

Detail Close-up: *After.*

Warehouse Addresses

Despite our best efforts, thirty years after JIT/Lean arrived in the West, most companies still have not achieved one-piece flow or its material corollary, zero inventories (not more than three hours of WIP). To the contrary, many companies are still packed to the rafters with stock. The following address solutions can help, whether you fit the above profile or are simply a distribution center, like the ones in the examples below, responsible for processing large quantities of just about everything.

Such centers have acquired a sophisticated understanding of the challenges associated with large inventories and have solved them in ways that I hope you find instructive for your own purposes. We begin with a widely-seen address modality: the airborne address.

Airborne Address: Basic. An airborne address is simply one that hangs from the ceiling—those yellow and black placards above the rows in Photo 8.58 (see red arrow). Here we again have generic number addresses ("9," "10," "11") that support the continuous loading of the stock in temporary residence between each person-width border. These addresses are easy for lift drivers to see at a distance.

>   *Question.* What is the readability problem with these airborne addresses as you see it here?

>   *Answer.* Blocked by mounds of inventory, we cannot see the airborne addresses without craning or stepping away from the rows.

>   *Solution.* Add floor addresses at both ends of each row (Photo 8.59; see red arrow).

Photo 8.58 Airborne.

Photo 8.59 Redundant floor addresses.

Airborne Addresses: Advanced. Make no mistake, warehouses and distribution centers have special needs—vast expanses of concrete, stories of racks, and a roof that is far far away. And beneath it, motion potential that ranges from suffering to near insanity. For most companies, the silver bullet is not SAP, TecSys or any other asset management software system—though a nifty RFID mechanism could lend a welcome and powerful assist in the pick-and-put process (if you can afford it). Why not, instead, decipher the operational logic of these systems and simply imbed that logic, visually, in your own warehouse?

We travel to one of the world's great automotive suppliers, Delphi, for a set of first-rate visual applications. I have been to dozens of Delphi plants, some when the corporation was still Packard Electric. All the sites are visual show stoppers, having been schooled by Sumitomo Electric in the 1980s. The Delphi Group continues to grow in its use of visuality. Let's follow Delphi's thinking.

First, in the photo sequence that begins with Photo 8.60, we see large (visible at 30 yards) airborne addresses: 01 and 02, the first of many rows. The blank space below these two numbers is a plastic pocket for more details. This is visible in Photo 8.61: Row 03.

Look at that hanging placard address. See how the same product shares two rows of finished goods. Look closer and you will see the double arrows, under "03;" each of them points to a separate row. The sheet below the "03" is a list of the 12 plants on the delivery route, the telling detail that will help us do a better job.

Photo 8.60 Lane addresses visible at 30 feet.

Photo 8.61 The list of plants on the delivery route is inserted in the plastic pocket.

PLANT 61- ZACATECAS	PLANT 86 - LINAPES
PLANT 62 - FRESNILLO I	PLANT 87 - ANAHUAC
PLANT 63 - FRESNILLO II	FLT 91/92 - VICTORIA I/II
PLANT 81 - N LAREDO I	PLANT 96 - GUADALUPE
PLANT 82 - N LAREDO I	PLANT 97 - CENTEC II
PLANT 84 - GUADALUPE	PLANT 98 - CENTEC

Detail.

Let's go to the tall shelves and locate, first, the home for the 5700s (Photo 8.62). Photo 8.63 shows the "5900 Mochis" in a low-cost flexible format—paper in a plastic sleeve. The row address (Photo 8.64) is an ever-splendid 3D tab. But look how it is constructed—not of costly metal, fabricated by an outside suppler but laminated paper, printed by you. Low cost, hands-on, flexible, and highly readable.

Photo 8.63 Simple plastic sleeve plus tape.

Photo 8.62 Two rows of part number 5700.

Photo 8.64 3D tabs you can make yourself.

Take a look at Photo Cluster 8.65. It shows how you can go to Rack Row 60 and find a handy *Table of Barcode Contents*. Travel further and see more detail—a vivid demonstration of driver-license address: the closer you get, the more information you get.

The point in showing this RFID barcode rack system is not to persuade you to buy one. If your company has the money and time to convert to RFID, it probably has already done so—or is in the process. The point in sharing this is so you can study the components of this sophisticated address system conceptually—the ideas, the elements—and select what will help make your current approach more visual and therefore more useful.

Look again at the Photo Cluster and notice the low-cost way in which the 3D tabs are created: just paper, laminated to give the material enough heft to make it into a 3D tab—then mounted on a strut. You may not be able to purchase the kit for this—but you sure can afford the idea. Put your home-made version in place with masking or duct tape. This becomes your pilot—your small beginning. All beginnings are small. That is the nature of starting anything. Beginnings are also powerful because they represent the new. They are the horizon and you must seek it.

Photo Cluster 8.65 RFID Elements. (How many can you adapt for your warehouse?)

ID Labels

Now the final element of the visual where: ID labels (red circle, Photo 8.66). Once a location is claimed by a border and address, put an ID label on the item that lives there. When you do, you make the match between the three elements of Automatic Recoil: Border + Home Address + ID Label.

ID labels are how items find their way back home if they wander off, go for a "walk" or just get lost. The location information you build into the visual where for these items is functioning. And the lack of an ID label on any tool could mean that tool may well "belong" to someone else by the morning. Similar to a soldier's dog tag, an ID label moves with the item—because it is on it! Look at the following three examples.

Photo 8.66 The final element of the visual where: ID label.

Photo Series 8.67 ID Label Opportunities.

This design-to-task system does such a great job controlling tool placement that we may not notice it lacks the ID label level—probably because the boxes are made by a vendor. Add ID labels and complete the visual where.

The Ultramarks area collects paperwork in this bin, carries it to the front office at the end of each shift for processing, and waits for the bin's return, empty, all thanks to the ID label on the bin itself.

This hand truck reflects the simple formula for the visual where: border, address, and ID label on the thing itself.

Time to clear up one small point: My "hard-and-fast rule" about the visual where for everything that casts a shadow loosens a bit related to ID labels. Why? Because you cannot put ID labels on consumables—the stacks of packing cardboard, those brackets, this bubble wrap, those commodity parts.

While you should (and will) put an ID label on the red bin on your bench that holds your wood screws, you will not—and cannot—apply ID labels to the screws themselves. In much the same way, I can ID label my coffee cup ("Gwenie's Cup") but not the coffee that's in it. But you already know that.

Addresses and ID Labels: Next Steps. Review what you just learned about addresses and ID labels and how your thinking has grown in ways to make your area safe and more operationally effective. Then, working alone or with a buddy, make a list of opportunities for them and update your visual workplace hit list (Figure 8.4), posting *all* your improvement ideas, even if you don't plan to tackle them yourself.

Figure 8.4

The Visual Where

We have completed our journey through the basics of the visual where—two chapters and over 150 examples in action. You have probably already begun to apply this powerful visual combination to your own work area and seen struggles lessen and work begin to make much more sense.

In the next chapter (9), you learn about visual mini systems and ways to drill these basic principles deeper into the information deficits of day-to-day work. Then in Chapter 10 (*Four Power Levels*), you learn how to make your visual solutions more and more powerful. This is when visuality becomes more of a language than an application—and you become masterful in that application.

Photo 8.68 Joyce Clark, ace visual thinker.

Before we do that, let me introduce you to Joyce Clark, a member of the Shipping Team at Seton Name Plate in Branford, Connecticut (Photo 8.68). Joyce took to visuality like a duck to water. For her, the visual workplace—beginning with the visual where—was the long-hoped for answer to the everyday struggles that spirited employees like Joyce find so discouraging. She, like many of you, came to work to make a contribution. And like you, she wanted her day to make more sense. Here are some of her words:

I worked out back at Seton Name Plate in the stacks, picking products that needed to be shipped. Those stacks used to feel like a gigantic maze. And I used to feel like the mouse traveling through it. I could never get to what I was looking for. It aggravated me. I felt like I was wasting my time.

Now that I put the visual where in place, I go to where I need to go, get my product, and come right back. That's the first thing that's great about visuality—I'm saving my time.

Everything is in its place. Everything is sorted. I cleared wasted space in my area that I use now to get my packages shipped. And because it is so organized and neat, my returns dropped from nearly ten a week to nearly zero!

My mistakes are down drastically. My returns—whether a mis-pick or wrong quantity or the order got the wrong label—are totally almost non-existent now. I got an award for it too. I had eight weeks straight without a return. No one has touched my record yet. I say it is because of the visual workplace. Because prior to that, I had my mistakes!

As you might guess, not everyone as Seton was quite as enthusiastic as Joyce about workplace visuality and would tease her about it. When they gave her the title of *Queen of Visual Order,* Joyce responded—visually, of course.

You can see her reply in Photo 8.69. I call it *ID Label Mania.* She called it *Joyce's Revenge.*

Photo 8.69 ID Label Mania: Joyce's Revenge.

People don't come to Toyota to work. They come to think.

Taiichi Ohno

Driving Visuality Deeper

Now that your area has a strong base of the visual where, many of the grosser forms of motion have begun to disappear and, with them, many of your day-to-day struggles. It is time for you to drill deeper into information deficits and invent visual devices that address them more completely.

In this final section of *Work That Makes Sense*, you learn to create *Visual Mini-Systems* for carts, benches, shelves, corners, and other narrowly-focused spots—inspired by the master visual thinkers introduced in these pages. Travel yet deeper into motion and you learn to satisfy the unanswered (and sometimes *unasked*) questions of your customers through your own need-to-share. You learn about *Customer-Driven Visuality*,

Then you are ready to make your devices more effective as you learn about the four power levels of visuality. From visual indicators to visual signals to visual controls, and culminating in *poka-yoke*/visual guarantees, these power categories can spark round after round of new visual thinking. Suddenly, the vital details of your work become increasingly transparent, inventive, and precise. More and more daily struggles dissolve.

In this book's final chapter, we come to appreciate visuality as a natural and inborn way of sharing vital information and connecting with others. Recognized as a birthright, your visual journey takes on new meaning. Visuality aligns you in right relationship with your company and with the contribution you make to it daily—your work. Finally work makes sense.

Chapter | Nine

Visual Mini-Systems & Customer-Driven Visuality

To this point, you have learned a great deal about implementing the visual where. Now we are going to drill deeper—deeper into eliminating motion and the information deficits that trigger it through visual mini-systems and customer-driven visuality. We begin with mini-systems.

Visual Mini-Systems: Major Motion Busters

Visual mini-systems (mini-system for short) are a major way to deepen and extend visual information sharing in your area. Here is our definition:

A visual mini-system is a cluster of visual devices that work together to promote a single performance outcome.

Look again at some of the community and workplace solutions you have already seen in this book (Photo Series 9.1, next page). They are *all* mini-systems—groups of visual devices that work together to make sure specific work outcomes happen.

In the workplace, a mini-system can be as simple as a visually-defined tool cabinet—or a single shelf in it. It can be a drawer or the entire desk. It can be one side of the machine that you have visually organized around small tools, lubricants, and fixtures. Or you can make a visual system out of the entire machining center.

The point is, a mini-system has a tight focus; its visual components share a purpose. They are located together and made visual for a reason: to create a specific outcome—to fulfill a fixed purpose.

Photo Series 9.1 Each mini-system supports a specific outcome.

The paperwork gets done on time.   The plane can now load/unload quickly.   Gas for money, fast.   Consumables are handy.

I get to find the special tool I need even if someone else has it.   Parts and tools for this assembly.   All my tools are at-a-glance—and I know the ones I'm missing.   What I need to wire an 80-foot trailer chassis.

Consider the neighborhood school bus—packed with visual devices, all aimed at the single outcome of keeping our kids safe (Photo Series 9.2, next page).

When Mini-Systems Begin

Start to apply mini-systems in your area after the visual where starts to take root. By then, you understand the basic visual vocabulary, know that details matter, and see the benefits of your visual efforts beginning to grow.

This does not mean your area has completed its basic visual transformation. It means that you and others have learned and are continually applying core visual concepts—smart placement principles, slanted borders, driver-license level addresses, color coding, and so on. It also means you have begun to operationalize your need-to-know (getting control of your corner of the world) and to recognize your need-to-share (helping others). As a result, a growing number of visual devices populate your area—and they are I-driven. They come from you and other visual thinkers.

Motion is on the decline. Work (value-adding activity) is on the increase. And information deficits have begun to evaporate. You and your colleagues have experienced, first hand, the early benefits of visual information sharing.

By the time visual mini-systems become the focus, your managers have completed the behind-the-scenes procedures supporting your efforts. For example, you know that: improvement supply carts will be regularly stocked; a process for releasing improvement time is in place; maintenance has set up a special work order system for visual inventions; and visual blitzes are becoming a regular part of your area's improvement schedule. The visual conversion is gaining momentum (see *Leadership Task 16*).

But that doesn't mean you have to wait until those things are in place to launch mini-systems. They are such a natural extension of visual logic, you may have created several early on, by coincidence. Now you are ready to implement mini-systems *by design*—to drill into the deeper levels of motion and hidden layers of information deficits, intentionally.

The phrase that applies here is: *one-foot square/one-mile deep.* When you invent mini-systems, you take the principles of the visual where to a highly detailed degree. This may take a bit of a special effort. As you have been often asked, you have to develop the ability to see what is *not* there. You have to see the motion—and the habit of motion—before you can address the information deficits that triggered it.

Take the story of John Pacheco (Photo 9.3, next page), visual workplace impresario and veteran machinist in the Model Shop at United Electric Controls (UE) (Massachusetts). We saw John's cut-saw bench in Chapter 3 and his pull-out paperwork shelf in Chapter 6. As you are about to read, John began his visual journey quite modestly—and grew from there. He generated dozens of visual mini-systems in the five years we worked together and many more since.

Photo Series 9.2 School Bus Safety Mini-System.

Have you ever counted the visual devices on a school bus? (1) Bus lights are on all four sides that flash as the bus is stopping, plus the Stop Sign arm extends. (2) A cow-catcher swing arm in the front activates at unloading to prevent kids from walking out of the driver's line of sight. (3) Cantilevered left and right mirrors on the bus hood are double insurance that small children will be seen if they walk in front of the bus. (4) An array of vital information is shared on the back of the bus. (5) The shade of yellow used for school buses is reserved by US law. All this makes the bus mini-system a maxi-system.

Leadership Task 16: Pay Attention to Beginnings

When you as a supervisor or manager go deeper into your own understanding of visuality—and the visual thinkers who report to you begin to create visual solutions—pay close attention.

It is now that the conversion is in its most delicate state because a single disparaging remark can undo the work of weeks or months. Every contribution, however humble, has a huge value at this point. That value is said this way: *It is a beginning.* And all beginnings are to be celebrated. They mark a break from the past and the promise of a tomorrow whose horizon is only partly understood.

Managers and supervisors, when you see that beginning, however small, make much of it. Give congratulations and take photos. Once ignited, people have such willingness to contribute. Though they may not yet have the skill to create a trackable bottom-line benefit, you still must recognize these early efforts. You must project the tangible benefits that small early steps can produce as the momentum gathers. Pay attention. Notice the good and give praise. The success of your improvement initiative depends on that, along with the growth of the enterprise.

The Visual Inventiveness of John Pacheco

Like so many people, John was first skeptical about visuality. He did not see how it would help him. Then he decided to give it a try and liked what he got.

Photo 9.3 John Pacheco, visual impresario.

Part of John's early success was due to the wisdom of UE managers to recognize and appreciate his small efforts. For example, John's very first visual device was a border for his coffee cup. You can see it on the upper right of Photo 9.4 (yellow arrow). That photo also captures John's first mini-system—a visual home for stainless steel scrap and his water basket. If you look closely at that basket, you'll see a series of six white ID labels that say "Water, Water, Water, Water, Water, Water." John was reaching.

He wanted to do more but had run out of ideas. So he asked his supervisor, Paul Plant, for suggestions (Photo 9.5). As the story goes, Paul mentioned the trouble the area had in getting visitors to wear safety glasses. Could John figure out a way to handle that?

The first thing John noticed was that the existing sign—"Wear Your Safety Glasses"—hung from the ceiling, 15 feet up (Photo 9.6). "Who looks up at the ceiling when they walk in?" John observed.

After more thinking and a scan through the Seton Name Plate catalogue, John came up with the fabulous visual mini-system in Photos 9.7 and 9.8. This mini-system stopped you in your tracks and practically put the glasses on your nose! It provided safety glasses at the exact point-of-use. No searching. No excuses. No motion.

And, on your way out, the back of the Stop sign tells you what to do next: Return the glasses to the same box you took them from. John's system is self-explaining so we can be self-regulating. I make sure to stop at UE whenever I go to Boston to see the latest of John's remarkable and (so far) never-ending visual inventions.

Photo 9.4 John's very first mini-system.

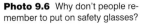

Photo 9.6 Why don't people remember to put on safety glasses?

Photo 9.5 Paul Plant.

Photo 9.7 Stop! Put them on right now.

Photo 9.8 Please return them as you leave.

Mini-Systems Opportunities

As you saw with John Pacheco, mini-systems have a narrow focus that often calls on you to drill deep. Because of this drilling action, you may need several hours over several days (or weeks) to complete one. This is part of the pleasure of creating a mini-system. You build the pieces gradually, gaining insight over time into what will make this system function better and better. As with all things discussed in this book, you are looking for a balance point between structure and creativity, between methodology and invention—even flights of fancy.

By methodology, I do not mean I want you to get *complicated*. No, I want you to get *systematic*—to do things step-by-step-by-step. When we create something systematically, the steps are in order because that order matters. Think of the steps in a cake recipe, an engine overhaul, or building a cabinet from scratch. In all these cases, the order of the steps matters. So it is when you build a mini-system.

Watch Your Steps

When you begin a mini-system, follow the same visual conversion protocol (recipe) we have been using. The steps are identical. Only your focus has shifted—to that drawer, that shelf, that cart or to some narrow purpose (such as: *Get people to wear safety glasses*). Here are the steps.

First do your prep:

> Tour your area and identify mini-system opportunities. Add these to your Visual Workplace Hit List. Pick the one you want to do first. Fill in your name (and a buddy, if you wish), along with your start and target dates. (Remember to divide complex mini-systems into smaller steps that you post and track separately.) Gather your supplies.

Now follow these steps:

1. Clear out the clutter. Make the spot clean and safe.
2. Think through and apply the principles of smart placement.
3. Implement the visual where for your mini-system. Be inventive.
4. Test out your mini-system through observation and use. Proof it.
5. Drill deeper: Identify the details and make them visual as well. (Look for hidden forms of motion and buried information deficits; address these.)

Follow this procedure (this protocol) and you will create scorching good visual mini-systems.

Mini-systems are meant to be satisfying. So plan to build them gradually over time. That's the point. Creating a mini-system should not overwhelm you. Keep a tight focus and simply keep going until the system achieves a high and detailed level of visual performance functionality.

Finding Mini-System Opportunities

Let's go on the hunt for mini-systems candidates. They are everywhere—in every cabinet, drawer, bench top and lower shelf, cart, tool box, and corner. The focus is tight and the need is evident. They are your *Befores*.

Mini-system opportunities are everywhere. Look at Photo Series 9.9 on the next page. (I've put a red box around several—but not all—mini-system candidates.)

Photo Series 9.9 Mini-System Opportunities are Everywhere!

This maintenance department is covered with small and large tools. It'll take several visual mini-systems to pull these pieces together.

This isn't just a mess. It hides several important functions that only a smart visual mini-system can reveal.

This HR office is a universe of mini-systems. Create them and you'll achieve a well-functioning department.

Grab 15 minutes of improvement time on Monday and Wednesday, and some more on Friday and you will make tremendous progress.

Offices offer so many mini-system opportunities because of the many individual business functions. The red boxes indicate just some of them—and notice the bulletin board is included.

We will go to Fort Worth, Texas to see an example of a mini-system that drills deeper in the visual where, one of the many invented by master visual thinker, Margie Herrera.

The Visual Inventiveness of Margie Herrera (I)

Margie Herrera is a long-time employee at Lockheed Martin Aerospace (LM-Aero) and a visual thinker of the first order (Photo 9.10). A material handler, Margie is in charge of stocking parts and materials for the Tube Shop (a tube fabrication and assembly area).

Photo 9.10 Margie Herrera, visual wizard.

When LM-Aero started to roll out visuality in operations, Margie was among the first to create powerful mini-systems. Here is the first of the two mini-systems we will discuss in this chapter that Margie created.

Margie's Tube ID Tape Mini-System

Tube identification tape (tube ID tape) is used in aerospace fabrication to indicate characteristics of each type of tube: part number, direction of flow, function (hydraulics, pneumatics, fuel or air), etc. The color coding is also critical; for example, blue/yellow striped tape is used for hydraulics. This information is vital to the work of field personnel, responsible for quick and precise repairs.

Tube ID tape also has a shelf-life limit: between 12 and 24 months. Towards the end of a tape's shelf life, its adhesive backing can lose surface stickiness, begin to ooze out the sides, and cause the entire roll to get glued shut. That's one reason tapes reaching their shelf limit need to be removed—another part of Margie's job.

Margie had to police all the tape—boxes and boxes of them on seven tall blue racks. You can see those racks on the left in Photo 9.11—stuffed with boxes of overstocked, out-of-date or nearly empty tube ID tape. Despite Margie's determined efforts, an out-of-date roll of tape sometimes reached an assembler. Margie and her supervisor knew why: There were just too many boxes of tape. When Margie decided to tackle this problem, she began there.

Photo 9.11 Helen Cherry and too many boxes.

With help from production control staff, Helen Cherry, and perishable materials engineer, Marty Harnish, Margie removed 130 boxes of tape (Photos 9.11 and 9.12). That's when Margie realized that she not only did not need all seven tall racks, she needed none of them. Instead, she set up a kanban pull mini-system that keeps her active inventory to a manageable minimum (two tapes per product code), ensures fresh tape, and makes certain no assembler ever runs out.

Photo 9.12 Marty Harnish with out-of-date tape.

Margie's new system was housed in a large blue tool cabinet, with partitioned drawers shallow enough to accommodate only two tape rolls per compartment, and enough drawers to store all her part numbers (Photo 9.13). With two rolls of tape per compartment, a second one is always ready for the next assembler if the first roll is in use or consumed.

Photo 9.13 Blue cabinet with "Need-to-Order" and "Already Ordered" cards.

Margie checks the cabinet daily, scanning the barcode card she has placed in each compartment so she has exact information handy, at the point-of-use, when more tape needs to be ordered.

Margie made the assemblers part of her mini-system as well. Look at the two plastic holders on the top of the blue cabinet. The first contains a set of laminated cards that read "Need to Order." They are for assemblers, such as Dorita (Photo 9.14), to place in a compartment when they pull the first roll; this alerts Margie to replenish the tape in case she missed it.

The second plastic holder contains cards that read "Already Ordered." Margie, in her turn, uses these, swapping it with the Need-to-Order card so the assemblers know that Margie got the message. The communication loop is visually complete. Both customer (Dorita) and supplier (Margie) know what each other knows. The partnership remains strong.

Photo 9.14 Margie's customer, Dorita, continues her work.

Margie's Tube ID Tape mini-system, brilliant in its visual detail, remained a LM-Aero Visual Best Practice until the industry developed print-on-demand technology that requires bare tape only, or tape that is pre-color-coded.

But for the purposes of this book, Margie has provided us with an excellent example of *making a system out of the visual where*—exactly what you and your colleagues will now focus on. And once you do, you will move that much closer to exchanging red dots on your area's laminated map for yellow ones. Remember?

The Laminated Map: Tracking Your Progress

The laminated map is a tool you learned about in Chapter 3. It is used to track the progress of visual improvement in your area. A report card of sorts, this map can be very valuable in driving visuality—*systematically*—through your department. If you are already using it, please continue. If you have not yet adopted it, I urge you to set one up now. Here's a refresher on how.

You and your colleagues begin by dividing a paper map of your department (laminated) into logical sub-sections. You put a blue dot in each sub-area (blue means: *We're not going to improve this area, yet.*). Then you exchange a red dot for blue when you began to improve an area visually. The red dot means: *We've started but there's a long way to go.*

Going to Yellow

That *red dot* is replaced by a *yellow dot* when you have installed the visual where thoroughly in a given sub-section. Another word for the visual where is *automatic recoil*. Both terms mean that there is a border, address, and (if possible) an ID label for everything that casts a shadow.

Your march to yellow gets even more focused when you undertake mini-systems. As discussed, mini-systems are about going deeper; and that is exactly what it takes for an area to *go to yellow*. You and your colleagues have to keep drilling in the details of your information deficits.

Since the specific rules for yellow are built directly into this map, there will never be any doubt when a sub-area gets to yellow—or needs further work. Set aside the audits, radar charts, and 5-point checklists. Your

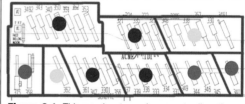

Figure 9.1 This map has two sub-areas at yellow, three *just started* at red, and three *not yet touched* at blue.

laminated map provides all that and more, with the added bonus that the standard—"everything that casts a shadow"—is both I-driven and *not* subjective.

So that is how to use the laminated map on your way to yellow. We will talk about *going to green* in a few pages and present a second mini-system that Margie Herrera invented to illustrate that. In the meantime, let's look at a common worry about mini-systems, common areas, and the people that share them.

Common Areas

Here's the worry:

> *What do I do when I want to improve an area that I share with my co-workers? What if they don't like my changes? What if they don't want me to change a thing? Or what if they change everything back after I changed everything forward? I'm liable to get pretty upset. It's happened to me before.*

And to that I say: This is a good worry to have. The fact that you have it means you are already in the process of making your area visual and want to go further. Terrific.

My response to this worry has several layers. The top layer is this: The problem of how to handle improving shared or common areas is not exactly yours. It belongs to your supervisor or boss. Why? Because to get solved, this issue needs re-framing and a structure—two things that only someone in authority (a boss) is position to create. In other words, unless you work in a self-directed team, you do not have the clout. Nor should you want it.

One of the things that makes your day-to-day interactions with colleagues workable is the fact that you are both—in your eyes and in the eyes of your employer—equal. Neither of you has more power than the other. You are peers. That balance is instantly upset if one of you suddenly acquires greater authority—the authority, for example, to resolve the above worry. Let your boss do that. It's her job.

And one way for her to resolve this issue and still get tremendous improvement mileage is to call for a *Prototype Mini-System*.

Prototype Mini-Systems

Here is a statement of the problem again: A person or group wants to improve something in a shared area while a second person or group does not want anything improved ("changed") or has a largely different idea of what "improved" means.

As I map out my approach, bear in mind that I am talking to your boss. You are eavesdropping—with our mutual consent of course.

The key to my solution is to set up what I call a "prototype" or pilot approach. The dictionary definition runs something like this: *A prototype is a representative or experimental model used as part of the design process to provide the designers (associates) a chance to explore design possibilities and confirm performance prior to launch.* In other words, you keep going until the darn thing works.

The process of building a prototype looks like this: design, test, evaluate, and then modify the design based on what you learn. Do this repeatedly—cycle after cycle, again and again; keep resolving issues until you get it right. (I could have just said: *to prototype means to pilot your idea*—but I like words, as I am sure you have noticed by now.)

The following process is based on an experience at a Seton Name Plate.

1. The company's shipping department is in the midst of a visual conversion. As in most shipping areas, nearly everything is a shared resource—eight packing stations, tons of materials, five pallet jacks, and, of course, the rows upon rows of racks. Most of the fifteen associates in shipping have waited a long time for the chance to improve the area—but not all of them.

2. Step-by-step, associates cleared out clutter, and made the area clean and safe. They moved on to smart placement which went surprisingly well as did the visual where for the floor—borders, addresses, and ID labels. But mini-systems got stalled. People had lots of ideas. Some were brilliant; others promising; still others seemed unworkable or vague. With some people clamoring to move ahead and others worried, emotions ran high. What to do?

3. As shipping supervisor (remember, reader, I am talking to your boss), you want to head off any chance of a skirmish and keep the focus on improvement. But you also don't want to squelch

people's ideas or homogenize everything into plain vanilla. You want *Cherry Garcia*—visual inventiveness. To get it, you decide to follow the prototype process described here.

4. First, you gather the group and tell them that the next focus for visual improvement is the eight shipping stations. Then you ask people to team up with a buddy or two (not more than two). You have each team pull a number out of a baseball cap—a number matching one of the shipping stations. Next you lay down a challenge:

   Over the next three weeks, I will release three hours of improvement time per team for you to use in visually transforming the shipping station you picked.

   I want you to start systematically. You know what that means: clear out the clutter, clean what's left and make it safe. Then get visual. You and your team get to decide what that means: what smart placement principles to apply, how to capture the visual where, and how to go deeper. You get to pour all your visual creativity into the shipping station you selected. Make it as visual as you wish. Go as far as you can go. Make it dazzling.

   Everyone still uses all the stations during regular work—but no one else gets to improve your station. Just you. I'll take photos every Monday and Friday. (Most of you noticed the white-dot shot spot this morning.) Also keep your eyes peeled for other people's cool ideas. But remember last week's quote: "Steal shamelessly. Just remember to say thanks!"

   Also, I nabbed two extra carts from Maintenance so you won't have to fight over supplies anymore. Maintenance also gave our area an extra two hours per week for visual improvement work orders, on top of the two we already have.

   At the end of three weeks (that's May 3), we'll check out all eight stations and see if we can develop a prototype shipping station—taking the best from all of them. Or we may decide to not make them the same. And yes, I know, it'll my turn to bring the Cherry Garcia.

5. Implement the above. And don't forget to get those extra supply carts and additional help from Maintenance so logistics don't sidetrack the process. Let the inventiveness run for three weeks—or longer if you know more time is needed or the ideas need to go further.

6. Then do as you said: Let everyone check out the visual thinking across all the stations, with an eye towards consolidating around best practices and making the station reach some level of uniformity. Just be prepared if the group balks at the notion of making the stations look the same. If so, try to edge towards some consolidation of best operational practices.

Use the *Four People Process Tools* you learned in Chapter 4 as needed. Don't push this phase of the process. You may have to go with eight different shipping station for awhile—as long as they are all performance functional. Later you can seek to nudge the thinking toward combining the more robust solutions across all stations. Handle this process effectively and you will have a better bottom line as well as a much stronger, more open, attentive, and inventive team.

Photo Cluster 9.15 shows you some of the results of this process at Seton Name Plate (Connecticut) in the 1990s. (Excuse the blurry photos. Back then cameras weren't what they are today.)

> *Note:* Adapt the prototype approach for other visual improvement targets. For example, if your group stalls in converting a machining center, divvy up the machines, letting each team tackle one. In the case of one machine, have one team tackle the incoming material and tools; another the outgoing material, and a third the machine itself.

Photo Cluster 9.15 The Prototype Process: Shipping Stations at Seton Name Plate.

Shipping Station

◀Before

After▶
▼

The Visual Inventiveness of Margie Herrera (II)

Now let's look again at the visual wizardry of Margie Herrara and the another mini-system she invented. Doing so will lead us to the second key principle of going deeper: customer-driven visuality.

Margie's PLS Mini-System

Margie created this next visual mini-system to solve a challenge her customers faced with commodity parts—called *Production Line Stock* (PLS) at LM-Aero. PLS covers a wide range of components that varies from shop to shop. In one shop, PLS refers to fittings, caps, and covers. In another, it means nuts, bolts, screws, and the like. Many such parts were look-alikes, differing only in minute attributes—thread depth, spring-compression ratio, etc.

Photo 9.16 The Working Side.

In the Tube Shop, PLS were stocked in small blue bins on double-sided, rolling carts that Margie kept stocked for several linked sub-areas.

When visuality came to LM-Aero, each area laid down a visual foundation of borders and addresses. Working from that base, Margie turned to mini-systems to drill into the details of her PLS approach.

First, she assigned an address to each side of the cart—the *Working Side* (Photo 9.16) where assemblers (her customers) pull parts. The other was the *Stocking Side* (Photo 9.17), what Margie kept replenished.

Margie scanned the barcode address on each blue bin for ordering. When a bin ran out on the Working Side, the operator walked around to the Stocking Side and swapped the empty bin for a full one. This is classic 2-bin kanban.

But, as Margie noticed, this didn't always happen smoothly. There were times when an operator found an empty bin on the Working Side and, when she went around to the Stocking Side to retrieve a full one, got stalled. Margie would see the operator reach for a bin and then just stand there. It didn't take long for Margie to realize that the person was trying to figure out which bin was the replacement. Was it the bin directly behind the one that was empty? Or, reading left to right, was it the bin on the opposite corner?

Photo 9.17 The Stocking Side.

The bin's barcode held the answer but it was far too small to read and compare—though Margie kept seeing people try. Eventually, they gave up and did nothing or looked for Margie so they could get an answer. In either case, they were doubtful, not confident—hesitant and not active. They were in motion.

Margie's customers were in motion because of her—because of a hole (an information deficit) in her delivery system. Even though the PLS system she had developed to this point was far superior to the prior approach, it was clearly not yet complete. Margie knew she needed to share more information if she was to help her customers do a better job. But what information? And how? She was going to have to stretch her visual thinking.

Then in a flash Margie understood the exact information deficit that had triggered that motion and what she would do to eliminate it, one hundred percent. She added a single brilliant visual detail and the problem disappeared entirely.

Instead of making the bin address more specific or the information on the bar code larger, she simply added numbers—ordinal numbers: 1, 2, 3, 4, 5, and so on. In the visual language you learned in Chapter 7, Margie applied *generic addresses*.

Photo 9.18 The addition of a single brilliant detail.

She added a number to each bin, left to right, on the Working Side, starting with 1 (Photo 9.18 and Detail). Then she put a matching number on the related bin on the Stocking Side. Although the assemblers did not know the following (nor did they need to know it), in a 2-bin kanban system, the opposite side reads from right to left. As a result, when an operator finds an empty blue bin, she just goes to the Stocking Side and exchanges it for the fully-stocked bin with the same number. As with her tube ID tape mini-system discussed earlier, Margie included two sets of laminated cards—one to indicate the *Need-To-Order* and the other to indicate *Already-Ordered* (Photo 9.19).

Margie's PLS mini-system is a splendid example of customer-driven visuality—noticing your customer's motion and eliminating it through solutions that are visual. Photo 9.20 shows Margie with one of her happy assembler customers, Diana.

Splendid motion detective work. Splendid visual thinking. And splendid customer-driven visuality.

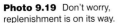

Photo 9.19 Don't worry, replenishment is on its way.

Photo 9.20 Margie assisting her customer, Diana.

Customer-Driven Visuality

We know two things about Margie at the time of the above solutions. We know that she applied the need-to-know and the visual where vigorously to her own corner of the world and was well on her way to mastering it (she was nearly at yellow). And we know she had begun to apply the need-to-share, shifting her focus to the information she needed to share so that other people could do their own work safer, smarter, better, and with less struggle. In the case of Margie's PLS system, those other people were her internal customers.

But they could just as well have been her internal suppliers—people inside LM-Aero who work upstream, downstream, and at stream from Margie. Add to these, Margie's suppliers and customers, external to LM-Aero. All these groups are her customers—the customers of her information.

Margie had become active in her search to serve. She paid attention to the motion her customers and suppliers got caught in, whether in the form of questions they asked, or moments when they were stalled, felt confused, unsafe or doubtful. Margie began to notice these things; and she began to tackle them, one by one, by inventing visual devices and mini-systems that removed the information deficits that caused the motion in the first place. She was beginning to master visuality driven by them.

Photo 9.21 The yellow strip on this bin is a customer-driven device to help Margie better serve her customers.

Notice the small yellow strip at the bottom of each blue bin for example (red box, Photo 9.21). It was put there for a customer-driven purpose. Margie color coded all PLS bins by department (yellow for the Single Flare area; green for Double Flare, another area), not so she could "catch" an assembler "stealing" from another department. Her motivation was entirely different. She did it so that, if she found the wrong color code in a department, she would know that department had run out of those PLS components—and that there was a hole in her replenishment system. She did it to better serve her customers.

This is the heart of the customer-driven process: to serve your customers (and we include your internal and external customers and suppliers in that single term)—and to serve them better by visually sharing the information you know that they need to know.

Sharing with Your Customers

Think about your internal suppliers and customers. Who are they? What kind of information do they need to know from you? Do the same for your external suppliers and customers. Who are they? What kind of information do they need to know that you need to share? Are you currently sharing that? How? Could a visual device do it better?

Listen to their questions. Invite them into your area for a walkabout and ask them what information would help—even delight—them to be able to access at-a-glance. There will be a sizeable difference between what an internal customer (from, for example, a downstream process or planning) wants you to share—and an external customer, such as General Smith from the Department of Defense. Both have a need to know and will love when, the next time they stop by, you have answered them visually.

In customer-driven visuality, your goal is to use visual devices and mini-systems to help your customers—all of them—feel safe, smart, and connected—and achieve greater success in their own day, in their own goals, and in their own work lives through your visual contribution.

Going to Green

Green on the laminated map means you have drilled deeper into the information deficits in your area, so deeply in fact that visuality is now sustainable. Part of that means implementing the customer-driven visuality you just read about—and part is what you will read about in the next chapter: *The Four Power Levels of Visual Devices*. When your area goes to green, visual information sharing devices—and the visual thinking that produces them—have become a way of life there. Yours is a *Visual Best Practice* department.

An area goes to green much the same way as it went to yellow—gradually, sub-area by sub-area (Figure 9.2). Unlike going-to-yellow, green has no specific criteria that defines it. Your area simply becomes more powerful and complete as it moves to green. Using a word I coined in the 1980s, it becomes more *transparent*. You can see into the operations of the department and retrieve…well, anything you want.

Like replacing a wall with a clear pane of glass, all is revealed. Nothing is hidden, secreted away or unavailable. When the area is green, the workplace speaks (Figures 9.3 and 9.4).

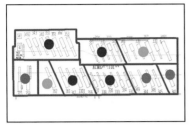

Figure 9.2 Gradually sub-areas shift from yellow to green.

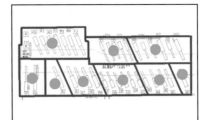

Figure 9.3 The area (your department) has gone full green.

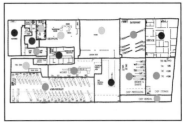

Figure 9.4 When the area goes green, the dot on the company map goes green too.

You will know it—and you will like it. Besides the smooth flow of work and the absence of struggle, you will like the way it feels to work with others; they have become master visual thinkers as well. They know what you know and with you have designed and re-designed your work area. Your supervisor will also have a big smile on her face. Because you can get to your work, without struggle, she gets to hers. And by now she knows that her main job is not answering questions or chasing down materials.

She has become a leader of improvement—but that is a topic for another book.

Just one thing more (by now you know there is always "just one thing more" in this book). Don't assign green to your area too quickly. Don't assign it for effort—as in "they meant well and are trying so hard." Assign green because the results are evident. Make green worthy of the horizon you sought when you first got started on your visual journey. You were full of hope then—and belief and energy. And then you learned and applied a methodology, diligently over time. Not for a few days but over a number of months. You kept going. Make that pay off. Make sure your area is worthy of green. When a department goes green, it becomes a showcase—a vision place—for others.

They have been watching and will turn to your area to learn what a visual workplace is and how it functions long before they get started. Your company needs at least one visual showcase area (discussed in Chapter 3) to set the pace for others. When that happens, then instead of having to travel outside the company to see a vision place, people from other departments will simply walk across the floor to yours. Going to green is an achievement to celebrate.

The Visual Inventiveness of Rick Ell

Throughout this book you have seen many visual solutions invented by Rick Ell (Photo 9.22), precision machinist at Denison Hydraulics (now Parker Denison/Ohio).

Though Rick admits that he was indifferent, even reluctant, when visuality was launched in his area, a few months later he decided to give visual information sharing a try. He liked the result and soon resolved to visually transform his entire area. You can't see those results, unfortunately, because they disappeared virtually overnight when his cell was moved—before I had taken any photos.

Rick was assigned a new area. Where the visual conversion of his first cell took about nine months, Rick converted his second cell in less than three. It was the first thing on his agenda. Rick had already made a name for himself with his

Photo 9.22 Rick Ell.

Photo Series 9.23 Denison's Visual Workplace Bulletin Board & Rick Ell's Dot Ceremony.

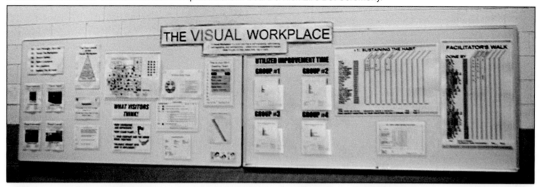

With Steve Harvey holding the map, the author removes the yellow dot and hands it to Rick Ell.

A green dot is retrieved from the stash of dots and placed to show the new visual status of his department.

Congratulations to Rick Ell, with his fellow Steering Team member, Deb Kelsey, joining in.

first cell as a master visual thinker. With his second cell, he went beyond his own high standard. Machinists on the other two shifts used to compete to work in Rick's area. They called it the *no-thinking cell*—because you didn't have to think when you were there; you just did the dance of work.

I was lucky enough to be in the factory the day that Rick's second cell went to green (Photo Series 9.23). Under the Denison Visual Workplace Bulletin Board that Steve Harvey (Denison's first-rate visual workplace coordinator) had created, Rick traded in his yellow dot for a green one, with champion, Bill Cornell, Rick's supervisor, and Steering Team looking on. What a moment.

Now take a tour of Rick's visual showcase (Photo Series 9.24). You've seen many of these devices elsewhere in this book. Now they are grouped together to give the full effect of Rick's level of visual mastery.

Photo Cluster 9.24 The Visual Mastery of Rick Ell (*continues next page*).

The Pattern of Work

Smart Placement Principles Everywhere

 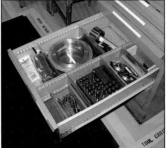 

The Machine That Speaks

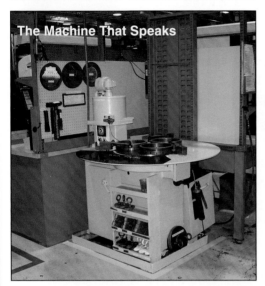

The Visual Machine®

Rick's fan is...never out of visual order

Visuality Behind Closed Doors

Drilling Deep into the Value Field

Mini-Systems: Next Steps

You have just learned a great deal about visual mini-systems. Now it's time to look for opportunities to apply them.

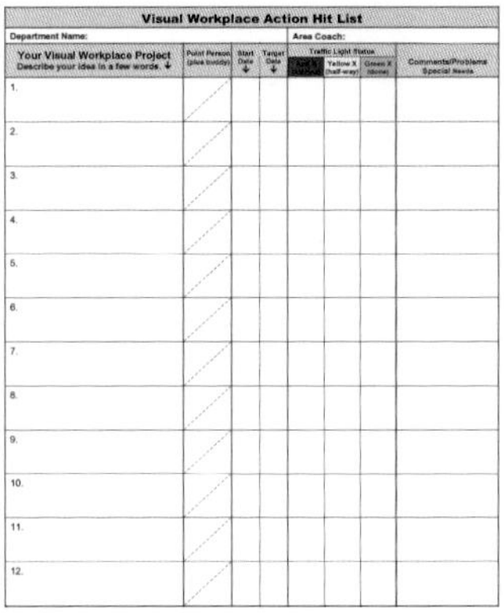

Figure 9.5 Keep track on the Hit List.

Consider the mini-systems you just studied, walking back through the pages of this chapter as you need to. How have they broadened your thinking about ways visuality can make your work area safer and more operationally effective? Think about that now.

Then, working alone or with a buddy, make a list of mini-system opportunities in your area. Add these to your visual workplace hit list (Figure 10.15), posting *all* your improvement ideas, even if you don't plan to tackle them yourself. Improvement is continuous so it all doesn't have to happen right away or happen through you alone.

You already know what happens after that: You keep going. You follow the methodology (the recipe). You keep thinking. And you keep using your hit list.

You also keep showing up for the visual blitzes scheduled in your area—and when I say show up I mean all parts of you: hands, feet, brain, heart, and your sense of humor.

Converting to a fully-functioning visual workplace is about just that: function, operational function. It means that you and the people who work with you are learning how to function on an entirely new level—a level that is captured visually in the many devices you and they are developing and imbedding into the landscape of work. Those who visit your work area see it as well. They see the level of operational excellence that the visuality you created in your area captures and expresses. They see work that makes sense.

The future ain't what
it used to be.

Yogi Berra

Chapter | Ten

The Four Power Levels of Visual Devices

Translating Information into Visual Devices

Let's go back to where we started. In Chapter 1, we said that visuality is about translating information into exact behavior through the mechanism of visual devices—through devices that share information visually. (Figure 10.1—a repeat—summarizes this process.) And that's what you've been learning about and applying ever since.

Nearly every person who works begins in a value field that is starved for information. The *Before* photo you see Photo 10.1 is such a value field—a work bench with zero information sharing and therefore flooded with information deficits and their accomplice, motion.

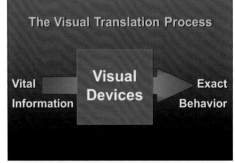

Figure 10.1 The translation of information into exact behavior—through visual devices.

But the situation doesn't have to stay that way. As we learn about visuality, we realize we can eliminate the info deficits—and the motion they

Photo 10.1 An information-starved value field.

trigger—through solutions that are visual. We become powerful visual thinkers, capable of creating increasingly powerful visual devices.

That's exactly what you see in Photo 10.2: the same work bench *after* visual thinking was applied—not once but repeatedly—until that value field functions visually on a very high level. You can almost hear the story of that progress. An assembly operator (let's call her Maryanne) decided to take some of the struggle out of her work by applying visual principles and methods. First Maryanne installed the visual where through borders and addresses. That cleared the way for her to find deeper levels of motion and she began to build more layers of visual power into her primary value field.

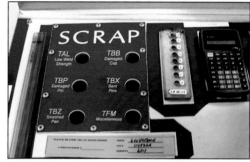

Photo 10.2 An information-rich value field.

Maryanne began to notice how much time she spent every day sorting and counting defective parts—counting scrap. She noticed her motion; and she decided to develop an easier way—a visual way—to get an answer to the question *how many defects?* The red scrap separator system in the upper left corner of her bench was her powerful visual response. This system allows Maryanne to sort a defective component into one of six categories *as she finds them.* She simply drops the defect in the matching hole; it lands in a waiting cup underneath. At the end of the day, she merely counts what's in each cup, gets a tally, and completes her report.

Photo 10.3 Foam Cups.

Maryanne's device did not eliminate defects. But it did streamline the task of tracking them; that, in turn, became an important step in solving the problem. Nor did her invention begin as the snazzy red system shown in the photo. It began as a set of six styrofoam cups (Photo 10.3), each marked with the name of a different defect, and held together with masking tape. Maryanne's device saved her so much time that other operators copied the idea for their own benches. Within months, Maryanne's solution was formalized into the powerful red scrap separator system in the photo. It had become a Visual Best Practice in her company.

Maryanne's system includes many levels of visual functionality—not just the visual where. That is what makes it so effective and so powerful. And that is exactly what we are going to discuss and explain in this chapter: the power levels of visual devices.

Learning and Pacing Yourself

The purpose of this chapter is to show you many, many different visual devices. Some of these have already been discussed in this book. If you are familiar with my other visual workplace books, others may have been presented there. You may wonder what I didn't just choose other examples. There reason is simply this: Certain devices are so outstanding they are classified in my mind as "teaching examples." They hold the principles of visuality so vividly and completely that they teach no matter the industry.

One more thing before we begin to study the four power levels of visual devices. Be aware that it may take longer than you think to absorb and apply what is shared in this chapter. My hope is that you do not rush through these pages, glancing at the photos, murmuring "uh huh I get it," and moving on. Instead, I encourage you to spend time as you learn about each power category and consider how it can and does change human behavior. As part of this, think about ways to apply what you are learning in your own area in order to improve first your own performance—and then the performance of others.

If I were teaching you directly, I would make sure to spend two to three weeks on each power level, working with you to develop applications and track their impact. Better not to rush. Keep this in mind as you move through these pages. If you want to build an even better result, ask your supervisor or trainer to walk through these pages with you—or help organize a Book Study Group so you can study and apply the power levels with colleagues. They will be happy to help; this was the subject of *Leadership Task 11*, discussed in Chapter 5. Here is a recap, this time with you as the leader.

Work That Makes Sense is an implementation manual. Put it to work for you and your department by starting a book study group for you and your colleagues. Your supervisor or trainer will help you set this up. Then meet regularly to discuss the ideas, concepts, and principles in this book—chapter by chapter. This usually means once a week, during lunch. Meet in a quiet place for 30 minutes, no interruptions (if it's during your lunch, management will sometimes provide another 15 minutes). Gate-keep for yourselves, rotate session leadership, keep a tight focus, and stay on a reading schedule. Discuss what you have read, listen, share insights, ask questions, learn from each other—and name or imagine possible applications. Get informed, get inspired, and take the lead for steady improvements in your area.

The Four Power Levels

The purpose of this chapter is to show you that visual solutions exist on different levels of power—and to show you how to make your own visual solutions more powerful. Power to do what? Power to get precise, predictable, and repeatable behavior. Power to make sure that what is supposed to happen, does happen.

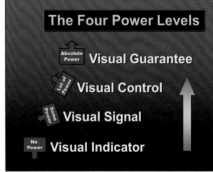

When you understand the four power levels, you begin to think beyond border, address, and ID label because the visual where is only one category of visual function, and a very basic one at that. Other categories include visual standards, visual displays, visual metrics, visual problem solving, visual controls, visual pull systems, and visual guarantees. You are about to learn how visual devices can be made increasingly powerful through your own visual thinking.

Figure 10.2 The Four Power Levels.

Look at the four levels in Figure 10.2, starting from the bottom up: Visual Indicator, Visual Signal, Visual Control, and Visual Guarantee (poka-yoke). The red boxes describe and point to each level of power. Notice that the yellow arrow moves from less power to more. We begin with visual indicators.

Visual Indicators

Like all visual devices, a *visual indicator* delivers a message. The railroad crossing sign in Figure 10.3

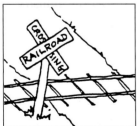

shares information vital to drivers and pedestrians: "Be careful! Trains often pass here!" But indicators are placed at the bottom of the power progression because they have *no power* to make us slow down. They simply announce the possibility of an oncoming train.

Because you and I are adults, we are likely to notice the indicator and, as result, slow down; we understand the concept of consequences.

Figure 10.3 A visual indicator.

But teenagers? For far too many of them, the railroad crossing post looks like an open invitation to step on the gas—especially if a train is in sight—and try to make it across the tracks without getting smashed. Immature? Childish? Dangerous? Yes, it's all those things. And no railroad sign would be capable of changing that.

Look at Photo Series 10.4 for three more visual indicators found in the community.

Photo Series 10.4 Visual Indicators in the community.

"Stroller Parking" at Disney World. Nothing forces you to park there. No stroller police. It's up to you.

The most famous indicator of all. Its power lies in the possible consequences of ignoring it—an accident or a ticket. It has no power of its own.

We pay attention to street signs only when we need them. Otherwise, they are practically invisible. We breeze right by.

Visual indicators convey important, even vital, information, but they have no power to make us obey, comply or adhere. They have no power to make us do the right thing.

This is not to say that visual indicators are not important. They are indispensable to our life and our work day. Imagine a world without street names, house addresses, stop signs, road signs, directions, maps, etc. Imagine your company without a name and an address on the front building, names on desks, departmental signs, names on each file drawer, signs that point us to the Men's Room vs. Ladies, and so on. Could you function without those? Probably. But why would you want to?

Photo 10.5 (plus Detail) shows you the glory of indicators: a great system of addresses at Seton Name Plate where thousands of catalogue orders are fulfilled weekly. Look at all the visual concepts captured here: big bold color-coded airborne and floor addresses and coded ID labels—plus *sort-the-universe, co-locate like functions,* and *put it on wheels.* The lowly indicator at its finest.

What self-respecting buyer could live without the two-sided, laminated, airborne driver-license address you see in Photo 10.6? Not Cindy Barter.

Photo 10.5 A mini-system of indicators.

CINDY BARTER

BUYER #6   EXT. 207

RESPONSIBILITIES

SCREW MACHINE PARTS
SINTERED METAL
BAR STOCK
WIRE & CABLE
MOTORS
BELLOWS

ALTERNATE: JON BIRKETT

Photo 10.6

Yes, visual indicators are valuable; they are just not powerful. Though we seem to automatically obey most indicators, in fact, anyone of us could decide—at any point—not to. Indicators leave us in charge of our own will. That is precisely why I once paid $57.75 for a cup of cappuccino—$2.75 for the coffee, the rest for the parking ticket—one day when

I chose to ignore a *No Parking* sign.

Ignoring indicators can trigger severe outcomes—or not. If someone, for example, does not see or follow the "Use First" indicator in Photo 10.7 (red arrow), the schedule may get thrown off—but no one dies.

But even if the consequences are severe, indicators do not—by their nature—help. They cannot; they are not designed to. You'll need more powerful visual devices for that, the kind you learn about later in this chapter.

Photo 10.7 A visual indicator with an urgent request: "Use me first!"

Visual Standards are Indicators. Managers love *Visual Standards*, such as the ones you see in the Photo Cluster 10.8. After all, their thinking goes, these signs make it perfectly clear what needs to be done, by when, and how—the technical and procedural details of adding value—so they are bound to happen.

Photo Cluster 10.8
Visual Standards from the shop floor.

Yes, visual standards—indicators all—hold vital safety and quality answers, but, because they are merely indicators, they have no power to make us adhere, follow, obey or comply. They depend entirely on our willingness to use them. If we accept that we need to know such detail and that the information is truthful and complete, we probably will decide to read and follow it. In some organizations, that is a pretty big "if."

Here's the story that triggered a splendid visual standard, created by operators working in the blade grinding area at Hamilton Standard (Connecticut). When arguments between shifts began related to machine cleanliness, it did not take long for people to recognize the complaints as a form of motion—bickering due to missing information. The missing information was what "clean enough" looked like. No standard had been set, therefore cleanliness remained a subjective condition—an opinion. Needless to say, opinions differed.

But associates in this area were already visual thinkers and their solution was brilliant: Photograph the grinder area when it is "clean enough" and post that on each grinder (Photo 10.9 and Detail). The quarreling stopped. This visual standard is an outstanding example of operator-led visual inventiveness.

By now, I'm sure you have begun to understand that, though visual indicators can not force us to do anything, they can still influence practically everything. Take measures, for example.

Photo 10.9

Detail

Visual Measures are Indicators. It seems that we watch, count, track, measure practically everything. What supervisor does not hope that sharing such measures would automatically improve them? That rarely happens. And yet, knowing the details of less-than-stellar results is important.

Look at the kiosk (or bird's nest) in Photo 10.10. This four-sided kiosk is built to show results across this area's key performance indicators (KPIs): safety, quality, delivery, and cost. Regular computer printouts get slipped into the plastic sleeves on each side. The kiosk rotates. It's on wheels. You can take it to lunch if you want to.

While this approach is a huge improvement over not collecting data at all, sharing results in this way is not, on its own, going to trigger improvement. Why? Because all this kiosk does is monitor and indicate.

All metrics (another word for measures) are indicators. They have no built-in power to make us change or even care. But that doesn't mean they are not important. They are. The question is: Can they be more effective? Yes, they can, and powerfully so, as long as: 1) they give you direct feedback on your own performance in as close to real time as possible; 2) they provide a point of comparison; 3) they help you discover cause; and 4) you use them.

Let's look at the first two requirements in more detail.

Photo 10.10 Metrics on wheels.

Feedback on Yourself and a Point of Comparison. First separate the metrics that speak to your boss (usually because they speak to her boss)—and the metrics that speak to you.

The ones that speak to you will almost always give you feedback on your own behavior, your own performance. And you will like that feedback the most when it is frequent, specific, and on demand—like the score at a ball game or the mirror in your bathroom. How interested are you in that feedback? The answer: very interested, never get tired of it, give me more.

Remember, the visual workplace is an I-driven methodology. You are at the center of it. That is not egotism; it is functional. The self at the center not only directs your interest in performing well, it clamors for feedback on just how well. That's one of the main purposes of I-driven measures. The motivation is on the inside—inside the measure and inside you.

Line operators at Alpha Industries (Massachusetts) were well on their visual journey when they decided to go after more feedback on their own performance related to on-time delivery. They constructed the airborne placard (an indicator) in Photo 10.11 that announced their current on-time performance (93%) and boldly proclaimed what their own previous best had been—which in this case was even better: 100%. They held their own feet to the fire of continuous improvement and included a meaningful point of comparison to spur them on.

Photo 10.11 A visual metric provides a meaningful point of comparison.

There's much more to know about visual metrics but this will get you started. Start experimenting with them. Put a metrics project on your hit list and explore. Your supervisor is sure to be interested in supporting your research, even delighted.

Visual Displays are Indicators. Similar to a visual metric, a visual display has no power to make us change, improve, or even listen. Its effectiveness comes from our interest in and need for the information that it contains. When we are motivated on the inside, we pay attention on the outside.

Photo 10.12 shows the maintenance display you saw in Chapter 1 when we discussed the ten doorways. Located on the main aisle of a 1500-person factory in Indiana, this board is divided into maintenance specialties (electricians, millwrights, pipe fitters, and so on).

Its purpose is to share the truth about work orders, first so the maintenance technicians know; and then so everyone else in the plant knows.

Look how honest it is. At the bottom of the display (in green), maintenance shows its completed tasks. In the middle (in yellow) are the new orders. At the top (in red) are the past due. Everyone can tell where most of the work is: past dues.

Visual displays are about telling the truth in real time, as the truth changes. You begin displays with the "I"—answering your need-to-know. Other people often need to know the same thing so it may seem as though you are organizing the board for others. But that is only a coincidence.

Photo 10.12 Maintenance shares order status visually.

Visual Display by Bill Antunes. More often than not, displays are developed by supervisors and managers. But there is nothing to prevent value-add associates—*you*—from inventing displays to support your own work and that of your area. That is exactly what Bill Antunes did (Photo 10.13); you saw Bill's splendid work bench in Chapter 2. Bill began his display, triggered by an urgent need-to-know.

Photo 10.13 Bill Antunes, ace visual thinker.

Bill had worked in switch and control assembly at United Electric Controls (Massachusetts) for nearly 20 years before he learned about visuality. For most of that time, his department was plagued by parts shortages or *stockouts*. Management tried to remedy the problem many times but without success. The latest attempt was a 3-sheet form you filled out when you saw a part running low. One sheet went to purchasing to alert the buyers. A second stayed with you as proof. Nobody knew what to do with the third sheet—so it usually got sent to the buyer as a reminder and double insurance. But that only confused the buyer since he already had one alert; as a result, he set both forms aside to investigate "later." The part never got ordered.

As a visual thinker, Bill realized his area's approach to parts shortages was triggering a ton of motion—piling up information deficits instead of reducing them. He decided to do something about it. He invented the visual display you see in Photo Series 10.14 (next page). Here's how it works.

1. The display has two sides. The red left side is for part numbers that are out: *Hot Shortages*. The blue right side is for part numbers that will run out soon: *Low Stock*.

2. When an assembler notices a part running low or an actual stockout, he or she marks the part number on the correct side of the display—and in the correct color (important to Bill).

3. The buyer (in this case, Lee Sacco) checks the display three times a day, noting any new items.

4. Lee returns to his desk, calls the supplier, orders the parts, and secures a promised delivery date.

Photo Series 10.14
Stockouts Display of Bill Antunes.

Lee Sacco, the buyer, posts the promised delivery date.

Lee at his desk on the shopfloor.

5. On his next trip to the board, he notes this information next to its part number—and, of course, looks for new items.

6. Bill—or whichever operator posted the shortage—then circles that promised delivery date as a way of saying *thank you*. The communication loop is complete.

This worked so well that within six months, Lee and the other buyers had moved their desks to the shopfloor to be where the action happened and to better support operations.

See Photo 10.15 for an associate-led display in another company, this one related to production output. Work orders are marked on small magnets and re-arranged by operators themselves as the schedule is completed or revised. Other cells in the grid hold quality data, problems, and special needs or comments. As with all visual indicators, this display *tells only*—and still makes a powerful daily contribution.

Visual Indicators: Next Steps. This concludes our discussion on visual indicators. Now it's time for you to consider them. How have the visual indicators you just studied expanded your thinking about ways to make your area safer and operationally more effective?

Think about that now. Then, working alone or with a buddy, review the previous pages and list opportunities for visual indicators in your area, as you remind yourself of the many kinds of visual indicators. Then add them to your visual workplace hit list (Figure 10.4), posting *all* your improvement ideas, even if you don't plan to tackle them yourself. Improvement is continuous so it all doesn't have to happen right away or happen through you alone.

Photo 10.15 An associate tracks her daily production output, defects, and problems on a shared display.

Figure 10.4 Post and track your improvement ideas on your visual workplace hit list.

Visual Signals

We now move up the power ladder to *visual signals* and see how they strengthen adherence. Look at Figure 10.6. What changed? Yes, we added flashing lights to the railroad crossing sign. Now when a train approaches, the lights start to flash and draw our attention to the fact that there's an oncoming train on the tracks we are approaching. We stop—the message was sent and received.

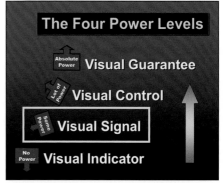

Figure 10.5 Power level 2: Visual Signals.

That is, you and I stop. But our teenage friend might still gun the motor and make a run for it.

A visual signal has a bit more power than a visual indicator because it first grabs our attention and then delivers its message. But it is still up to us if we heed the message—or not. A visual signal is only slightly more effective than a visual indicator—and that means hardly at all.

Figure 10.6 Visual Signals.

Examples of visual signals abound, from the stop light you see in Photo 10.16 to the beep-beep sound (annunciator signal) as the forklift backs up. Visual signals first get our attention—and then they deliver their message.

You can see this process in the simple rumble strip at the side of the road (Photo 10.17). You are driving home from turkey dinner at Grandma's house, and the whole meal hits your nervous system. You fall asleep at the wheel. The rumble strip springs into action the instant your tires touch it....bounce, bounce, bounce! "Wake up wake up, you dunderhead!" it shouts. "You're heading for the ditch!"

What a perfect visual signal. The device simply lies there, mute but waiting, until the very instant you need it—when your wheels hit the strip on their way to the ditch. Instead taking the dive, you swerve and get back on course, thanks to a few indents in the pavement.

Photo 10.16
Traffic lights.

Photo 10.17
Rumble Strip.

What makes visual signals effective is the fact that they change. When a signal stops changing, we ignore it. Just like the stop light that gets stuck in the middle of the night in the middle of nowhere—we ignore it and move ahead, because it has lost the message it is designed to deliver. (Needless to say, I have never done that.)

Now let's look at some more examples.

Red Clothes Pin Visual Signal. Here's a story about a visual signal found in an unexpected place and in an unexpected form.

Camilla came in early every morning to prepare a report by 8:00 a.m. for Nate, the head engineer. Nate came in early every morning and hovered around Camilla's desk to make sure she got the report to him on time. Camilla put up with this for a while because, well, Nate was her boss. Then she spoke up, in the language of visual thinking.

"Look Nate, I really respect you. But honestly you get me off to a bad start every morning because you hover around my desk, worrying about the report. Can't we do something about that?" Nate had also been trained in visuality. He knew arguments were just another form of motion, caused by missing information, unanswered questions; and he recognized that in this case his unanswered question was his need to know exactly when his report was ready.

"Yes, Camilla," said Nate, "Let's do something about this together." So together they figured out how to eliminate Nate's information deficit. Check Photos Series 10.18 for how they did it.

Photo Series 10.18 A great visual signal solution.

Before. Is the report ready? Nate has to either go and look—or ask Camilla. He always asked Camilla.

After-1. When the report is ready, Camilla puts it in a blue bin and clips a red clothes pin in place—Nate's signal the report is waiting.

After-2. When he picks it up, Nate takes the clothes pin down—Camilla's signal that Nate picked up his report and all is well with the world.

The device in Photo 10.19 is a combination visual signal (the lights) and visual indicator (the words in Spanish that are fixed on the lights). Here is the translation:

- Green-*trabajand*: The machine is running. Everything is going smoothly.

- Yellow-*no trabajand:* The machine in not running because of planned downtime.

- Red-*ayuda problema*: Oh no, we are having a problem. The machine is down, and we did not plan for that.

The purpose of this excellent visual signal application is to show the status of a process. In the case of our example, the machine is on planned downtime.

Photo 10.19 The yellow light means planned downtime. No worries.

***Andon*/Stacked Lights.** The technical name for these stacked lights is *andon*—Japanese for "paper lantern." Andon is a system of stacked lights that share status information on core performance parameters: faults/stoppages, readiness, waiting state, help needed, and so on. But one of the challenges in using these systems is that the color order and number of lights varies from vendor to vendor.

Photo Cluster 10.20 An array of andons or stacked lights—but what do they mean?

The six sets of andons you see in Photo Cluster 10.20 were just a few of the dozens that surrounded me at a mail processing center in Minneapolis. Few were alike in number or color sequence, yet all were lit. I had no idea what any of them meant or if I was in mortal danger. When I asked, my escort replied, "Oh there's nothing to worry about. They're always on."

Instead of creating the sense of stability, control, and safety that visual devices are meant to provide, stacked lights used in this manner have the opposite effect. As a result, people either ignored the lights completely—because they were always on—or felt a growing sense of danger for the same reason. And only a handful of people actually knew what they meant. Here's what to do about that.

When you use lights to carry a message—whether a single light or a stack—add a name list or legend that translates each color into a precise meaning. The example in Photo 10.21 uses an adhesive label you fix directly onto the surface of the light. The other (Photo 10.22) uses cardboard and duct tape effectively on a two-sided legend. Stacked lights are an important way to share vital information, instantly, close at hand and at a distance. There should be no mystery about what that information is, what it means, or what to do in response. Don't let your andon lights cause motion when their purpose is to minimize it.

Photo 10.21 A stick-on label provides meaning.

Photo 10.22 Cardboard and tape is the answer here.

Visual Signals: Next Steps. This concludes our discussion on visual signals. Now it's time for you to think about and apply what you have just learned. How have the visual signals you just studied expanded your thinking about ways to make your work area more visual, safer, and more operationally effective?

Think about that now as you review the examples in the preceding pages. Then, working alone or with a buddy, make a list of opportunities for visual signals in your area. Identify one or several that interest you the most. Then update your visual workplace hit list (Figure 10.22), posting *all* your improvement ideas, even if you don't plan to tackle them yourself.

Improvement is continuous so it all doesn't have to happen right away or happen through you alone.

Figure 10.7 Keep track on your hit list.

Visual Controls

A visual control is a mechanism that limits, restricts, and directs our behavior through structure—like the railroad crossing gate you see in Figure 10.9. Visual controls have a good deal of power; the gate now prevents vehicles from crossing the tracks when a train is coming. That physical barrier replaces the less effective railroad crossing sign, even with flashing lights.

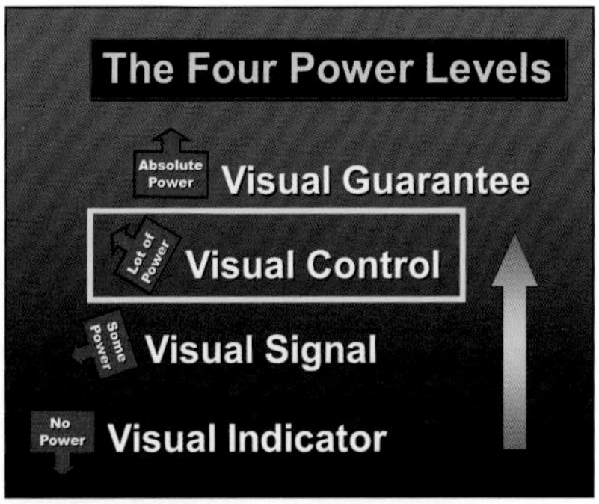

Figure 10.8 Level 3: Visual Controls.

Because visual controls are structural, they directly impact the power of the individual will—choice—except if a person is determined

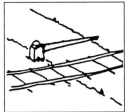

Figure 10.9 Visual Control.

to ignore them. Our teenage friend is still in jeopardy because his will is his main organizer. We can see him now, racing against the train, zigzagging through the very gates that are designed to protect him. Even if there were a cluster of *railroad cross buck signs* (their technical name), flashing lights, bells ringing, and a train in sight, that teenager might still make a run for it.

For the rest of us, visual controls are powerful deterrents—or enablers, whichever side you look at. When we reach the control level, our behavior becomes less and less optional because the device itself structures (controls) our response. Here are examples.

The Power of Lines. To some, Photo 10.23 looks like a parking lot. They are wrong. It is instead a highly sophisticated visual control system. How do we know? Because 120 strangers will park 120 cars uniformly there. No injuries, dents or even thinking twice, even the very first time they enter the property. How does that happen? It happens thanks to the position of the white borders (some called them "lines"), the length and angle of those borders, their number,

Photo 10.24 Snow erased the pattern.

Photo 10.23 A powerful visual control system first—then a parking lot.

and the space between them. In short, it happens because of the strength of the pattern in the value field we call *a parking lot*. Adherence—control—is built into that landscape, visually. And we seamlessly obey.

Consider this. You know you are in the presence of a powerful visual control system when the behavior the system produces simply stops when the control structure is removed—in this case, due to a heavy snow (Photo 10.24). All information disappears and with it adherence, compliance, and uniform behavior. In the absence of the control pattern, one might wisely decide not to park there.

We see the same control application with the pallet jack parking (Photo 10.25): four slots, four jacks—location and quantity in the same device. Add visual indicators—addresses and ID labels—and you get a complete solution system (Photo 10.26).

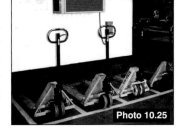

Photo 10.25

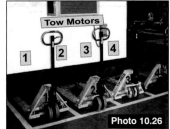

Photo 10.26

Lines as Structure. You may be wondering how 2-dimensional "lines" on a floor can have the power to control anything. After all, you may say, they are flat and have no tangible structure. The explanation lies in the discussion we already had about the power of pattern. Each of the floor (or ground) border examples shown above (including the parking lot) creates an enclosed space—a containment structure. Test this out by raising each of those "lines" up in your mind's eye. What do you get? Walls. It is those walls that we intuitively envision when we see or work around borders that contain. That is how "lines" can function as powerfully as structure. Consider this further as you study the three examples in Photo Series 10.27.

 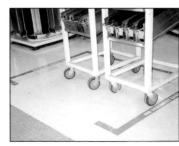 

Barry Controls, a cellular manufacturer in Boston, favors broad bands of color as borders. These imbed the pattern of work across the factory, creating a production environment that feels sane and stable, no matter what. Are they visual indicators or controls?

The green border for this rack has a door—that front gap. The GM associates who created it push racks in and out through that gap as though it had walls on either side—a measure of the power of that opening. Is this border solution an indicator or a control?

Some see this work station and say, "Just a bunch of yellow lines." But you and I know it's the power of limits that regulates, even governs, as seen on this Scania takt-time driven assembly line (Holland). Is that yellow square an indicator or a control?

What do you think? If you are undecided, check it out further through your own visual applications and the behaviors that follow. Challenge your buddies in discussions about this. A clear and final answer, in this case, is not possible; nor is it as important as exploring the question itself. You will all gain a much greater understanding of lines as controls through your lively exchanges and experiments. And that is answer enough. Now we'll add to the mix.

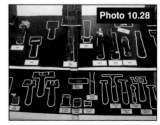
Photo 10.28

Raising Shadows/Making Walls. Photo 10.28 shows the visual application called *shadow boards* where a home for a tool is its outline (or shadow). Shadow boards are commonly used to keep tools in order. And then a tool is in use (or borrowed), the same 2-dimensional surface tells you that it is *not at* home. But why not go further?

Make the basic concept more powerful by raising up the shadow and making a wall—exactly what you see in Photo 10.29 (also shown in Chapter 7). Stiff blue foam cut out in the shape of the tools provides

Photo 10.29

a tight control function. A bright yellow background, in this case, allows us to spot at-a-glance when a tool is missing. The control element in that visual device—and in all visual control devices—is some manner of physical barrier, structured or built into the device itself, in this case the foam.

While this particular set of tool boxes were made by an outside vendor, you can mimic the concept, using foam or even drawer liners from a hardware store (for more revisit page 132 in this book).

Here is the same raising-walls principle (Photo 10.30), applied to a machine changeover cart in the Tube Shop at LM-Aero in Fort Worth, Texas. The thick foam on the top was carved to fit a needed set of hand tools and machine fixtures, making the tools not only handy, and securely in place, but also automatically alerting us if something is missing.

Photo 10.30

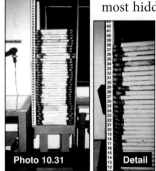
Photo 10.31   Detail

The need to count or measure is a one of motion's most hidden forms. Jose and Roberto worked the day shift and spent a lot of time daily counting up silk screens to make sure they had made enough to supply the night shift. Visual thinkers in-the-making, one day they realized that meant they were in motion—motion caused by the missing answer to the *how many* question. Their solution is in Photo 10.31 (and Detail): a wooden box that could contain (that structured in) the maximum number of screens they needed to prepare: 52.

Lines as Triggers/Min-Max Levels. In Photo 10.32, a dashed red line triggers the correct human response, lowering the risk that we might stack bales of used cardboard too high on the loading dock at Seton Name Plate. And notice the good double use of existing architecture: the wall. Great visual thinking.

Besides the controlling aspect of the floor borders in Photo 10.33, the bright yellow "Re-Order Level" line on each barrel (red arrow)

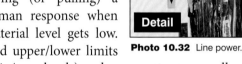

Photo 10.32   Line power.

is a visual control, triggering (or pulling) a human response when material level gets low. Add upper/lower limits

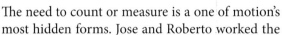

Photo 10.33
Line power.

(min/max levels) and you create more pull, which in turn imbeds time into the process.

Photo 10.34 shows a storage spot for welding wire, used in the axle (aka, "bogie") assembly at the Trailmobile factory in Toronto—a simple visual where. Nothing more. Add a "line" (see red arrow) and you add an important dimension of meaning. You have defined what "enough" means—in this case 30 boxes of wire.

Photo 10.34

Photo 10.35

In doing this, you cross the line (pun intended) from location to pull. That so-called line represents a limit—and that limit triggers behavior. In exactly this way, human response is designed into the physical landscape of work.

A simple "line" can help us—and everyone else—see when something is getting low: the visual how many. It becomes a min-max (minimum/maximum) device, a popular and useful visual control.

Min/max devices make it easy to tell at-a-glance when the item is in full supply or running out—whether raw material, parts, medicine, paper clips or customers. Notice how the min-level of the visual controls described above trigger a pull from us (and/or material handlers) to replenish the supply. This is the link between visual controls and our next control application: *visual pull systems*.

Visual Pull Systems/Kanban. With visual pull systems, we reach the land of *kanban*—the imposition of limits to control the pace of material consumption and replenishment.

Photo 10.36 Visual pull.

There are many ways that visible pull can be installed. In Photo 10.36, the physical limits of the control border itself—four kanban squares—ensure that the nearby process never runs out of material. The squares convey the friendly message: *Don't worry; you won't run out—and you won't have to hoard stuff to keep on working.* There are four bins or squares of material (and not three or two) because the site had one forklift driver per shift; he requested four squares so he would have time to make his circuit without shutting down an area because he was running late (Packard Electric/Mississippi).

Actual cards were used to trigger pull in the inventive supply kanban system shown in Photo Series 10.37. "Kanban" means "laundry ticket" in Japanese.

Photo Series 10.37 Kanban replenishment system for welded parts.

With eight metalworking mills and over 800 employees, Plymouth Tube Company manufactures high-precision tubes and extruded shapes. Plymouth started its excellence journey in 1999. It continues it to this day. In the West Monroe (Louisiana) plant, stock outages and parts hoarding were a problem.

Robin Griggs, supplies purchaser, decided to solve the problem and created the innovative kanban system shown here. If you think visual pull could help take some of the struggle out of work in your area, talk with your supervisor and/or purchasing.

You don't begin with fancy laminated color cards. Robin did her thinking first; then she experimented with cardboard. Later she made things pretty.

1. Welding parts are stored in cubbies in this rack. Robin installed time card racks on each side (red arrows) when she saw the parts bins were so small.

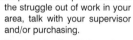

2. Each bin is numbered (red circle), marked with part numbers plus min/max replenishment levels.

3. Cards are numbered as well to correspond to each small bin and have clear instructions.

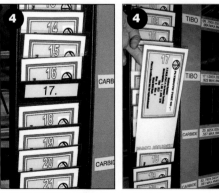

4. Each slot for a card is also numbered.

5. Parts running low? Turn the card upside down, put it back into the same slot. Robin will pick it up on her rounds.

Traffic Light Pull. Another frequently used visual pull method uses traffic-light color coding (red/yellow/green) to signal and control material delivery and pick up. This is an approach so simple, its effectiveness continues to surprise.

For a fine example, we go to the Delphi Rimir (Matamoras/Mexico; now part of Autoliv), air bag supplier to the auto industry, with value streams that include many cutting and sewing processes. In Photo 10.38, you see a roll of air bag material mounted on a cutting machine at the top of the stream (start of operations). The traffic light device is that painted placard on the side of the machine, in plain sight of forklift drivers (red arrow). They keep an eye on the color bands to make sure the fabric does not run out. If the fabric still reaches the green band, there is still plenty of time. If it drops to yellow, time to pay attention—a new roll will be needed soon. If it's down to the red, you are late.

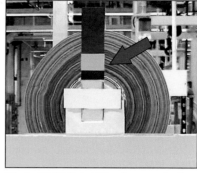
Photo 10.38 Material Handlers pay attention.

An excellent system. Here's what else. This plant employed 1500 people at the time of these photos and this simple traffic-light pull system was the only material handling approach used throughout the facility. See Photo Cluster 10.39 for several more examples from this plant. Could such a system help your area?

Photo Cluster 10.39 Traffic light pull plant-wide.

Animal Pull. Pull systems are so much a part of lean operations that we sometimes forget that these are also visual systems. Remembering this can help you improve an existing system. Here is a case in point.

The men and women on the machining floor at Freudenberg-NOK (Georgia) had devised a system, using color-coded kanban cards to pull parts to specific machines. For example, parts with green cards go to the "green" machine. Match the card with the machine (Photos 10.40 and 10.41).

This simple system should have worked well—but it didn't. Costly mix ups kept happening. Finally, the plant discovered that a number of male employees were some degree of color blind (the national average is one in twelve). What to do?

Photos 10.40 & 10.41 A simple system that did not work.

The team met. "Gee, color coding is such a great concept but it just doesn't work here." They thought and talked and thought some more. And then they solved it. Here's how….

One of the technicians remembered that his toddler came to breakfast one morning in a mismatched outfit: a rabbit head on her shirt but an alligator pants. "So I told her," he recounted, "Tonya honey, put a rabbit with a rabbit or an alligator with an alligator."

Photo 10.42

Photo 10.43

"That's it! Garanimals!" exclaimed the parents in the room. The Garanimals solution worked perfectly as you can see in Photos 10.42 and 10.43—matching animal heads and bottoms instead of color. If this appeals, make sure to choose animals whose bottoms look different: alligators, rabbits, turtles.... This is kanban at its most inventive.

Visual Scheduling/Heijunka. Whether you work in a factory or hospital, the tool called *heijunka* can apply. "Heijunka" means "make flat and level" in Japanese and is a system of logic for sequencing and smoothing out the flow of work. Kanban pull needs to be in place for heijunka to work, as does *standard work* (standard work is the pre-set flow of exact work content, based on the technical and procedural standards we discussed in Chapter 2.)

Heijunka is most effective when applied within a strong visual framework, especially when the base scheduling is computer-driven. That is one reason I call this approach: *Visual Scheduling.* With few exceptions, visual scheduling involves a physical box or structure that segments work orders into actual physical slots. Photo Series 10.44 shows several of the many ways to do this. This need for physical structure is why heijunka is in the power category of a visual control.

Photo Series 10.44 Visual scheduling/heijunka boxes.

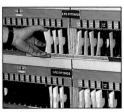

Each card is an order, each slot, a time period (say 15 or 30 minutes). Cards are slotted in work sequence for the day.

Orders across the company are placed by days of the week in physical sequence.

The actual barcode labels are used as the work orders (the green card signifies a model change). The structure is a rack bought at K-Mart, turned upside down and secured on the workbench.

While visual scheduling is nearly always the job for engineering and planning, I introduce you to it in case you see possibilities for your work and want to check it out further. No matter what, knowing of these matters could you think of further ways to imbed the need to know and need to share more completely in your work area.

Photo 10.45

At Wiremold (Connecticut), where visual scheduling has entirely replaced computer and paper scheduling, hundreds of kanban cards are loaded into 350 boxes each morning, the plant's production schedule for that day (Photo 10.45). This is the power of visual scheduling.

Figure 10.10

Visual Controls: Next Steps. As you just read, visual controls have a wide array of applications. Consider these now, walking back through the pages as a review.

Then, working alone or with a buddy, list visual control opportunities in your area. Discuss them. Sketch them out in a notebook or on a flip chart. Present your thinking to others and listen to theirs. When you are ready, post them on your hit list, even if you don't plan or want to tackle them all yourself (Figure 10.10). Keep going. Keep learning. Keep improving.

Visual Guarantees

A visual guarantee is a mechanism that builds information so deeply into the process that it becomes the work. When that happens it also becomes impossible to do the wrong thing. We can do the right thing *only*. *Poka-yoke* and mistake proofing are two other names for this kind of device.

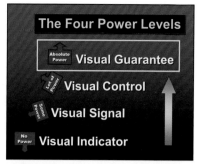

Figure 10.11 Level 4: Poka-yoke devices.

Figure 10.12 shows us what happened to the train and our teenager. Re-routing the train to the bridge makes it impossible for them to collide. (This is a far more expensive option than usual when you move from visual control to visual guarantee.)

We go to the community for our first actual visual guarantee (Photo 10.47, provided by Annie Yu, licensed QMI affiliate, Boston). Study the photo and answer the following questions, based solely on what you see there. To get you started, I will tell you this device is located on ship.

Question: What is the device? Answer: Some manner of ladder.

Question: How does the device work? What does it make sure you do?

Answer: You have to start climbing with your right foot. (You can try to start with your left foot. It's a free country. But you won't get far.)

Question: What does the device (these stairs) make sure you do not do?

Answer: The stairs make sure you do not skip a step. You can't. Not even Julia Roberts—not even Michael Jordan—has the wing span to skip a step.

Good job! And those answers tell us that this device is a visual guarantee, requiring us to do the right thing while preventing us from doing the wrong thing. Visual guarantees or poka-yoke devices are the highest level of visual devices because behavior is so deeply imbedded in it. Before we leave our ship, I have one more question: *Where did the idea for this visual guarantee come from? Why was it invented?*

Photo 10.46 What is the device? How does it work?

Here's a hint: Imagine yourself a sailor on a ship, sweetly asleep in your hammock, surrounded by fifty other sailors, likewise cozy in their "beds." Suddenly the alarm blasts: *Eurnh! Eurnh! Eurnh!* You leap up and, along with fifty others, make a mad rush for…. For what? Where are you? Where are they? Where are you rushing off to?

Yes! You are on a battleship in the middle of World War II, under attack. You and your buddies are rushing topside to the guns. Part of getting topside really fast is ensuring—*guaranteeing*—that the instant you put your foot on that ladder, you are already in exact unison with everyone else trying to go up that ladder. Right/left. Right/left. Micro-seconds matter. *In visuality, the need leads.* This is a case in point.

The design of the stairs ensures you and your buddies will get topside, fast and safe. In guarantees, the attributes talk to each other. In this case, your foot communicates directly with each step. And that is the point: *we humans are no longer part of the equation.*

Photo 10.47 Dr. Shigeo Shingo, receiving an honorary doctorate from Utah State University in 1989, the inauguration of The Shingo Prize.

Dr. Shigeo Shingo. Dr. Shigeo Shingo nearly single-handedly brought visual guarantees to the world of work Photo 10.47). He, along with Taiichi Ohno, was the co-architect of the Toyota Production System. Dr. Shingo dubbed these amazing information-packed visual solutions poka-yoke or "mistake-proof" devices. I call them visual guarantees to keep the message that they are part of the same continuum of logic I call workplace visuality.

I had the honor of working with Dr. Shingo through the 1980s. Three years before he passed on, he asked me to use his book, *Zero Quality Control* (Productivity Press, 1986), as a base for creating a poka-yoke methodology for the West. As part of that, I developed a classification framework to help companies implement poka-yoke (see book's Resource Section for more). Here is a part of that framework: the three types of poka-yoke devices. Like the power levels, they work from the ground up:

Type 1 Device: Eliminates the possibility of the error.

Type 2 Device: Detects the error causing the defect while making it.

Type 3 Device: Detects the defect after it is made and contains it.

Type 3 Device: This visual guarantee from Chapter 2 is a Type 3 device because it captures a quality defect and prevents it from traveling downstream (Photo Series 10.48). Study it again, this time focusing on the principles that make it work.

Photo Series 10.48 Type 3 Visual Guarantee: Detect the defect after it is made and contain it.

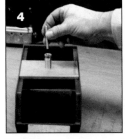

Problem: On some plungers, the outer diameter is too large to slide inside the bushing without rubbing. This hard to see defect was rarely discovered before Final Test.

Challenge: Develop a way to ensure no defective plunger travels downstream.
Solution: Imbed the answer to the question "Is this a good plunger?" as deeply as possible into the process itself. Create a visual solution.

Visual Guarantee: First a plate is mounted on the blue bin, with a hole in the center the size of the bushing.

With the bushing mounted on the plate, the operator drops each plunger through and checks its size. If the plunger gets stuck, it is set aside. The attributes "talk" to each other.

Then think: *Can I use a mechanical device to contain a defect or problem in my area and prevent it from traveling downstream and contaminating someone else or some other department?* When you do, you leave time to solve the real problem—in this case, a machine that moves out of calibration too easily.

As part of that solution, you may decide to install a sensor or limit switch, a type of visual guarantee that can apply to all three levels. They are often used to shut down machines that have begun to run defects or to warn us if we are about to get into trouble. Look around and you will see the result of using them—in fast food places, gas stations, and other settings that have high human traffic. Most are absolute in their power. They simply shut you down and don't let you proceed if you are doing the wrong thing.

Type 2 Device: The second guarantee type detects errors as they are being made. At this level, we begin to hold ourselves directly accountable for product and process attributes—the execution of minute characteristics.

The example in Photo 10.49 shows us the 72 "pins" that need to be inserted into a subassembly. Instead of

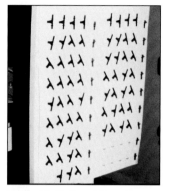

simply picking them out of a bin of hundreds, we count them out exactly in advance and position them on the board. In that way, we know at-a-glance if we have correctly completed the task—before we send it downstream.

Mounting a complete set of pins on the board makes it easy for the assembler to "see" that he needs to insert all of them. And he will know, in real time, if he did not, without doubt or excuses. If he thinks he is done with the job and a clip is left on the board, he has made a mistake. And he will notice it in time to correct his error—instead of sending the unit downstream in the belief that it is well made.

This is precisely why we say this level of guarantee allows us to notice when an error is being made as we are in the process of making it. As long as we stay alert and pay attention, a category 2 poka-yoke can be very effective.

Photo 10.49 Type 2 Guarantee: see your mistake as you're making it.

Type 1 Device. The final guarantee level is absolute. Whatever mistake you may have made in the past that resulted in damage, a defect, or accident, that mistake can no longer be made. Training is no longer a part of this success equation—nor are binders, OJT or your will. The device itself holds the product and/or process intelligence.

A guarantee on this level cannot stop you from doing *something else* is wrong. But it can tightly control your behavior (or a machine's) towards a single attribute. For our example, we go to Finish Machining at the Rolls Royce plant in Oberursal, Germany. George is an ace visual thinker and the machinist responsible for this final process— the high value-add segment of the value stream. He

has taken pains to put all his yellow boxes of bits and chucks in excellent visual order, even building a cubby unit to keep mix-ups to a minimum. Grab the wrong yellow box and you ruin the unit. Photo 10.50 shows his excellent visual solution.

Photo 10.50. *Before:* An advanced level of the visual where is not powerful enough to keep George from making mistakes.

But George knew the visual where could only reduce his mistakes. It was not powerful enough to eliminate them. He needed a surefire way to guarantee that his hand did not grab the wrong box. And one day he knows what he will do: Hide all the wrong yellow boxes so he can only get to the right ones. Seems far-fetched? His simple and brilliant poka-yoke solution is in Photo 10.51—a set of masking templates, color coded to product. Genius!

Photo 10.51 *After:* This masking template is product-specific, covering cubbies that hold the wrong yellow boxes so none can be wrongly taken. George has access to the right ones only. Other templates mask different cubbies.

Visual Guarantees: Next Steps

In this final section of the four power levels, I introduced the concept of visual guarantees/poka-yoke systems. There is so much more to learn about them—but not here, not today. Yet, I hope and believe you know enough to look for and find applications. Do that now. Working alone or with a buddy, make a list of guarantee opportunities in your area. Then post on your hit list, even if you don't plan or want to tackle them all yourself (Figure 10.13).

Visual Workplace Action Hit List

Department: Mag Test and Clinic | Supervisor: Donald x426 | Visual Coach: Maryanne x444 | Date: June 16

Your Visual Workplace Project Describe it in a few words. ↓	Point Person / Buddy	Start Date ↓	Target Date ↓	Traffic Light Status: Red X	Yellow X (half-way)	Green X	Comments Problems Special Needs
1. We are missing real time feedback on our defect tracking—huge info deficits.	Sue / Dave	5-14	5-25				We need 1/2" drill bits for plastic.
2. Incoming and Outgoing keep getting mixed up—by us and forklift drivers.	Gary / Henk	May 14	May 30		X		Please get us some more blue and green Floor-Mark.
3. The Stamper SOPs are too hard to get to, especially for newcomers.	Geo	05/18	05/25	X			What can stick to the Stamper sides?
4. We need a match between parts and blueprints. Will do.	Mary / Dan	May 21	June 3				Who's color-blind in our area?
5. All shipping stations are disorganized in different ways. We need to develop at least three prototype benches.							
6. We want to develop a way to store + track test samples while in our area.	Dan / Joe	May 21	~~May 30~~ June 20				We need a white board by the door.
7. Our consumable supply area is a mess, no order, no visuality, lots of mix ups. We will fix.	Mary Pat / Nate	6-4	6-14				Can we work with purchasing, please?
8.							
9.							
10.							
11.							
12.							
13.							
14.							

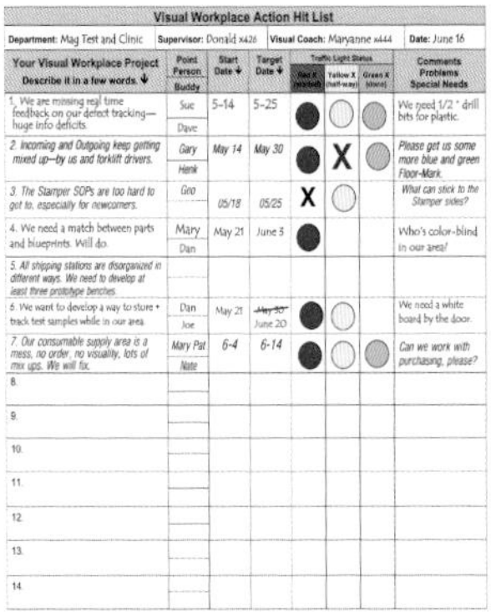

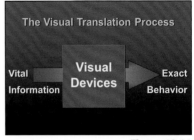

Figure 10.13 Track your improvement progress on your hit list.

Learning to See

As mentioned early in this chapter, its purpose is to show you many, many different kinds of visual devices, some you saw in earlier chapters of this book. But they, along with the many new visual devices these pages share, are presented in a new way—from the vantage point of power. The four power levels of visual devices offer you a new way to explore workplace visuality and its ability to translate information into exact behavior. Remember the image in Figure 10.14? It is fundamental to understanding visuality and the role of the visual thinker: *you*.

Figure 10.14

Because you have already learned so much about visuality, you are now able to see deeply into almost any device that share vital information through any of our five senses. As with the teaching examples, every visual device has many layers or dimensions of meaning. Some of them are already captured. Already in the device. Others are waiting for you to discover and implement them. Or, if you are not in charge, then you must look for and "see" the potential that has yet to be realized.

I call this *inverted visual thinking* or *sight inversion*, and you must develop a skill at it and an appetite for it. It is one of the most rewarding and delicious aspects of thinking visually.

Because of that, expect to "see" visuality, everywhere—even, as mentioned, when it is missing. Expect to go the mall and see cluster after cluster of visual devices influencing, even limiting your behavior. And expect to appreciate the thinking behind it. Expect to see this at sport stadiums, and the library, and the hardware store. Expect to see it at your workplace and at the places where the world works. You'll see visual devices—or you will see the absence of them. You'll see the device that is not there—the device that has not yet been installed or maybe even invented—because you'll see the motion caused by its absence.

Visual thinker, apply the lessons of this book, experiment with the possibilities. Visually answer your need to know until you are in control of your corner of the world through visuality. Then turn to others and recognize your need to share. Help other people gain control over their own work. When you do, the sense of safety, precision, alignment, and service becomes stronger in you and soon stronger in others.

Inspire your own life.
Be an inspiration to others.
Gwendolyn Galsworth

Chapter | Eleven

We Live in a Visual World

We live in a visual world because we are visual beings. Not the other way around.

The world did not teach us to understand the visual devices that surround us—those on our roads and highways, in our hospitals and supermarkets, at the airport, and in workplaces around the world. We understand these devices because visuality is a language we already speak and thoroughly know. That knowing is imbedded in our chemistry, in the way our mind works, the way it seeks and recognizes patterns, and the way we think and perceive, naturally and with elegance. Visual is how we are made. We are visual beings, therefore we live in a visual world.

It's the same way with visuality at work. The visual workplace is a physical workplace. It exists because visual devices and mini-systems exist in it. Visuality is not a world of the imagination even though our imagination helps us create it. It is real, actual, immediate, and natural.

Across the length of this book, I have introduced you to many visual principles and practices. You have worked through a ton of examples. And I hope and believe you have begun to apply these principles and practices to trigger a ton of visual solutions of your own.

If you are lucky, you will be surrounded by people who are doing the same, applying the two driving questions repeatedly, the principles of smart placement, the elements of visual where, and drilling deeper and wider, powerfully, I-driven, and with great satisfaction.

If you are very lucky, your supervisors and managers are not only supporting you, they are making their own value fields speak. That makes them lucky too. And you know what? The very next book I write is going to be for them—*Visual Leadership*—so they can go even further and get even luckier.

Together, you are transforming your work area and your company, and in the process you are transforming yourself and each other. Because there is no way you can gain expertise in a language without that language changing you. You are thinking and speaking visually.

An Uncommon Solution

Workplace visuality is an uncommon solution. Its rewards are both obvious and understated. The obvious part is operational transparency and the elimination of searching, errors, mix-ups, defects, rework, scrap, accidents, overdues, and other grosser forms of motion. As we locate work items closer to their points-of-use, we automatically reduce the distance travelled. As we make the workplace physically and psychologically safer, we begin to relax on the inside. And as we imbed the pattern of work in the physical landscape, operational details surface visually and we become masters of our work day.

That's when the understated rewards start. Unwanted questions and interruptions begin to evaporate. Things no longer get in our way. Struggle begins to recede. The workplace becomes our partner in delivering value to our customers and suppliers, downstream, upstream, at stream, and in the marketplace.

Over time, the area we move within becomes more focused and requires less attentiveness. The order and logic of work become so visual that a harmony settles in. Our movements become efficient and less scattered. We begin to notice less obvious forms of motion and we find ways to visually minimize these.

Workplace visuality has turned motion reduction into a science and an art and has become the perfect ally to your other improvement efforts: TPM, six sigma, A3 Thinking, quick changeover, lean, and other methods that make up the excellence journey. Aligned with visual, they forge a powerful partnership.

As that alliance deepens, operations in every venue come to be executed efficiently, smoothly, and within the context of time, speed, safety, and quality. If you have ever observed or worked in a department that has mastered visual and lean, you have seen people maneuver in a space defined by the value that gets added there—the work. All the waste has been removed from the process and motion is at an absolute minimum. In the best of these areas, work looks more like dancing. Every step and each hand movement is choreographed, measured, fluid, and intentional.

The same can be true of all work settings, including traditional manufacturing. Whether you work in a city hospital or country clinic, a machine shop or stamping plant, on an assembly line or in purchasing, in a bank, a military depot or an open-pit mine, visuality is central to it and can create an entirely new level of work, one that blends focus, intention, and results for outputs that are superior.

As your focus becomes more precise, suddenly it's just you and your work. When the struggle has been minimized and all the tiny extraneous interruptions removed, you can simply do your work. You are alert and relaxed as you bring a new dimension of your attention to the task at hand.

This state is possible at work, on the shopfloor, in your company. You have experienced it before, but perhaps not yet at work. It is a state of intent stillness where all your resources are at your disposal and they surface to assist you when and as needed. They flow from you. Motion as you have known it no longer exists in any form. It is just you and the silent, steady rhythm of your breath as value is added.

This is what you have always wanted work to feel like. This is what work is meant to be—the ease of your contribution flowing through you and into the process your company has asked you to perform. This is work that makes sense.

Appendix

Resource Section

Visual Products & Services

In addition to more details on Dr. Galsworth's company, QMI/Visual-Lean Institute, this section provides information on companies that specialize in visual workplace products and services (including 5S)—and offer assistance in visuality along with other continuous improvement methods.

Contact them directly for service details, product brochures, free samples, and a schedule of events. They are happy to help.

QMI/Visual-Lean® Institute
The 5S Store
Brady Corporation
Visual Workplace Inc.
5S Supply
MEP Utah
The Shingo Prize
Visual Workplace Australasia

Index

QMI ⦙ Visual-Lean® Institute   *Mastering Workplace Visuality*

Under the leadership of Gwendolyn Galsworth, Quality Methods International (QMI) is the premier resource for products and services that support visual thinking, workplace visuality, and visual conversions. The Visual-Lean® Institute is QMI's educational arm, training and licensing in-house instructors and external consultants in any of the Institute's fifteen visual workplace methodologies.

Based on nearly thirty years of research in the field, our visual methodologies are robust, complete, and well-tested. Our clients include a wide range of industries and settings—from factories and military depots to banks, medical centers, and open-pit mines.

With licensed affiliates in the United States, Canada, Mexico, Europe, and Australia, QMI sets the pace for the industry with visual workplace offerings that include seminars, workshops, on-site visual workplace consulting and troubleshooting, train-the-trainer licensing, complete visual conversions, conferences, webinars, online courses, keynotes, and study missions with an exclusive visual workplace focus.

VisualEdge Off-the-Shelf Series
Package 1: Visual Basics
One of dozens of self-training packages, using the exact same materials Dr. Galsworth uses when she trains her own clients.

With over 35,000 visual solutions in our database, we continually refine and upgrade our instructional materials, implementation designs, and behind-the-scenes support. Visit our website for our full range of on-site services and off-the-shelf training packages, including videos, DVDs, and our latest VisualEdge packages.

QMI offers a week-long train-the-trainer licensing process in *Work That Makes Sense*, the subject of this book, in the United States, Canada, Europe, and Australia. Visit our website for these and other details.

QMI/Visual-Lean® Institute
Phone: 503-233-1784
Fax: 503-233-3091
Email: admin@visualworkplace.com
Website: www.visualworkplace.com

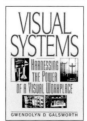
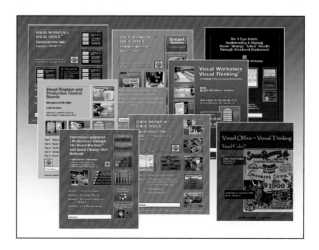

Visual Workplace-Visual Order DVD Training System (+ Spanish subtitles)

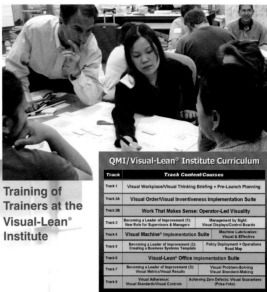

Training of Trainers at the Visual-Lean® Institute

QMI/Visual-Lean® Institute Curriculum

Track	Track Content/Courses	
Track 1	Visual Workplace/Visual Thinking Briefing + Pre-Launch Planning	
Track 2A	Visual Order/Visual Inventiveness Implementation Suite	
Track 2B	Work That Makes Sense: Operator-Led Visuality	
Track 3	Becoming a Leader of Improvement (1): New Role for Supervisors & Managers	Management by Sight: Visual Displays/Control Boards
Track 4	Visual Machine® Implementation Suite	Machine Lubrication: Visual & Effective
Track 5	Becoming a Leader of Improvement (2): Creating a Business Systems Template	Policy Deployment + Operations Road Map
Track 6	Visual-Lean® Office Implementation Suite	
Track 7	Becoming a Leader of Improvement (3): Visual Metrics/Visual Results	Visual Problem-Solving Visual Standard-Making
Track 8	Visual Adherence: Visual Standards/Visual Controls	Achieving Zero Defects: Visual Guarantees (Poka-Yoke)

Webinars

Keynotes

Conferences

Public Seminars

Visual Benchmarking Tours

Training Aids and Tools
Wall Charts, Audio CDs, Tool Kits, Resource Folios with adaptable forms, checklists, hit lists, and templates.

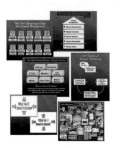

On-Site Assessments & Implementations

THE 5S STORE℠

Your one stop shop for all your 5S needs!

The 5S Store, LLC, founded in 2006 is an easy to use one stop shop for 5S supplies and Lean Manufacturing products. "Our stated purpose is to help businesses improve their competitiveness by providing materials for organizing their workplace utilizing 5S principles." The 5S Store is more than just a reseller of products. Our knowledgeable staff can help you address any challenges you may have with your implementation such as choosing the right floor tape or determining which video fits your training needs or helping you come up with that challenging visual control solution.

We pride ourselves on providing a friendly and value-added service as can be seen by the testimonial below:

Testimonial

"When we began our transition from Traditional to Lean Manufacturing we fell short on planning. We were into our first 5S Event and realized that we needed more Red Tags and Foam Tool Organizer Kits. Our consultant suggested that we call the 5S Store. Within an hour of my phone call, in a terrible rain storm, a staff member of the 5S Store met me at a service station on the highway to provide the material we needed for that same day. The extraordinary service that was provided, at no additional cost, helped to make our event successful. Since that first impression, the 5S Store continues to be a special supplier that is helping Spincraft successfully transition to a permanent culture of Continuous Improvements."
~ Murray Pitchman, Spincraft, Billerica MA

We also launched *5S Best Practices* in 2010. "Many of us know that the most challenging aspect of a successful 5S program is sustainment" says David Visco, founder and co-owner of The 5S Store. "We therefore created 5S Best Practices (www.5sbestpractices.com) to provide a forum for 5S and visuality practitioners to talk amongst themselves, get ideas, discuss challenges, and also to show off their before and after pictures."

The 5S Store, LLC
Phone: 978-842-4610
Fax: 978-842-4633
Email: sales@the5sstore.com
Websites: www.the5sstore.com
www.5sbestpractices.com

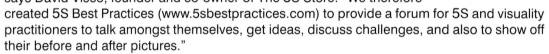

Sort: *Remove unnecessary items*   **Set in Order:** *Everything in its place*   **Shine:** *Nice and neat everyday*
Standardize: *Everyday, Everywhere*   **Sustain:** *Today and in the future*

Our Purpose

"To help businesses
improve their competitiveness
by providing materials for
organizing their workplace
utilizing 5S principles"

The 5S Store, LLC
www.the5sstore.com

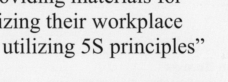

Brady Corporation is a global provider of solutions that identify and protect people, products and premises. Headquartered in Milwaukee, Wisconsin, Brady employs more than 7,000 people with locations in over 25 countries.

Brady North America, a division of Brady Corp., helps companies achieve operational excellence through the creation of a visually instructive plant that reinforces work standards and highlights abnormalities at a glance. Brady's visual workplace solutions make it easy for lean practitioners to post critical information right at the point of need, ensuring that the latest best practices remain clearly visible and consistently adhered to long after the rapid improvement event is over.

Brady North America's line of products include 5S marking supplies, visual management boards, plus software and printing systems that allow users to create custom signs, labels and tags onsite and on demand. These high-quality, high-performance products are designed for use in industrial environments and are capable of withstanding harsh conditions. When performance matters most, rely on Brady!

USA	Canada	Mexico
1-888-272-3946	1-800-263-6179	1-800-262-7777
www.BradyID.com	www.BradyCanada.ca	www.BradyLatinAmerica.com

Lean Information Boards
Expand shop floor communication by displaying:
- Production Goals & Trends
- Kaizen Improvement Ideas
- Schedules & Assignments
- Lean Activities & Results

Toolboard & Workbench Marking Supplies
Identify a place for everything that casts a shadow.

Shadow vinyl

Border tape

ToughStripe™ Floor Marking Tape
The most durable floor marking tape.

Floor marking   Floor signs   Floor labels   Pre-spaced markings

GlobalMark®2 Industrial Label Maker
The ultimate visual workplace system.

Multicolor printing   Cutout shapes   ½" - 4" tape widths   Magnetic tape

BBP™31 Sign & Label Printer
Fast, simple and powerfully versatile.

Monocolor printing   ½" - 4" tape widths   Photolum tape   Pre-printed safety headers

BMP™71 Label Printer
Most versatile handheld labeler on the market!

   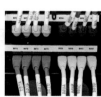 

Monocolor printing   ½" - 2" tape widths   Wire & cable markers   Control panel labels

For more on Brady's innovative workplace solutions including application ideas, best practices, webcasts, white papers and more go to **www.BradyID.com/visualworkplace.**

Are you spending too much time and money on signs?

Facilities have no idea how much time and money is wasted on signs. Employees solve signage needs with different approaches in different departments, driving unseen cost and inefficiency.

Try a Mobile In-House Sign Shop and find out what high-impact signs you can make, while saving time & money! Use the Sign Shop in combination with Floor-Mark to label borders and add floor graphics for increased impact. *The possibilities are endless!*

- Safety Signs
- Floor-Graphics
- Tool Shadows
- 5S Locators

- Directional Signage
- Visual Management Boards
- Facility Signs
- Office Signs

- Maintenance Signs
- Key Performance Boards
- Banners
- Magnetic Labels

5S Supply is the premier provider of Lean related items including training materials, books, DVDs, tags, boards, kits and supplies to support and enhance your Lean implementation.

We pride ourselves in offering unique and innovative products and services based on our real-work experience and application of Lean through hundreds of clients in all types of industries including manufacturing, service, government and healthcare.

Our goal is to provide you want you want, when you want it. We understand that you do not want to waste time during a kaizen event searching for items. We did the work for you and offer a one-stop shop for all your Lean needs.

Our Mission: To help organizations on their Lean journey.

This is 5S Supply

Lean simplified. Everything you need… all in one place.

5S Supply
www.5Ssupply.com
info@5Ssupply.com
888 4 LEAN 5S

Join us at

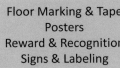

Manufacturing Extension Partnership

Understanding and meeting the needs of small businesses

The Manufacturing Extension Partnership (MEP) is a national network with thousands of specialists who understand the needs of manufacturers and small businesses. Collectively, we are the number-one resource in the United States for helping manufacturers realize cost savings, new sales, and retained sales.

The mission at MEP Utah is to sustain and improve the performance, growth and profitability of our clients. Realizing the importance of visuality and visual thinking, we have incorporated them into our core offerings.

In addition to conducting on-site visual workplace assessments and seminars, we train, coach, and support advanced levels of operator-led visuality—namely, *Work That Makes Sense*. Our staff of trained and certified visual workplace instructors is ready to help you, your operators, and your senior leaders think through, plan, implement, and support a highly successful visual conversion.

As one of our clients recently said:

"The visual workplace is the cornerstone of lean. I cannot imagine implementing lean without first creating a visual workplace. It's a superior way to get your employees involved and excited as you move down the path of lean thinking—or whatever your improvement initiative is called."

Doug Reilly, YESCO Electronics, Logan, Utah

Before MEP Utah came to assist, efforts to create a visual workplace at our company met with strong workforce resistance. Then the MEP's field staff trained value-add associates in the *Work That Makes Sense* methodology, and they got directly engaged in visually transforming their own work cells. The resistance completely faded away. An authentic work culture of continuous improvement began to take hold.

Lean Werks (Ogden, Utah)

Manufacturing Extension Partnership of Utah
800 W. University Parkway
Orem, Utah 84058
801-863-8637 (main office)
800-MEP-4MFG (toll-free)
801-765-9739 (fax)
info@mep.org (email)
www.mep.org (website)

MEP Utah is a licensed affiliate of QMI/Visual-Lean Institute. Our field staff is trained and certified by Dr. Gwendolyn Galsworth, leading visual workplace expert and author of this book.

THE SHINGO PRIZE
for OPERATIONAL EXCELLENCE

...the Nobel Prize of operational excellence

Established in 1988, The Shingo Prize is internationally recognized as the premier award for operational excellence and provides an organizational roadmap for attaining the highest standards. Named after Dr. Shigeo Shingo, co-architect of the Toyota Production System, the award is a milestone on the journey to operational excellence and a sustainable cultural transformation.

The Shingo Prize is more than an award. It is a means for creating alignment, synergy, and purpose throughout an entire organization. We teach that a sustainable culture of continuous improvement is achieved by focusing on a distinct set of principles, aligning management systems, and implementing improvement techniques throughout an entire organization.

The focus is on principle-based leadership; vision and strategy alignment; employee empowerment; continuous improvement; innovation and development; quality and sustainable results.

Whether or not you plan to challenge for The Shingo Prize, there is no better diagnostic format than The Shingo Prize model and the application criteria it includes. Download both at: www.shingoprize.org.

The Shingo Prize, The Visual Workplace, & The Shingo Online Course on Visuality

Visual Workplace/Visual Thinking is now an on-demand course in the Shingo online e-curriculum, created and narrated by Gwendolyn Galsworth. This course introduces you to the logic and application of workplace visuality, along with key definitions, core principles, and hundreds of visual solutions.

Robert Miller, executive director of The Shingo Prize, says this about the visual workplace:

> *"Galsworth's visual workplace methodology is in perfect harmony with the model of Operational Excellence represented by The Shingo Prize. Visual concepts, tools, and thinking are essential as we pursue other guiding principles of seeking perfection, quality at the source, and the continuous flow of value to customers. As I learn more about this important approach, I am hopeful that it will reach the hands of all of the great experts who know their jobs so well and want to ensure that what is supposed to happen does happen."*

Begin your Visual Workplace journey today. To register for this and other Shingo online courses, call us at 435-797-2279, or register at www.shingoprize.org and click on Learning Center > Course Catalog.

The Shingo Prize for Operational Excellence
3521 Old Main Hill
Jon M. Huntsman School of Business
Utah State University
Logan, Utah 84322-3521

Phone: 435-797-2279
Fax: 435-797-3400
Website: www.shingoprize.org

We change the way people see and work

Visual Workplace Australasia (VWA) assists companies in Australia and Asia stay locally and globally competitive through the technologies of the visual workplace.

VWA director and founder Oscar Roche and his team of certified visual trainers, use workplace visuality as a core component of their project-based learning approach to mentoring companies as they "build the house of Visual-Lean®."

Oscar Roche

Client companies such as DeBortoli Wines, Orlando Wines (makers of the famous Jacobs Creek brand), Casella Wines (home of the *Yellow Tail* brand), Markerry Industries, Gannon Vietnam, and Tetra Pak (Vietnam) have all benefited significantly from the delivery of visual workplace seminars, workshops, and facilitation. These organizations recognize the power of workplace visuality for embedding the process of continuous improvement into the enterprise on their journey to operational excellence.

Visuality is a mission-critical process in the complex market environment of SE Asia. With great diversity of language and culture, businesses here have come to understand the power of visual solutions to embed the details of work into the physical environment in nonverbal forms. With those in place, the entire company then becomes a gigantic adherence mechanism.

Ben Chopping

If you are a traditional manufacturer, VWA will help you optimize your existing approach. If you are already on the journey to lean, we will help extend and support your lean conversion and make those gains sustainable through visual workplace methods and tools.

Visual Workplace Australasia (Management Resource Plus)
Phone: 0427 066348 (+61 427 066348)
Fax: 02 692 6689 (+61 2 69626689)
Website: www.vwaust.com.au

Visual Workplace Australasia is a licensed affiliate of QMI/Visual-Lean® Institute. Our trainers are trained and certified by Dr. Gwendolyn Galsworth, leading visual workplace expert and author of this book.

Index